Wait Ten Minutes:

A Guide to Central Ohio Weather

Marshall McPeek,
Meteorologist

Quox Creek Publishing, Grove City, Ohio.

ISBN: 978-0-578-41074-6

Table of Contents

Preface

I'm a weather nerd. No surprise there.

While it may make some folks yawn, I find science and weather statistics fascinating. So do you. That's why you just picked up this book. Welcome aboard! Embrace your inner geek!

We'll learn about Central Ohio's fascinating weather and history. We'll look at past and present. We will be a resource for information about local weather events and climatology. And, along the way, we will take the mystery out of what's floating around in our skies.

Obviously, we can't cover everything but we will answer the most common questions and keep our focus on Central Ohio. (And, you can suggest things you'd like to see in a future edition!)

Our focus is Central Ohio. We are not trying to cover the globe or even North America. We are going do our best to stay local. When we say "Central Ohio," we are referring to the 23 counties that make up the Columbus television market. It's a little different from the definition used by the U.S. Census, but it should be familiar. Right here in our backyard, there is plenty of wonderful weather and weather history to talk about!

Thank you for your incredible support!

Now, let's learn about Central Ohio weather!

Acknowledgments

Thank you to WSYX's Tony D'Angelo and Jamie Justice for green-lighting this project and having the patience to wait for it to finally come to fruition.

We owe a huge debt of gratitude to our indomitable editor, Linda Grist Cunningham, who, with her loyal cats at her side ("The Cat 5"), slogged through thousands and thousands of words to whittle this beast down to a more manageable size.

Many thanks to Jym Ganahl who has unknowingly served as a mentor, teacher, and guide for nearly two decades. There aren't enough words to describe how much I (and much of Central Ohio) have learned from you and your enthusiasm for weather.

My mother, Libby, who has been a faithful supporter and cheerleader through so many projects. Thank you for believing in me and offering encouragement whenever things seemed bleak. I love you.

Foreword

Math, statistics, and science are not often used with the term "comfort reading." Books that are bland are not read. Marshall has thought of everything to create a book that is appealing to look through, easy to read, and colorful.

With that done, he is just so knowledgable and views weather as a hobby and it reads that way -- with enthusiasm.

For decades, he has stored his love of weather, statistics, science, and math now to present it for all of us to enjoy. You will never need another book other than this one for answers to astronomy, meteorology, records, and folklore. You will love this.

I've watched Marshall for decades grow and continue to be so excited about the amazing study of weather.

- Jym Ganahl, Meteorologist

INTRODUCTION

*"All of us could take a lesson from the weather.
It pays no attention to criticism."*

- Anonymous

You Know the Joke

You know the joke: "If you don't like the weather in [insert the name of the village, city, state, island, mountain, or resort where you happen to be right now], just wait ten minutes."

Mark Twain made a similar line famous as he mused about the weather during a trip to the northeast:

"If you don't like the weather in New England, just wait a few minutes," he is credited with saying. It applies around the world. And, to a certain extent, it's true. If you wait a quick spell, the sun may peek through the clouds again. Give it some time and that thunderstorm will, indeed, move to a new spot.

Boaters know how quickly the weather can change on Lake Erie. In less than an hour, the water can turn from calm and tranquil to choppy and churning, from sunny and warm to stormy and dangerous.

Wait ten minutes. The weather will probably change.

Weather Affects Us All

Weather is the single thing we all have in common. (Okay, other than, say, gravity or a strong fondness for breathing.) We all have to contend with that stuff churning around in the atmosphere.

That's why it's such a great subject for small talk.

Weather Is Fun!

But what causes that weather? What forces are at work? Why does it happen when, where, and how it does? And can we actually predict it?

Humans have been watching and studying the weather for thousands of years and new discoveries are made all the time.

Meteorology, the study of weather and how it affects our world, is one of the few disciplines in which the physical sciences and the social sciences collide. Once we can detect or predict a tornado's path (physical science), we can send out warnings about it; but we also have to understand how people will react and how to get them to pay attention (social science).

All the while, Mother Nature remains belligerent and quirky, unwilling to give up her secrets easily and occasionally seeming to defy her own rules. The weather captivates us. Not just nerds like you and me, but *all* of us. It has for tens of thousands of years. We can't help it. Our Neanderthal predecessors learned to pay attention to it (in some cases, the hard way) and our modern lives are just as intertwined with its beauty, fluctuations, and annoyances. The weather influences what we wear, how we behave, even what we talk about at chatty dinner parties.

Most of the time, the weather is part of the background in our busy, daily routines. It's always there even though we tend to pay it little or no attention. But every now and then, Mother Nature makes a big fuss to ensure we're respectful.

The weather doesn't have to be severe or extreme to be interesting (or even amazing). Something as simple as a raindrop or a cloud is actually a fascinating feat of complex physical processes and myriad series of intricate interactions in the atmosphere! Once we understand how difficult it is to create a single raindrop and to know that it happens billions of times in each rain shower, we're blown away by the incredible power of nature.

A Quick Note About the Data Herein

We've crunched a lot of data to crank out the climatology records, averages, facts and figures you'll find in this tome. There have been more spreadsheets than we care to admit. Unless otherwise noted, the general, daily, dataset we're using is provided by the National Weather Service (formerly, The U.S. Weather Bureau) and covers the Columbus area, July 1878 through December 2017. Reliable snowfall and snow depth data started in the winter of 1947-1948. The Storm Prediction Center (SPC) tornado database covers the nation starting in 1950.

You may sometimes hear meteorologists and climatologists talking about "normal" temperatures or "normal" amounts of precipitation. In general, they're talking about an average covering the most recently-established 30-year period. The 30-year standard was established during the 1935 International Meteorological Conference in Warsaw, Poland. The American Meteorological Society says, "[t]his practice is used to take account of the slow changes in climate and to add more recently established stations to the network with observed normals." In general, we're using the same "normal" period as the National Weather Service, 1981-2010.

WEATHER 101

The Sun

One of my favorite questions to ask school groups (it's even more fun with adults) is, "What is the single thing that causes our weather?" You probably noticed the name of this section, so you have a pretty solid clue. Clouds, wind, air pressure, and seasons are popular answers. But the ultimate driving force for our weather is... the sun.

When you hold out your hand in the bright sunshine, your skin feels warmer. Even in the winter. Those little rays of light have traveled 93 million miles and still

A brilliant, autumn sunrise with the downtown Columbus skyline. Photo by Chris Mazivanhanga.

have enough energy to warm your skin. Expose yourself to enough of those rays and you'll end up with a pretty nasty burn. That's a lot of energy coming from so far away.

That incredible energy is the root of our planet's success. It makes life possible. And it creates the complex weather patterns that we forecast every day.

The little yellow dot in the midday sky (and the big, orange ball on the horizon at sunrise and sunset) is an enormous glob of superheated gases and plasma that sits at the center of our solar system. It's a huge, flaming ball of gas made up mostly hydrogen and helium, the most basic and abundant elements in the universe. The forces of gravity and electromagnetism are so strong that they force atoms to give up their electrons (nuclear fission) or take on new ones (nuclear fusion). The energy released in those processes is so powerful, it warms the surface of our planet tens of millions of miles away. It's enough to power solar cells to make electricity. It can warm the solar panels that heat the water for pools. It provides abundant light for photosynthesis, even when there are clouds in the way. And it warms our atmosphere, creating our weather patterns.

Uneven Heating

There's a catch. The sun doesn't heat the earth evenly. It makes some parts warmer than others.

At the equator, the sun's rays hit the earth at almost a right angle. That part of the world gets nearly the full energy of those rays. At the poles, the rays arrive at very low angles akin to a glancing blow. There's much less energy delivered to the planet from those rays. Think of a boxer punching you directly in the nose instead of a glancing blow off your cheek. The direct hit delivers much more energy to your nose (and will do more damage) than the glancing blow to your cheek.

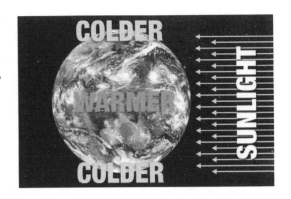

The energy difference makes the equatorial regions much warmer than the polar regions.

Mother Nature prefers things to be homogenous (the same), so air masses and pressure centers form and move around the earth in an effort to equalize the discrepancies between hot areas and cold areas. That works to a certain extent, but will never fully succeed. As long as those air masses and currents keep trying to balance and equalize, we'll continue to have weather.

The Seasons

In 1615, Galileo Galilei wrote a famous letter arguing, despite The Church's objections, that the earth moves around the sun (heliocentrism), not the other way around. Copernicus wrote about the geometry of heliocentrism in the 16th century. The Pythagoreans already had suggested the idea by the 4th century BCE. They did the math and figured out that it takes 365 1/4 days for the earth to make the whole trip. That's one year. (See Leap Year.)

Since then, we've also learned that the earth is tilted on its axis. We don't feel it but the whole planet is tipped over a bit. If you draw a line from the north pole to the south pole, you'll notice that line sits at a 23.5-degree angle.

Our built-in tilt aims some parts of the planet toward the sun and some parts away from the sun. As the earth travels around the sun, it doesn't wobble back and forth every six months. The tilt is the same all the way around its orbit, always pointed toward Polaris, the North Star. As earth travels around the sun,

Galileo Galilei by Justus Sustermans, 1636.

Why is the sky blue?

The molecules in the earth's atmosphere scatter the sunlight as it passes through. The majority of the atmosphere is nitrogen (no, oxygen is not the most abundant gas), and nitrogen absorbs and scatters the blue end of the spectrum more than the red. With all that "blue" light bouncing around in the atmosphere, the sky takes on a beautiful tint.

On a day with high pressure and low humidity, the clear sky becomes a brilliant blue. Township Hall Park, Lewis Center.

there are times when the northern hemisphere is tilted toward the sun and times the southern hemisphere is tilted toward the sun. Whichever hemisphere is tilted toward the sun gets more direct radiation, gets warmer, and we call it summer!

There are four points in Earth's orbit to which we pay some attention:

+ Vernal (Spring) Equinox,

+ Summer Solstice,

+ Autumnal Equinox,

+ Winter Solstice.

The AMS Glossary of Meteorology defines a solstice as:

Either of the two points on the sun's apparent annual path where it is displaced farthest, north or south, from the earth's equator, that is, a point of greatest deviation of the ecliptic from the celestial equator.

Yikes. In other words, the solstice is when the sun appears farthest north or south during the year. It marks the beginning of summer or winter and is the turning point for the days (hours of daylight) getting shorter or longer.

Why are sunsets orange?

As the sun dips lower and lower toward the horizon, it becomes progressively more orange.

Learn why at WaitTenMinutes.com!

The equinox is when the sun appears to be directly above the equator. It marks the beginning of spring or autumn and is when we have "equal day and equal night," roughly 12 hours of daylight and darkness. It's also the only day the sun rises due east and sets due west at every point on the globe.

If you're lucky enough to be at the equator at noon on the equinox, your shadow will disappear because the sun will directly overhead.

Tens of thousands of years ago, the Ohio Moundbuilders noticed those patterns and they built enormous earthworks to mark the sun's positions. (One of the world's greatest examples is right here in Central Ohio: The Newark Earthworks.) The Ancient Druids built Stonehenge to do the same thing. The Mayans, Aztecs, and Egyptians did it with pyramids and temples.

Vernal Equinox: Beginning of Spring

The Spring Equinox, usually around March 20, is when we finally cross the threshold into more daylight than darkness. The northern hemisphere's days get longer and hope returns for warmer weather.

Summer Solstice: Start of Summer

Rejoice in the longest day of the year with the summer solstice around June 21 each year. The sun slides into its northernmost position and we enjoy the most direct sunlight of the year. The warm season begins and we break out the shorts and t-shirts, open the pool, and get the grills ready!

Eggs balancing on end on March 16, 2010, which was *not* the spring equinox.

Balance an egg on the Spring Equinox

Many people believe that you can balance an egg on end on the Spring Equinox... and only on the Spring Equinox.

They claim it has to do with the earth's position around the sun and how that position affects the planet's gravity. They'll tell stories of modified electromagnetism. Tidal forces. All kinds of things.

The truth is: you can balance the egg any day of the year.

The earth's gravitational field, electromagnetic field, and the tidal forces produced by the moon don't change just for the 24-hour period that humans have designated as the equinox. Even if they did, the impact wouldn't be on your single, tiny egg.

Autumnal Equinox: Fall Begins

Fall begins with the Autumnal Equinox. The days have slowly been getting shorter, and the nights longer until around September 22 when they are nearly equal length. The sun rises due east and sets due west and the temperatures begin to cool as the sun appears to move farther south in the sky.

Winter Solstice: Welcome to Winter

As the days cool, the sun appears for fewer hours each day and moves to its southernmost point in the sky. The Winter Solstice, the shortest day of the year, usually happens around December 22nd and ushers in the Northern Hemisphere's coolest part of the year. South of the equator, it brings the warm season.

Hours of Daylight

	Summer Solstice	Winter Solstice
Columbus, Ohio	15:00	9:20
Minneapolis, Minnesota	15:37	8:46
Anchorage, Alaska	19:21	5:27
Auckland, New Zealand	9:38	14:41
McMurdo Station, Antarctica	0:00*	24:00**

*At McMurdo Station, the sun is down for the entire month of June. No sunrise, sunset, or twilight.

**At McMurdo Station, the sun is up for the entire month of December. No sunrise, sunset, or twilight.

Solstice & Equinox Dates

	Season Beginning	2019	2020	2021	2022
Vernal Equinox	Spring	March 20 5:58 p.m.	March 19 11:49 p.m.	March 20 5:37 a.m.	March 20 11:33 a.m.
Summer Solstice	Summer	June 21 11:54 a.m.	June 20 5:43 p.m.	June 20 11:32 p.m.	June 21 5:13 a.m.
Autumnal Equinox	Fall	September 23 3:50 a.m.	September 22 9:30 a.m.	September 22 3:21 p.m.	September 22 9:03 p.m.
Winter Solstice	Winter	December 21 11:19 p.m.	December 21 5:02 a.m.	December 21 3:59 p.m.	December 21 4:48 p.m.

All times Ohio local (EST/EDT).

The word "Equinox" comes from the Latin "equi" meaning "equal" and "nox" meaning "night," in other words, "equal night." On that day, we expect 12 hours of daylight and 12 hours of darkness. But if you look at the sunrise and sunset times, you may notice a discrepancy. Instead of sunrise at 7:40 a.m. and sunset at 7:40 p.m., it may be more like 7:21 a.m. and 7:27 p.m., a few minutes more or less than "equal." The day closest to 12 hours may actually happen several days before or after the equinox. Why?

It comes from several things:

1. how we mark and measure the sunrise and sunset and

2. how the earth's atmosphere bends sunlight.

Sunrise is the moment the top edge of the sun's disk first appears above the horizon. Sunset is the moment the sun's disk disappears below the horizon. ("Twilight" is the time when there is light in the sky but the sun itself isn't visible. "Dawn" is the moment the sun's light first appears in the sky, leading to twilight.)

To get equal day and night, you would need to measure from the center of the sun's disk as it rises and sets. Waiting for leading and trailing edges adds a few minutes to the timing on each end.

And just to make things even more complicated, the gases in the earth's atmosphere bend the sunlight before it reaches our eyes. We get to see the edge of the sun's disk before the geometry says sunrise is actually occurring. It's a similar situation for sunset. Bottom line: it throws off the timing.

Meteorological Seasons

Using astronomy, the dates of the solstices and equinoxes vary slightly from year to year. The variances become an issue for scientists and meteorologists who study the weather and its patterns, because they need a consistent way to compare data from year to year.

So they use a different calendar that sets the seasonal begin-and-end dates at more regular intervals. Each of the meteorological seasons begins on the first day of the appropriate month.

+ **Meteorological Spring:**
  March, April, May

+ **Meteorological Summer:**
  June, July, August

+ **Meteorological Autumn:**
  September, October, November

+ **Meteorological Winter:**
  December, January, February

Sometimes you'll hear forecasters refer to "Meteorological Winter" (December 1 - February 28) as compared to "Astronomical Winter" (roughly December 21 - March 20). Yes, there's still the Leap Year to deal with every four years but that still requires much less calculation than figuring out the solstices for each of a hundred (or thousand) years.

We're Slowing Down

The days on Earth haven't always been 24 hours. NASA scientists postulate that, in its early years, our still-forming planet was spinning much faster and an Earth day was only about 6 hours.

Since then, the earth has been continually slowing down. The moon's momentum plus friction from the oceans and the tides slow us down just a tiny bit year after year, millennia after millennia.

Our days will continue to get shorter and shorter (and the moon will inch farther and farther away) until the end of the solar system. Estimates say we're losing about 2 milliseconds every 100 years. That's about 1/500th of a second. You're really not going to notice.

The atomic clock, however, does notice. So, to make up the difference, a "leap second" is occasionally added to the world's timekeeping devices. Between 1972 and 2014, the International Earth Rotation and Reference Systems Service implemented 25 leap seconds. The most recent was added on December 31, 2016.

Length of Days Around the Solar System

Planet	Time for a Single Rotation (Measured in Earth time)
Mercury	58 days, 15 hours
Venus	243 days
Earth	23 hours, 56 minutes
Mars	24 hours, 39 minutes
Jupiter	9.9 hours
Saturn	10 hours, 47 minutes
Uranus	17 hours, 14 minutes
Neptune	16 hours, 6 minutes
Pluto*	6 days, 9 hours

*Yes, we know, Pluto isn't, technically, a "planet" any more. Thanks, IAU. By including our beloved Pluto in the list, we're simply clinging to our childhood.

Daylight Saving Time

The idea of "springing forward" and "falling back" is a relatively new concept. We've only been doing it regularly for a few decades.

Depending on your version of history, Daylight Saving Time (DST) was first proposed either

a) in an 1895 paper to the Wellington Philosophical Society by a New Zealand entomologist named George Vernon Hudson who proposed a two-hour time shift to keep up with the available sunlight (so he would have more time to collect bugs) or;

b) in a 1907 publication by English outdoorsman William Willett who noticed Londoners sleeping through the early-morning daylight hours in the summer months (he also wasn't thrilled about cutting short his golf game in the evening).

In the United States, before 1883, every town kept its own time, roughly based on the position of the sun. The local folks synchronized their timekeeping to a clock in the town square, the church steeple, or a jewelry store's window. But the new transcontinental railroads needed a more reliable way to keep track of the train schedules, so they created their own system with standard time zones.

By 1918, Congress finally got in on the action and passed the Standard Time Act, creating our modern time zones. The boundaries have changed a bit over the years, but the general concept remains.

Senate Sergeant at Arms Charles Higgins pushes the hour-hand forward on the Senate Chamber's Ohio Clock for the first Daylight Saving Time, while Senators William Calder (NY), William Saulsbury, Jr. (DE), and Joseph T. Robinson (AR) look on, 1918. Image from the United States Senate Historical Office.

Congress also approved the first period of Daylight Saving Time. Not everyone was thrilled about it and it was repealed the next year. DST was reinstated nationally during World War II in an effort to conserve energy then tossed out again at the end of the war.

The Uniform Time Act of 1966 was passed by Congress to "promote the adoption and observance of uniform time within the standard time zones" and it made permanent the annual, nationwide time shifts for DST. With a few rules and regulations, individual states and territories can still opt out of DST. Arizona, Hawaii, Puerto Rico, the US Virgin Islands, Samoa, and the Northern Mariana Islands don't change their clocks. The Navajo Nation follows DST but the Hopi Nation doesn't.

Columbus is in the Eastern Time Zone along with New York, Washington, Atlanta, Miami, Indianapolis and Detroit. In the winter months, during Standard Time (EST), we're five hours behind Greenwich Mean Time (GMT/UCT/Z). We're four hours behind GMT during Daylight Saving Time.

As of 2007, Daylight Saving Time begins on the second Sunday of March and ends on the first Sunday of November. The change happens at 2:00 a.m. on the appropriate day.

Map of the time zones of the United States from The National Atlas by the U.S. Geological Survey.

	DST Begins (Spring Forward)	DST Ends (Fall Back)
2019	March 10	November 3
2020	March 8	November 1
2021	March 14	November 7
2022	March 13	November 6
2023	March 12	November 5

Fall Colors

A mild, wet summer followed by a sunny, cool early-autumn produces the best and brightest fall foliage colors.

As the trees begin to change, you'll notice the colors peaking, generally, from north to south. Toledo and Cleveland peak during the first week of October. Central Ohio hits its brightest point around the second or third week of October. And southern Ohio, from Cincinnati to Athens, tends to peak in late October or even early November.

The state parks are great places to go to see fantastic fall colors. Hocking Hills State Park in southeastern Ohio usually is incredible by mid-October. (If you want to spend a weekend in a cabin around that time, book really early!) It's great for hiking and enjoying the crisp autumn air. Ohio also has 13 National Scenic Byways with great views.

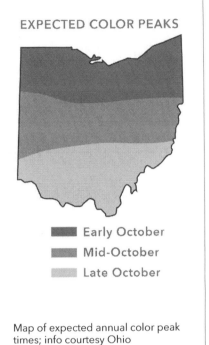

EXPECTED COLOR PEAKS

■ Early October
■ Mid-October
■ Late October

Map of expected annual color peak times; info courtesy Ohio Department of Natural Resources.

The autumn colors often are brilliant during mid- and late-October in the Hocking Hills.

Temperature

We think of temperature simply as how hot or cold something is but, technically, temperature is a measurement of how fast molecules are moving in a substance. The faster they move, the warmer the material.

Making them move faster or slower is simply a matter of adding or subtracting energy. Add some heat to an ice cube and you'll make the water molecules vibrate faster; as they get warmer, the water changes from solid to liquid. If you keep adding energy, they'll vibrate even faster and eventually convert from liquid to gas, creating water vapor (or clouds).

In the United States, we measure temperature using the Fahrenheit (°F) scale. Most of the world uses a metric scale called Celsius or Centigrade (°C). Scientists and meteorologists also use the celsius scale. Sometimes, scientists use a scale called Kelvin (°K) which is based on the actual vibration of molecules; Absolute Zero (0°K) is when there is no heat energy left in a molecule and it completely stops moving.

Temperature plays an enormous roll in our weather. It affects how weather systems form and behave, how air rises, and when and where water condenses into clouds. On a practical level, temperature influences what you wear to work or school.

When we record the weather conditions for the day, temperature is a fundamental piece of data. Many people note the day's temperature in their diary entries. NOAA's National Climatic Data Center (NCDC) keeps detailed records about temperature, precipitation, wind and other conditions for thousands of locations around the United States. The World Meteorological Organization keeps similar data for locations across the globe.

Temperature Scales

	°F	°C	°K
Boiling Point of Water	212	100	373
Hot Summer Day	90	32	305
Comfortable Summer Day	75	24	297
Cool Winter Afternoon	40	4	278
Freezing Point of Water	32	0	273
Inside Your Freezer	0	-18	255
°F and °C Scales Meet	-40	-40	233
Nitrogen becomes liquid	-321	-196	77
Absolute Zero	-460	-273	0

Temperature Extremes

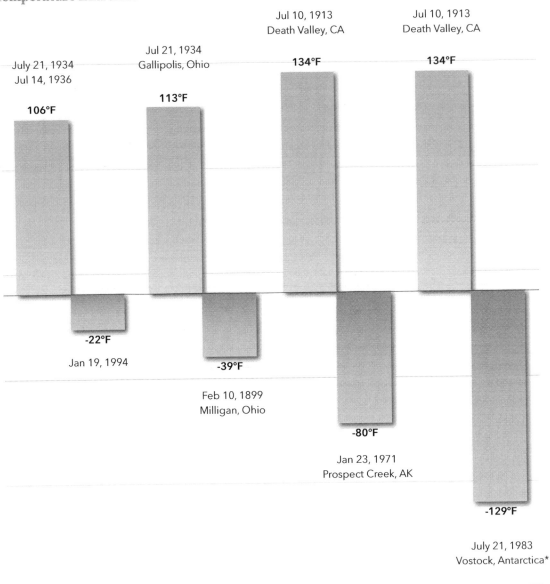

July 21, 1934
Jul 14, 1936

106°F

Jan 19, 1994

-22°F

Jul 21, 1934
Gallipolis, Ohio

113°F

-39°F

Feb 10, 1899
Milligan, Ohio

Jul 10, 1913
Death Valley, CA

134°F

-80°F

Jan 23, 1971
Prospect Creek, AK

Jul 10, 1913
Death Valley, CA

134°F

-129°F

July 21, 1983
Vostock, Antarctica*

Columbus   Ohio   United States   World

* This is the record reported by the World of Meteorological Organization. Another reading, taken by the Landsat 8 satellite, estimates a temperature of -135.8°F on a 3,900m ridge in Antarctica on August 10, 2010; that reading, though, was never confirmed by a thermometer on the ground and is considered a provisional reading.

Columbus Normal Temperatures, 1981 - 2010

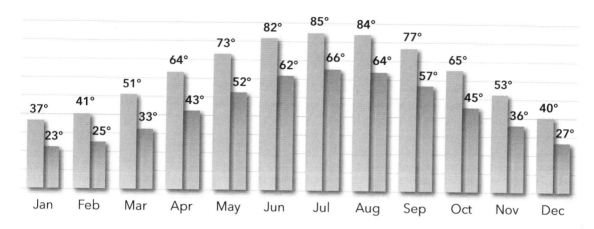

Temperatures in the mid-latitudes tend to vary a bit on a daily basis (diurnally) and significantly throughout the year. In Ohio, we often get 30-degree swings from the morning low temperature to the afternoon high temperature.

The low-latitude tropics are much more consistent day to day and even month to month. Sometimes, a tropical morning low and afternoon high may only differ by four to six degrees.

Columbus Monthly Record Temperatures, 1878-2018

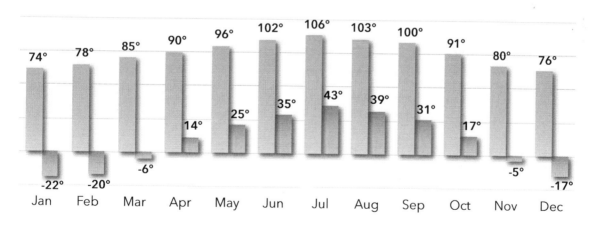

Ohio is a land of modest extremes. We're a mid-latitude continental climate and we don't have enormous bodies of water to moderate our temperatures. (The Great Lakes have a mild effect but not like being near the ocean.) So, we can get some pretty big swings in temperature from season to season and even day to day.

From extreme low to extreme high, we've racked up a 128° difference!

Columbus' Warm Weather

Warmest High Temperature Ever
106°F on July 14, 1936
and July 21, 1934

The low temperatures the following mornings
were in the mid-to-upper-70s.

Warmest Low Temperature Ever
82°F on July 10, 1881

The high temperature later that day was 103°F,
one of the Top-10 Warmest Days.

Columbus' Top 10 Warmest Daily High Temperatures

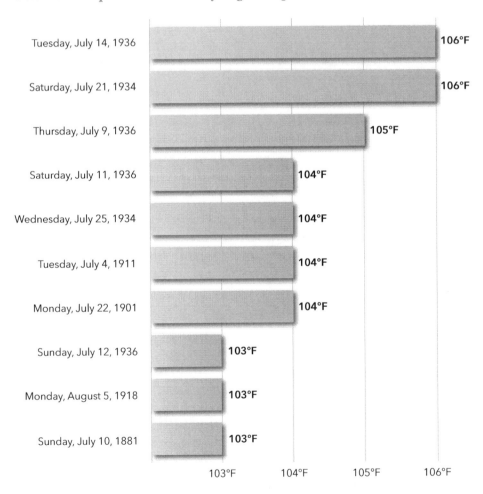

Tuesday, July 14, 1936	106°F
Saturday, July 21, 1934	106°F
Thursday, July 9, 1936	105°F
Saturday, July 11, 1936	104°F
Wednesday, July 25, 1934	104°F
Tuesday, July 4, 1911	104°F
Monday, July 22, 1901	104°F
Sunday, July 12, 1936	103°F
Monday, August 5, 1918	103°F
Sunday, July 10, 1881	103°F

Columbus' Warmest Low Temperatures

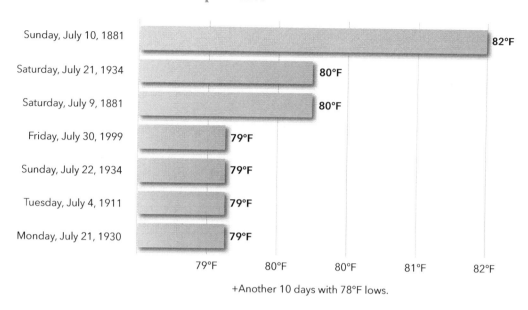

+Another 10 days with 78°F lows.

Columbus' Top 10 Warmest Summers

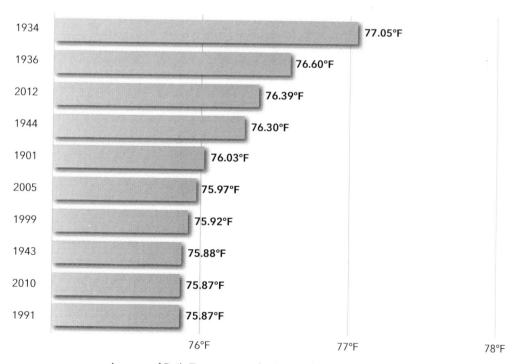

Average of Daily Temperatures for June, July, and August, 1879-2018.

90°F+ Days Annually

Between 1879 - 2015, the Columbus area has averaged 20 days each year at 90 degrees or warmer. The years with the most 90-degree (or warmer) days are 1936 and 1955. The fewest number of 90-degree days is one day each for 1979 and 1992. There are no years on record with zero 90-degree days.

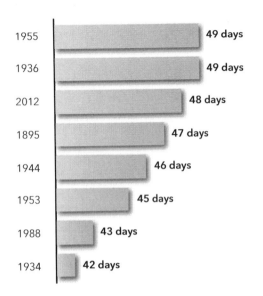

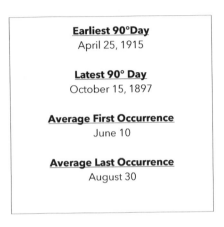

Earliest 90°Day
April 25, 1915

Latest 90° Day
October 15, 1897

Average First Occurrence
June 10

Average Last Occurrence
August 30

95°F+ Days Annually

Between 1879 - 2015, the Columbus area has averaged four days each year at 95 degrees or warmer. Four years have endured 13 days at 95 degrees or warmer and there were 12 of those days in 1999.

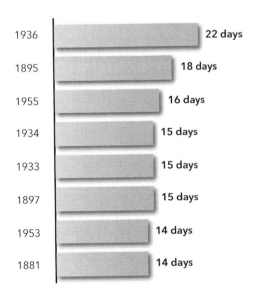

Earliest 95°Day
May 30, 1895

Latest 95° Day
September 29, 1953

Average First Occurrence
July 6

Average Last Occurrence
August 9

100°F+ Days Annually

Thankfully, in the Columbus area, 100-degree days are relatively rare. Between 1897 and 2015, a span of about 50,403 days, only 137 of them reached the three-digit mark. That's only 0.027%!

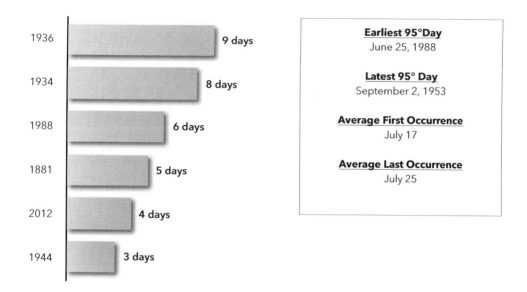

Earliest 95°Day	June 25, 1988
Latest 95° Day	September 2, 1953
Average First Occurrence	July 17
Average Last Occurrence	July 25

Columbus has also endured eight years with two days at or warmer than 100°F and six years with one day.

105°F+ Days Annually

Since 1879, Columbus has recorded only three days with daily maximum temperatures of 105°F or warmer: one day in 1934 and 2 days in 1936.

Columbus' Cold Weather

Coldest Low Temperature Ever
-22°F on January 19, 1994

The high temperature
later that day was -1°F.

Coldest High Temperature Ever
-7°F on February 9, 1899

The low temperature
the next morning was -20°F.

Columbus' Coldest Daily High Temperatures

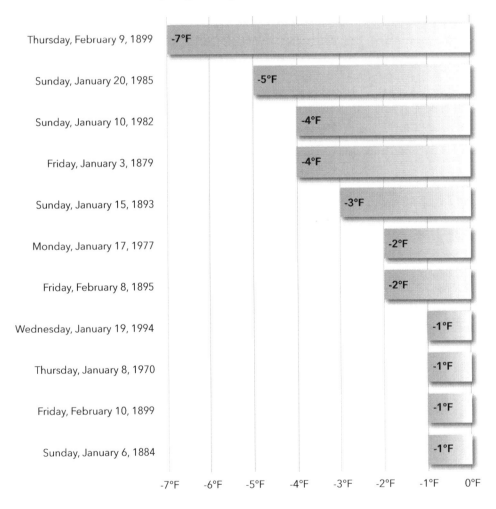

Thursday, February 9, 1899	-7°F
Sunday, January 20, 1985	-5°F
Sunday, January 10, 1982	-4°F
Friday, January 3, 1879	-4°F
Sunday, January 15, 1893	-3°F
Monday, January 17, 1977	-2°F
Friday, February 8, 1895	-2°F
Wednesday, January 19, 1994	-1°F
Thursday, January 8, 1970	-1°F
Friday, February 10, 1899	-1°F
Sunday, January 6, 1884	-1°F

-7°F -6°F -5°F -4°F -3°F -2°F -1°F 0°F

Columbus' Top Coldest Daily Low Temperatures

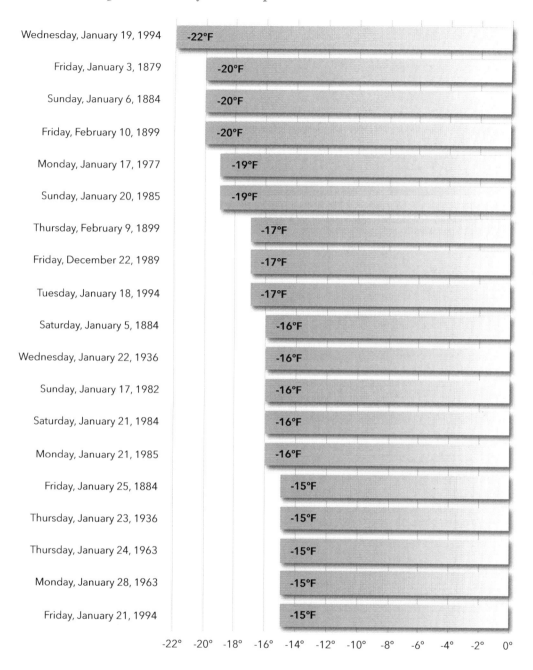

Wednesday, January 19, 1994	-22°F
Friday, January 3, 1879	-20°F
Sunday, January 6, 1884	-20°F
Friday, February 10, 1899	-20°F
Monday, January 17, 1977	-19°F
Sunday, January 20, 1985	-19°F
Thursday, February 9, 1899	-17°F
Friday, December 22, 1989	-17°F
Tuesday, January 18, 1994	-17°F
Saturday, January 5, 1884	-16°F
Wednesday, January 22, 1936	-16°F
Sunday, January 17, 1982	-16°F
Saturday, January 21, 1984	-16°F
Monday, January 21, 1985	-16°F
Friday, January 25, 1884	-15°F
Thursday, January 23, 1936	-15°F
Thursday, January 24, 1963	-15°F
Monday, January 28, 1963	-15°F
Friday, January 21, 1994	-15°F

-22° -20° -18° -16° -14° -12° -10° -8° -6° -4° -2° 0°

The Columbus area has also endured six days at -14°F and another five days dipping to -13°F.

Days -5°F or Colder Annually

Between 1879 and 2015, Ohio has averaged at least one day per year at -5°F or colder. Brrrrrr!

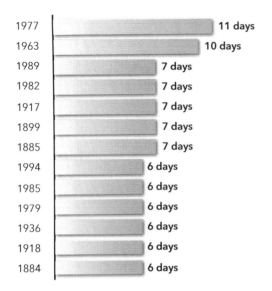

Earliest -5°Day
November 22, 1880

Latest -5° Day
March 9, 1984

Average First Occurrence
January 10

Average Last Occurrence
January 28

Days -10°F or Colder Annually

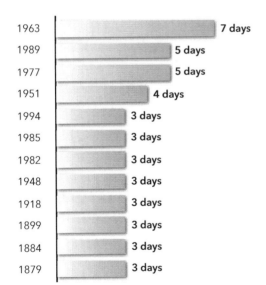

Earliest -10°Day
December 16, 1951

Latest -10° Day
February 27, 1963

Average First Occurrence
January 14

Average Last Occurrence
January 23

Days -15°F or Colder Annually

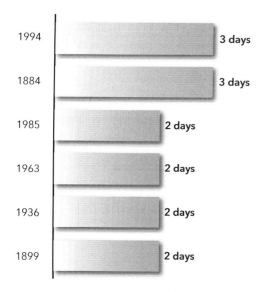

1994	3 days
1884	3 days
1985	2 days
1963	2 days
1936	2 days
1899	2 days

Earliest -15°Day
December 22, 1989

Latest -15° Day
February 10, 1899

Average First Occurrence
January 16

Average Last Occurrence
January 18

Days -20°F or Colder Annually

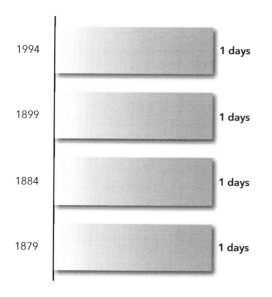

1994	1 days
1899	1 days
1884	1 days
1879	1 days

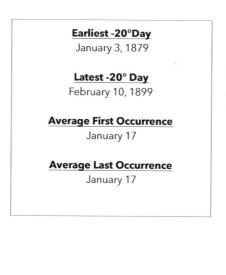

Earliest -20°Day
January 3, 1879

Latest -20° Day
February 10, 1899

Average First Occurrence
January 17

Average Last Occurrence
January 17

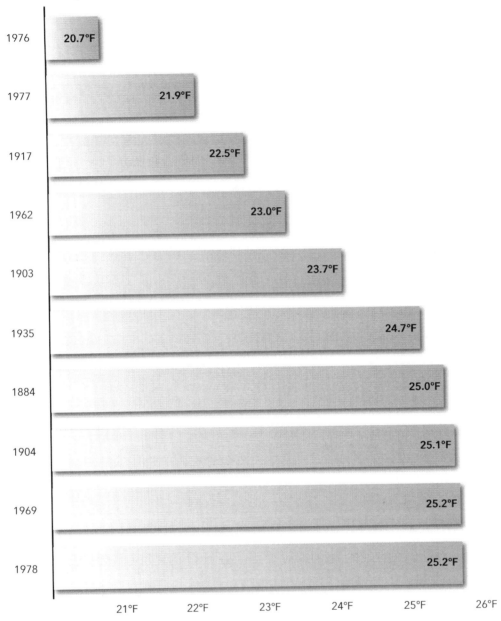

Year	Temperature
1976	20.7°F
1977	21.9°F
1917	22.5°F
1962	23.0°F
1903	23.7°F
1935	24.7°F
1884	25.0°F
1904	25.1°F
1969	25.2°F
1978	25.2°F

Average of Daily Temperatures: December, January, February, 1879-2018.

Temperature Perception

Temperature is a tangible, measurable condition. We can scientifically show how higher or lower temperatures affect the world and the objects around us. But temperature also influences our senses, our mood, and our feelings, things that are much more difficult to measure. Think about how differently you feel (physically and emotionally) on a 25-degree winter day, a 70-degree spring afternoon, and a humid 95-degree summer scorcher. It's much more than simply being hot or cold.

In meteorology, we have two formulas that attempt to capture what you're feeling as the temperatures fluctuate. On TV, you'll often hear them referred to as "feels like" temperatures: the Heat Index and the Wind Chill.

Heat Index =

$$-42.379 + 2.04901523T + 10.14333127R - 0.22475541TR - 6.83783 \times 10^{-3}T^2 - 5.481717 \times 10^{-2}R^2 + 1.22874 \times 10^{-3}T^2R + 8.5282 \times 10^{-4}TR^2 - 1.99 \times 10^{-6}T^2R^2$$

T is the ambient dry bulb temperature in degrees Fahrenheit and
R is the relative humidity in integer percentage.
There are a few "adjustment" formulas for varying relative humidities; this is the base formula.

Heat Index

The Heat Index uses a complex mathematical formula to combine the temperature and the humidity to figure out how you might perceive the atmosphere. When the temperatures are very warm, high humidity makes us feel as though it's even warmer.

That feeling has a lot to do with how your body is designed to dissipate heat. When it's hot, you start to sweat. As the water sits on your skin, it absorbs heat from your body until it evaporates. That "latent heat of evaporation" releases the heat into the air and your body cools down. However, when the air is already humid (filled with moisture), it's more difficult for the sweat to evaporate and your body holds on to its heat. You feel warmer.

The Heat Index is an approximation of that feeling or perception of the temperature.

Here's what the formula cranks out:

+ On a 60°F day with low humidity, it feels like 60°F.

+ On a 60°F day with high humidity, it feels like 60°F.

There's not a big difference when the base temperature is low.

+ On a 90°F day with low humidity (30%), it still feels like 90°F.

There's not a big difference when the humidity is low. However,

+ On a 90°F day with moderate humidity (50%), it feels like 95°F.

+ On a 90°F day with high humidity (80%), it feels like 113°F.

Cricket Thermometer

In 1897, noted physicist (and Ohio Wesleyan graduate) Amos Dolbear published a research paper called "The Cricket as a Thermometer." He noted that there was a definite relationship between temperatures and the speed of a cricket's chirps. His formula works for the snowy tree cricket, *Oecanthus fultoni*, but also seems to hold true for the more common field cricket.

His findings and formula became known as Dolbear's Law:

$$T_F \cong 40 + N_{15}$$

Where T_F is the approximate temperature in degrees Fahrenheit;

and N_{15} is the number of chirps in 15 seconds.

So, count the number of cricket chirps in 15 seconds, add 40 and you'll have a fairly close approximation of the temperature in degrees Fahrenheit! (It would seems that crickets aren't fond of chirping below 40°F.) If you want the result in celsius, count the number of chirps in 8 seconds and add five ($T_C \cong 5 + N_8$).

The Heat Index becomes more dramatic when base temperatures are high.

The National Weather Service will issue advisories, watches, and warnings when the Heat Index is likely to affect your health. The criteria for heat advisories and heat warnings vary slightly from place to place in the U.S., but in general, they involve a heat-index threshold of 105°F.

Heat Advisory: In the next 12 to 24 hours, the Heat Index is expected to reach 100°F to 104°F for at least three hours, it's likely to happen two days or more consecutive days, and the overnight lows are likely to remain warmer than 75°F.

Excessive Heat Watch: There is a potential for the Heat Index to reach or exceed 105°F for at least three hours within the next 24 to 72 hours or to be that warm for two or more consecutive days.

Excessive Heat Warning: The Heat Index is expected to reach or exceed 105°F for at least three hours within the next 12 hours, the heat is likely to continue for at least two consecutive days, and the overnight lows are likely to remain warmer than 75°F.

In the midst of a multi-day heat wave or early in the warm season, the watches and advisories may be issued at lower criteria.

It's better to be safe than to find yourself in a dangerous or compromising situation. Stay hydrated. Find some shade. And try to keep cool.

Wind Chill

This is the formula that was updated and adopted by the National Weather Service in November 2001:

$$\text{Wind Chill (°F)} = 35.74 + 0.6215T - 35.75(V^{0.16}) + 0.4275T(V^{0.16})$$

In the formula, T represents the current air temperature in degrees Fahrenheit and V is the wind speed in miles per hour. Plug in the numbers, do the math, and you'll get the wind chill!

In the winter, you'll hear forecasters spending a lot of time talking about the wind chill. "Bundle up when you head outside," they'll say, "because the wind chills are really brutal!"

You won't find the wind chill on a thermometer. It's another "feels like" number.

When the chilly, winter wind blows against your skin, it makes you feel colder because it causes moisture to evaporate from your skin. Again, that perception isn't something you can physically measure, but it can be estimated by doing some math.

The colder the air temperature, the faster the wind chill falls. For example, at 20°F, it takes a 60 mph wind to drop the wind chill to -5°F. But at 5°F, it only takes a 5 mph breeze to drop the wind chill to the same -5°F (a 60 mph wind will drop it to -26°F).

At wind chills of -20°F, enough moisture can be wicked from your skin to cause frostbite in a matter of minutes.

The wind chill only affects living things. Your car doesn't perceive it and the engine block won't get colder than the actual air temperature. The picnic table in the yard doesn't either. But your dogs do. So, make sure to let them back inside as soon as they've done their business!

Wind Chill Advisory: Wind chills of -10F° to -24°F are expected along with winds of 10 mph or stronger.

Wind Chill Warning: Wind chills of -25°F or colder are expected along with winds of 10 mph or stronger.

Coldest Wind Chill in Columbus

January 20, 1985, was one of the coldest days in Columbus history, so it's not surprising that it also holds the record for coldest wind chill.

National Weather Service Science & Operations Officer Seth Binau went digging through the climate records for Columbus and discovered this for the day:

"During daylight hours temps never got past -13F and it was still -16F air temp at noon! The -47F wind chill is from the 10AM hourly ob (air temp of -19F with a sustained west wind of 20 mph). This is the coldest wind chill I've ever found in the hourly CMH database."

While it may not be THE coldest morning low (that's -22°F on January 19, 1994) or the longest duration of über cold, it is definitely the day that FELT the coldest!

70 Degrees v. "70 Degrees"

A great question about temperature perception arrived by e-mail.

> Dear Mr. McPeek,
> Here is a burning weather question I have had for years!!! Please put an end to this mystery.
> 70 degrees is beautiful and comfortable during the day - with sunshine! Why is it such a miserable temp at might when there is not any sunshine?
> Thank you for answering this question!
> Tami
> Cardington, Ohio

The answer is more about perception than any real weather phenomenon. Seventy degrees is seventy degrees whether it's daytime or nighttime, in the sunshine or in the dark; it's a number on the thermometer. But our perception of 70°F may be radically different at certain times of the day.

Humans function pretty well at 70°F. In fact, most people consider it a beautiful temperature to be out and about. It's neither too hot nor too cool for outdoor activities. However, we tend to sleep better when the temperatures are cooler. A 55-degree night with a blanket is great weather for sleeping. Leave the windows open and enjoy. Seventy degrees, though, makes the bedroom feel like an oven — unless you're in Key West where 70 degrees is positively chilly sleeping weather.

Some experts say a cooler body temperature is associated with better sleep. Here's an explanation from the National Sleep Research Project in Australia:

> To drop off we must cool off; body temperature and the brain's sleep-wake cycle are closely linked. That's why hot summer nights can cause a restless sleep. The blood flow mechanism that transfers core body heat to the skin works best between 18 and 30 degrees [64-86°F]. But later in life, the comfort zone shrinks to between 23 and 25 degrees [73-77°F] - one reason why older people have more sleep disorders.

Our bodies want to be cooler when we sleep. That's why a 70-degree bedroom is so uncomfortable but a 70-degree office is pretty comfortable.

Comfort also has a lot to do with humidity. When it's muggy, it's more difficult to get comfortable for sleeping.

Sleeping in the Heat

Here are some great tips for getting to sleep on a hot night:

+ Increase the air circulation by opening opposing windows or use an electric fan to create an artificial breeze.
+ Cooling your feet will help cool the rest of your body; wear a damp pair of socks to bed.
+ Heat rises; sleep downstairs where it tends to be cooler.
+ Lightly dampen the bed's top sheet with a spray bottle; the evaporation will cool the bed.

Dew Point and Comfort

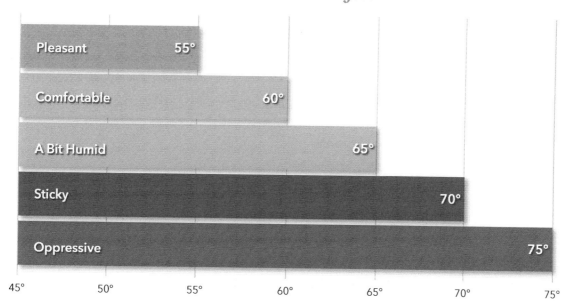

Central Ohio's Growing Season

Central Ohio's growing season is, in general, determined by the last frost in the spring and the first frost in the autumn. In between, we're lucky enough to have some of the most incredible agricultural conditions in the world and farmers know how to make the most of it.

Average First and Last Frost and Freeze Dates in Central Ohio

	Avg. Last Spring Freeze <=32°F	Avg. Last Spring Frost <=36°F	Avg. First Autumn Frost <=36°F	Avg. First Autumn Freeze <=32°F
Columbus	Apr 19	May 02	Oct 10	Oct 23
Marion	Apr 29	May 09	Sep 30	Oct 11
Circleville	Apr 26	May 09	Oct 04	Oct 14
Coshocton	May 02	May 13	Sep 30	Oct 09

Between 1879 and 2016, the latest spring freeze in Columbus was May 16, 2016, and the latest spring frost happened on June 11, 1972. That's why the general recommendation in Central Ohio is to wait until at least Mother's Day weekend to plant your annuals! The earliest autumn frost was September 18, 1959, and the earliest, growing season-ending freeze was September 21, 1962.

Of course, the actual length of the season varies a bit from year to year. Plus, rain can cause wet conditions that keep farmers (and gardeners) out of the fields (and flower beds) well into April and May, delaying planting and taking a bite out of yields.

NWS Frost & Freeze Program

The NWS Freeze and Frost Program issues watches and warnings at the beginning and end of the growing season. In the spring, notices will be issued any time cold temperatures may cause damage to new plants and crops. The program ends when the threat of frost has passed for the season. In the fall, the program runs until the end of the growing season when most of the area has experienced a widespread killing frost or hard freeze.

Freeze Warning: Issued when significant, widespread freezing temperatures are expected during the growing season.

Freeze Watch: There is a potential for significant, widespread freezing temperatures within the next 24-36 hours.

Frost Advisory: Low temperatures are expected to be 33°F to 36°F (often on clear and calm nights) during the growing season.

Defending the Garden from Frost

Frost often forms on cold, clear nights when there is a little bit of moisture in the air. It's nearly the same process as when dew drops collect on the morning grass but, in this case, the temperatures are cold enough that the water turns to ice crystals.

What is a Killing Frost?

When the thermometer hits 36°F, a light frost is possible. That seems odd because water can't turn to ice until 32°F, right? Well, it's because standard temperature readings are taken about six feet above the ground. At ground level, though, it may be a few degrees cooler, making it all the way down to freezing. Viola! Frost at "36°F!"

The amount of damage caused by a frost or freeze depends on the actual temperature and the length of time the plants are near or below freezing. Some annuals are just hardy enough to survive a very light frost. The edges of their leaves may turn brown but they'll survive. A hard or "killing" frost will finish off most plants for the season.

- Light Freeze: 29°F to 32°F for an hour or so. It'll do some damage to hardy plants but they'll survive. Tender annuals are pretty much done for the season.

- Moderate Freeze: 25°F to 28°F for several hours. Even hardy annuals will have a difficult time but a few will make it. Most will call it a season and die.

- Killing Freeze: 27°F or below for four hours or more. It's over.

Hoarfrost is white and feathery and forms when ice crystals collect on the plants. Rime is similar to a freezing rain in that it collects on the plants as water and then freezes, creating a glaze on the leaves. A black frost isn't actually a frost at all; it's when the temperatures get cold enough to damage the plant even if ice doesn't form at all.

Interestingly, your thermometer may show temperatures above freezing but frost will still form. That's because the air on the ground is slightly cooler than the air near the thermometer, which we tend to keep three to six feet above the ground at a height that's easier for us to read. While the reading may say 35-37°F, the air near your plants is actually closer to 29-32°F.

To protect the garden, you have to either keep the water from collecting on the plants or keep the environment warm enough to avoid freezing.

There are two kinds of cooling that cause frost: advective and radiational. Advective cooling happens when a cooler air mass moves into the area. Radiational cooling happens when heat radiates away from the ground and into the air.

When a cold front rolls in and brings much colder air into your garden, temperatures can drop quickly and significantly. Protecting your plants from those changes can be very difficult, if not impossible, because the temperature drop is so severe. Radiational cooling, however, is much easier to mitigate, especially when we're still early in the cool season.

When trying to salvage the garden, the goal is to trap and hold heat near the plants. You can often use the radiational cooling itself to your advantage.

During the day, the sun warms the air and the ground. The soil retains much more of the heat than the air and stays warmer even after the sun goes down. At night, that heat radiates away from the soil and warms the air in the process. If you can trap that warmer air and keep it near the plants, you can sometimes prevent frost from forming and harming those plants.

Before dusk, cover the plants with a dry blanket to hold in the heat. If the blanket gets wet, change it out before evaporative cooling has a chance to make the plants cold again. Newspaper usually isn't recommended because it gets wet too quickly. Be sure to remove the covers soon after sunrise so the sun has a chance to warm the soil.

Plastic covers can be effective because they act like a greenhouse. But be very careful with them. Make sure there's a vent in the top during the day otherwise the plants will overheat as the sun beats down on the enclosure. Seal the vent at night to hold in the heat collected during the day. Be sure the plastic doesn't touch the plants; the material itself can get cold enough to freeze the leaves even while it traps some of the warmer air in the tent.

Covering small plants with an inverted, large, plastic pot can be helpful.

Mulch also adds a layer of insulation throughout the garden.

The Colorado Master Gardener Program suggests putting medium-sized (C-7) holiday lights inside a framed, plastic tent. Their tests showed a strand of 25 lights was much more effective than a single, large, warming bulb.

As counterintuitive as it may seem, give the garden a good watering during a sunny day before the cold air arrives. Water holds heat even better than the soil. Wet dirt stays warmer than dry dirt.

A fan can help. Circulating the air in the garden can keep the moisture from collecting on the leaves where it has a chance to freeze and form frost.

Degree Days

Degree Days are a useful way of comparing how much energy we use trying to keep our homes and offices comfortable. It's handy for comparing one part of the country with another. Degree Days are also a good method of determining when crops may be ready for harvest.

Let's start with energy. For that, we use Heating Degree Days (HDD) and Cooling Degree Days (CDD). They start with a "base" of 65°F, a temperature at which many people are relatively comfortable. To be warmer than 65°F, we need energy to heat the room. To be cooler, we'll need energy to run the air conditioning. If the room is already at 65°F, we need neither the furnace nor the AC and we save the energy.

Corn growing in the fields near Hilliard. Corn needs 2,500 or more GDD to reach maturity.

To determine HDD/CDD, first find the average temperature for the day by adding the high and the low then dividing by two. If the number is warmer than 65, it will take energy to cool it down (CDDs). If the number is cooler than 65, it'll take energy to warm up (HDDs).

The heating degree year runs July 1 until June 30. The cooling degree year starts January 1 and runs until December 31.

As examples in different parts of the United States: Barrow, Alaska, is much colder and people there need to heat their homes almost continuously. They pile up a lot more Heating Degree Days than the homeowners in Hilo, Hawaii, who never need to switch on the furnace. Cleveland lies in the middle.

Air conditioning is not all that necessary in Barrow, Alaska, and their Cooling Degree Days are practically nonexistent. Hilo, Hawaii, and Key West, Florida, though, use the AC a lot. Bismarck, North Dakota, and Cleveland have fairly similar cooling needs.

Real-world HDD/CDD Examples

Example #1: Today's high in Columbus was 74°F and the low was 42°F.

Find the average temperature for the day:

(74+42) / 2 = 58°

Then you can determine the HDDs:

65 - 58 = **7 Heating Degree Days**

Example #2: Today's high in Columbus was 86°F and the low 62°F.

(86+62) / 2 = 74°

74 - 65 = **9 Cooling Degree Days**

Farmers and gardeners can use degree days to get an idea of when crops will be ready for harvest. Growing Degree Days (GDDs) use a baseline of 50°F and assume that plants will do no growing below 50°F or above 86°F.

So, if a Franklin County Farm Bureau member in Hilliard records a morning low of 59° and an afternoon high of 81°, the crop has accumulated another 20 GDDs and it's that much closer to harvest.

According to an Extension fact sheet written by Ohio State University Horticulture and Crop Science professors Donald J. Eckert and Peter R. Thomison, corn can take up to 2500-3000 GDD to reach maturity, depending on where it's planted in Ohio. Other research suggests soybeans average about 1600 GDD to maturity. Oats need up to 1750 GDD. But that forsythia bush in your front yard can start to bloom with bright-yellow flowers after only 15 GDD.

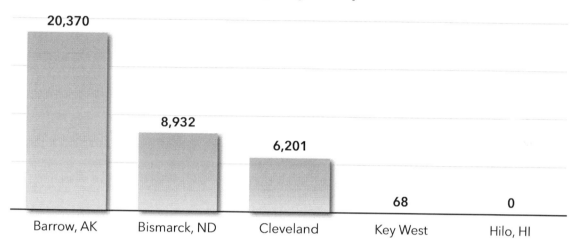

Heating Degree Days

Barrow, AK	Bismarck, ND	Cleveland	Key West	Hilo, HI
20,370	8,932	6,201	68	0

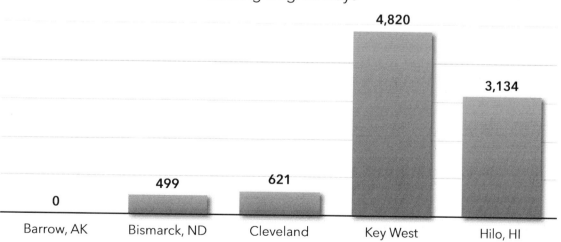

Cooling Degree Days

Barrow, AK	Bismarck, ND	Cleveland	Key West	Hilo, HI
0	499	621	4,820	3,134

Clouds

They drift by every day and we barely give them a thought. Puffy, streaky, white, gray, rainy, or icy, they're almost always there. On the rare, totally-clear, bright-blue days, we miss them and the shapes they create.

Clouds are woven into the fabric of our language. We may exercise "cloudy judgement" or make unusual decisions because we have "clouds in our eyes." We know there are plenty of positives in life because "every cloud has a silver lining" and when we are happy, we are "sitting on Cloud Nine."

Clouds fill the atmosphere on Earth and on several of the other planets in our solar system. They're simultaneously practical and whimsical.

What are clouds?

On Jupiter and Saturn, researchers think the dense layers clouds are made primarily of ammonia and sulfur. They're mostly methane on Neptune and Uranus. On Earth, our clouds are overwhelmingly made of water vapor.

Most of the air in our atmosphere has at least a little bit of water vapor in it. When that air rises, it cools and the water molecules in it begin to vibrate less and less until they eventually condense into tiny water droplets and visible clouds. When it's really, really high and really, really cold, those water droplets can freeze to create clouds made of ice crystals.

Cloud Spotter Guide

Until 1803, clouds were just "clouds." They didn't have actual names. No one had systematically studied their differences and given them classifications. Then along came Luke Howard. His essays and writings have earned him the title "Father of Meteorology." He was an all-around science guy and amateur meteorologist in London who kept extensive records of the daily conditions.

In a lengthy paper, "On the Modifications of Clouds," presented to a London debate club, Howard proposed an entire classification system for clouds. It was later adopted by the meteorological community and is still in use today. The World Meteorological Organization (WMO) has updated it several times and it now comes in two volumes[1].

For many of the clouds you see each day, naming them is as easy as stringing together some root words that describe their altitude and shape.

So, a high (cirrus), flat, widespread (stratus) cloud would be called "cirrostratus." Mid-level (alto), puffy (cumulus) clouds are "altocumulus." Low, flat clouds are "stratus." And puffy, rain-producing clouds are "cumulonimbus."

There are also lots of specialized clouds that have their own names like lenticular, orographic, pileus, and undulatus. Roll, funnel, mammatus, shelf, and wall clouds are often associated with strong thunderstorms.

Fog

Fog is a cloud on the ground. It can create an eerie mood, snarl traffic, and even cause school delays.

Heat radiates away from the earth and, on a cloudless night, it can happen fairly quickly. As temperatures fall, the temperature and the dew point get closer and closer. When they meet, the water vapor in the air begins to condense and we get clouds. In this case, they are clouds on the ground. Fog.

We need two ingredients to create fog: moisture and cool air.

Fog often forms in valleys and low-lying areas because that terrain often provides the perfect ingredients. Rivers, streams, ponds, and other bodies of water are often found in low-lying areas because water tends to roll downhill and collect in the lowest spot. Cold air behaves the same way. It also tends to collect in low-lying areas. That's called Cold Air Drainage. Cool air is denser than warm air, so it sinks instead of rising. Since it's not traveling far enough or fast enough to warm up as it travels downhill, it pools in the valleys, just like water.

When the temperature and the dew point meet, the air becomes fully saturated and water vapor begins to condense.

---

[1] Volume I is titled "Manual on the Observation of Clouds and Other Meteors" (ISBN 92-63-10407-7). Volume II is titled "International Cloud Atlas" (ISBN 92-63-12407-8).

Combine the cool air with water and viola! Fog.

When fog is at its thickest, many schools in rural areas will issue delays for the safety of walking students and buses in rural areas. Safety is the overwhelming concern.

Driving in Fog

When driving in fog, it is best to use low beam headlights so there is less reflection of the fog and more light on the road. Having your lights on also makes it easier for other drivers to see you because it activates your tail lights, too.

Dense Fog Advisory: Widespread fog is expected to reduce visibilities to 1/4-mile or less over a large area for two or more hours.

Freezing Fog Advisory: Freezing fog is expected to leave behind a light accumulation of ice on exposed surfaces.

Fog often dissipates by mid-morning as the sun warms the atmosphere. The sun doesn't actually "burn off" the fog; it boosts the temperatures so the air temperature and the dew point separate. Once the two temperatures are separated, new condensation stops, evaporation reoccurs, and the fog disappears. During the day, as a breeze develops, the wind can also help break up the fog.

Fog shrouds a Central Ohio golf course on a cool, October morning. Photo courtesy Edwin Wilson.

Here's a question from Bryan about clouds:

> "Can you help me out? My 3 yr old daughter asked me why the clouds were a little bit grey today, I told her they had only a little bit of rain in them."

Well, it does have something to do with the volume of water vapor in the clouds -- but probably not in the way you're imagining.

When you're in an airplane, seeing the clouds from above, no matter how tall they are, they're white. That's because you're seeing them from the top where the sunlight is hitting them directly.

From the ground, we usually see the bottom of the clouds, the shadowed side. As the cloud gets taller, less sunlight gets through it, and so it looks darker from below. The cloud is dark because it's shadowing itself.

It's just like holding your hand up to block the sun from your eyes or standing under a leafy tree; it's darker in the shadow. The top of your hand and the top of the tree are still bathed in bright sunlight. Similarly, the top part of the cloud is white as it starts blocking the sunlight and it gets darker and darker as more layers of the cloud block and scatter the light more and more.

In many cases, taller clouds are, indeed, more likely to include rain. So, while there seems to be a connection between the rain and the darkness of the clouds, that's a misidentified cause-and-effect relationship. The dark color of the clouds is all about the shadows.

Water vapor clouds are nearly always white but sometimes they cast shadows on themselves making their lower portions look dark and ominous.

Big, puffy altocumulus clouds may block a lot of the sunlight but not have any rain to drop. Thick stratus clouds may not be as tall and may not block as much of the sunlight (so they look a little lighter) but they still have lots of rain with them (in which case, they become nimbostratus).

Clouds become darker because they are taller or thicker and are blocking more sunlight, not because they're necessarily "carrying more rain."

Eerie, wavy, *undulatus* clouds over Columbus.

The "Cloud Blanket" and Earth's Solar Budget

When you crawl into bed on a cold, winter night, you pull a thick blanket up to your neck and, in a few minutes, you're cozy and warm, ready for a good snooze. When you first climb under the covers, the sheets and blankets are the same temperature as the room but, once you're in, they warm up. The blanket traps your body heat and the temperature rises in your sleepy-time cocoon.

The same thing happens outside when we have a thick deck of clouds. The Earth soaks up sunlight and the surface gets warmer, even on winter days. At night, when the sun stops adding energy, that heat radiates away from the surface. Some of it gets absorbed in the atmosphere, some radiates away into space, and some is reflected back to the surface by the clouds.

Ah ha! The clouds! When they reflect the heat back toward the surface, the air stays a little bit warmer! That's why, on the same night, areas with clouds are much warmer than nearby areas with a clear sky. Sometimes fog will form under the clear sky because those areas loose enough heat to reach the dew point but places with an overcast sky will be only hazy or even fog-free.

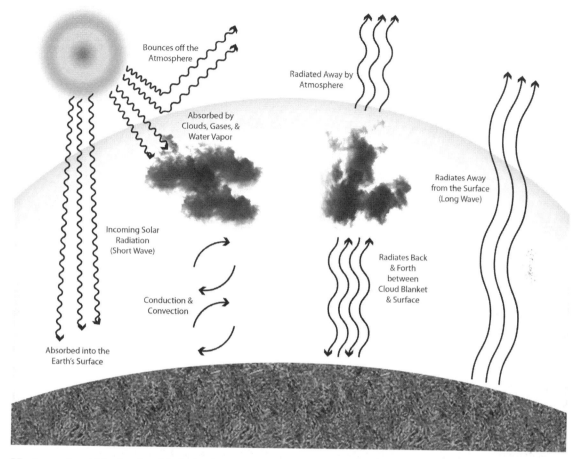

Having a cloud blanket is a big help during a cold winter night. It's like a comfy quilt for your entire region.

Precipitation

"Precipitation" is a generic term and refers to any form of water falling out of the sky (see hydrometeor).

Here is the AMS Glossary of Meteorology definition:

> All liquid or solid phase aqueous particles that originate in the atmosphere and fall to the earth's surface.

Rain, snow, sleet, hail, and graupel are all forms of precipitation and they are an important part of any forecast.

Rain

It rains a lot here. In fact, on average, Central Ohio gets nearly two inches more rain each year than Seattle, Washington, and 2.38 inches more than Chicago. We're *that* wet.

Columbus Normal Precipitation

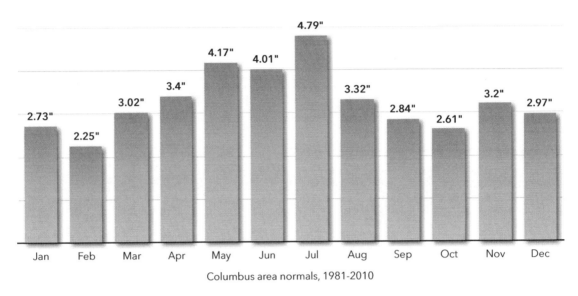

Columbus area normals, 1981-2010

Columbus gets a little more than 39 inches of precipitation each year, on average. Most months average less than 3.5" but we have a relatively clear "wet season" in May, June, and July when the averages pop up above four inches.

Bear in the mind, the averages include more than just rain. For the winter months, the precipitation totals may include rain and snow or both. When it's snow or ice, it's melted down and measured as a liquid, like the rain. Separate records are kept for the depth of new snow and the amount of snow accumulated on the ground.

In an average year, Columbus will have about 22 more rainy days than dry days. Most of those days only have a trace of precipitation. About 24 days collect half an inch or more. Thankfully, it's a very rare day that sees three inches or more. Only twice, has Columbus recorded four inches or more: 5.13" on July 13, 1992 and 4.79" on January 21, 1959.

Is that moderate or heavy rain?

The definitions for rainfall rates are very specific:

"Light" rain falls between a trace and 0.10" per hour, but no more than 0.01" in six minutes.

"Moderate" rain comes down between 0.11" and 0.30" per hour, but no more than 0.03" in six minutes.

"Heavy" rain falls at more than 0.30" per hour or more than 0.03" in six minutes.

What makes it rain?

Like many things in meteorology, rain is all about rising air. Whether it's caused by convection, orography, or frontal boundaries, lifting the air is the name of the game. It sounds counterintuitive because we think of rain as something that falls from the sky. But it begins with the air going in the opposite direction.

With a combination of water vapor, cooling, condensation, nuclei, the right pressures and conveniently-shaped molecules, we eventually form raindrops and gravity pulls them back from the atmosphere onto our picnics and parades.

Rain is part of the essential water cycle that makes life on our planet successful. Without it, rivers wouldn't run, aquifers would dry out, there would be much less erosion (e.g. no Grand Canyon), the rain forests wouldn't be as lush, and your favorite snow-capped mountain probably wouldn't have much of an annual ski area. Agriculture depends on rain, even where there is irrigation. (Think about how much water a typical Ohio farm needs in a season.) And it's even good for occasionally washing your car.

> **Heaviest Rain**
>
> The WMO reports that the greatest one-hour rainfall in the world happened on June 22, 1947, in Hold, Missouri. They collected 12.0" of rain in only 60 minutes; that's nearly a quarter-inch every minute!

While it is sometimes inconvenient, we depend on water falling from the sky. So, the next time we feel like complaining about the drizzle, we may consider being thankful instead. Let's try singing in the rain!

How do raindrops form?

You need at least two things to form a raindrop:

+ water vapor and

+ a nucleus.

When the atmosphere reaches a saturation point — it is holding as much water as it can — adding a tiny bit more water vapor or just barely dropping the temperature will start the condensation process. If there are tiny particles in the air, say, for example, minute dust particles, the water molecules can begin to collect around them. As they coalesce, the mass grows and becomes a raindrop. The larger and heavier it gets, the more likely it is to become heavier than the wind can support and then it falls toward the ground. Thanks, gravity.

The same process happens millions and millions of times in every shower and thunderstorm.

> **Turn Your Headlights On When It's Raining**
>
> Ohio law requires you to turn on your headlights when your windshield wipers are on.
>
> ORC 4513.03 says, unless you're driving a "motorized bicycle," your vehicle's headlights have to be on from sunset to sunrise, whenever the natural light isn't enough to see a thousand feet ahead, or "[a]t any time when the windshield wipers of the vehicle are in use because of precipitation on the windshield."
>
> It's a secondary offense, so the police can't stop you just for that, but they can tack it on to a speeding ticket or onto something else for which they legitimately stopped you. It's a minor misdemeanor which generally carries a fine of up to $150.

Drizzle

Drizzle is different from rain because the drops are smaller and they tend to reduce visibility more than rain. Still, the droplets are heavy enough to fall to the ground instead of being suspended in the air like fog. Technically, it's also slightly different from "mist" but, in practice, the terms often are used almost interchangeably.

Columbus' Top 10 Wettest Calendar Years

The wettest month recorded in Columbus was July 1992 with 12.36" of rain. The same month includes the wettest single day ever recorded in Columbus: July 13, 1992, when 5.13" of rain fell at (what was then called) Port Columbus.

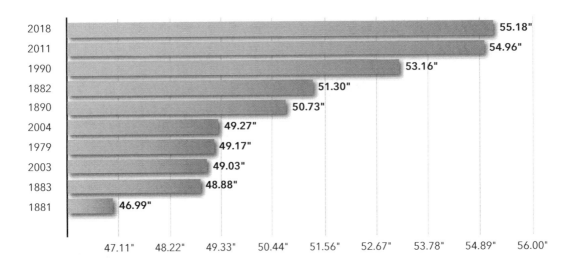

Columbus' Top 10 Wettest Calendar Days

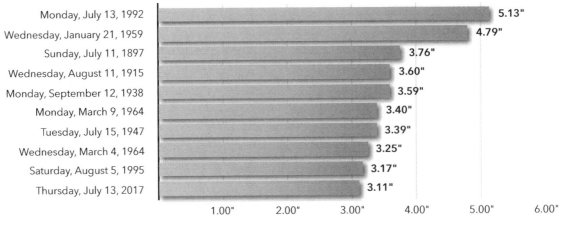

Daily Precip Totals, Columbus area, 1879-2018.

As the sun shines through the mist, a rainbow forms in a fountain at Township Hall Park in Lewis Center.

The leprechaun's treasure is safe, y'know. You'll never actually get to the end of that rainbow, even though, plain as day, it's coming down right there, in those trees, just beyond the neighbor's house.

A rainbow is an optical phenomenon caused by both reflection and refraction of light through water droplets or ice crystals in the air. It's always in the sky opposite from and at a 42° angle to the light source. That light is most often the sun but the moon can sometimes cast just enough light to create rainbows of its own (moonbows).

We usually see partial arcs, depending on what's generating the water droplets (rain, a waterfall, spray from waves, steam from a geyser, etc.). If we're in just

Optical Illusions

When you see a vivid rainbow, you usually see distinct bands of colors, red through violet. However, if you see a black-and-white photograph of a rainbow, you won't see bands at all, just a gradation of bright fading to gone. The bands themselves are just an illusion created by the anatomical construction of our eyes.

the right place and have just the right conditions, you might be treated to a bright, half-arc. Sadly, from the ground, we can't get high enough to see a rainbow's entire arc. From a plane, though, you can sometimes see the whole circle!

Remembering the Colors

Mnemonics are a great way to remember a list of things like the order of the planets, the notes on a staff, or the colors of the rainbow. They're usually a simple word or phrase that helps jog your memory.

A vivid double rainbow forms outside the ABC6 studios after a brief, heavy rain.

For rainbows, the colors of the spectrum appear as red, orange, yellow, green, blue, indigo, and violet. That's a lot to try to remember unless you use a simple memory crutch. Try one of these:

- Roy G. Biv
- Richard Of York Gave Battle In Vain
- Read Out Your Good Book In Verse
- Rinse Out Your Granny's Boots in Vinegar

Thunderstorms

Thunderstorms, as you'd guess from their name, inherently include thunder. Thunder is produced by lightning. Therefore, thunderstorms must include lightning.

The National Severe Storms Laboratory in Norman, Oklahoma, says there are nearly 16 million thunderstorms around the world every year, and almost 2,000 are raging at any given moment. The United States is home to an enormous percentage of them. NOAA estimates there are nearly 100,000 thunderstorms in the US every year and Ohio gets its fair share.

Thankfully, not all thunderstorms are severe.

Map depicting the average number of thunderstorm days each year throughout the United States. Ohio averages 30 to 40 days while Central Florida has more than 100. Courtesy: NOAA/NWS JetStream

A thunderstorm, in general terms, is any convective storm (a storm with a strong updraft) that produces lightning and thunder. Individual storm cells usually last less than two hours but a group of them can produce new generations of cells for long periods of time. If they're powerful enough, thunderstorms can grow taller than 50,000 feet and produce rain, hail, strong wind gusts, and even tornadoes.

Types of Thunderstorms

All thunderstorms start with rising air. (Sound familiar?) And there are several mechanisms that produce strong enough updrafts to create significant thunderstorms.

Most thunderstorms involve convection, a process that causes less-dense air to rise through more-dense air. It's kind of like what happens when you hold a beach ball under the water in the swimming pool; it pops to the surface. The air inside the ball is less dense (the molecules aren't packed together as tightly) than the water outside the ball, so it rises until it gets to the surface where the inside and outside densities are about the same. A helium balloon floats for the same reason. The helium inside the balloon is less dense than the air outside the balloon, so it forces the balloon to rise.

The strength of a thunderstorm often depends on the strength of the convection. Weak convection tends to produce smaller, garden-variety storms. Strong convection can produce violent or severe storms. Convection is essential in the formation of super cells that produce tornadoes. Convection also is one of the essential forces for powering and sustaining hurricanes.

Airmass Thunderstorms

Airmass thunderstorms are usually not very strong. They have relatively weak convection and often don't last long. They are usually not much more than very strong rain showers, barely strong enough to have the uplift to generate lightning and thunder.

Some can even be referred to as "pure convection." They are the "pop-up" storms we get on a summer afternoon when the sun is hot and the humidity is high. With just a slight nudge, a bit of air begins to rise and pulls the air beneath it up, too. Eventually, there is a column of rising air that reaches a point in the atmosphere where condensation happens, raindrops form, and the cloud finally becomes tall enough to produce a strong enough charge for lightning.

Once in a while, airmass storms can happen in groups and become severe. A hot, humid, summer afternoon is the ideal breeding ground for these storms.

Frontal Thunderstorms

Frontal thunderstorms occur with fronts. Cold fronts are the usual suspects. It's not unusual for a cold front to be the focus of a line of storms. The frontal boundary can generate storms for long distances and create updrafts strong enough to become severe.

A cold front can act like a bulldozer, nosing through the atmosphere, and lifting the air in front of it as it crashes forward. On radar, it often shows up as a very distinct line of storms.

A very strong cold front, with very warm air on one side and much cooler air on the other, can generate particularly strong storms with deep convection. It is not unusual to see them become severe storms.

Thundersnow

Thunderstorms can happen any time of the year, even during our cold weather months. The mechanics (rising air) are the same whether the temperatures are 85°F or 25°F.

> Buckeye Macks
> Oct 29th, 8:51am
> With the horrible whispers that snow might be on it's way, my 10 yr old Kaitlyn Mack asked this morning "I know it thunders in a rain storm, but does it ever thunder in a snow storm?" And I was utterly perplexed because I really had no idea if that was possible... Any help you could give to solving our mystery would be greatly appreciated. Thanks!

Sometimes when a thunderstorm forms during the winter, there's just enough "warm" air to create an updraft, but the surrounding air is still cold enough that the precipitation stays frozen all the way to the ground. So, we get lightning and thunder as the snow falls! It's a thundersnow!

Thundersnow is a relatively rare occurrence and it tends to make The Weather Channel's Jim Cantore very excited: http://youtu.be/PdRWGMyeSYY.

Lightning

Lightning is Mother Nature's way of equalizing opposing electrical charges. It's very similar to scuffing your socks on the floor and getting a shock as you touch a doorknob. As you shuffle your feet, you build up an electrical charge. The doorknob has an opposite charge. When your finger gets close to the knob, the two charges jump out to cancel each other out and you get a shock.

In this case, it's a thunderstorm building up a charge. Updrafts and downdrafts move water and ice particles around in the storm and electrical charges build up in the cloud. The ice crystals in the top of the storm bump each other around and build up a positive charge, the bottom of the cloud develops a negative charge. NOAA researchers have found that storms that don't produce a lot of ice, also often fail to produce lightning.

The Earth, in general, has a net negative charge; so do the attached trees, houses, and you. But as the negatively-charged base of a storm approaches, a positive charge can begin to collect on the surface below it, almost like a shadow. (The opposite charges attract one another, just like magnets.) When a storm (or another cloud) builds up enough of a charge and gets close enough to an opposing charge, the electricity is released and we see lightning.

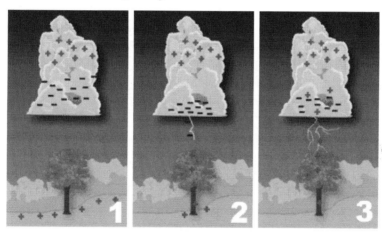

Thunderstorms build electrical charges because of ice and friction then lightning lashes out to neutralize those charges. Images courtesy NWS JetStream.

The process starts when the cloud sends down a "stepped leader," like negatively-charged fingers reaching toward the earth. At the same time, where there's a strong enough positive charge, similar fingers called "streamers" reach up toward the cloud. It's all invisible and happens in tiny fractions of a second. Until they connect. When the leaders and streamers join together, they form a channel that lets enormous amounts of electrical energy (an average of 30,000 amps and 100,000,000 volts at 50,000+ degrees)[2] travel between the cloud and the ground, briefly neutralizing the charges.

---

[2] By comparison, the typical household current in the United States is 15-20 amps and 110-120 volts. And you know how much it hurts when you get zapped by one of <u>those</u> outlets.

Cloud-to-Ground

Lightning monitors in the US track nearly 25-million lightning strikes from clouds to the ground every year. They are the most dangerous form of lightning. Hundreds of people are injured by lightning every year as it hits the ground or things connected to the ground.

Cloud-to-ground lightning connects the electrical charges in the sky to the charges on the earth. It releases immense amounts of energy as it strikes its targets.

Cloud-to-Cloud

It's much less common but lightning bolts can also jump between clouds to create an incredible show. Charged regions of separate storms can attract each other and lightning discharges then leap between the two. Thankfully, while they light up the sky, their destructive energy stays high in the atmosphere and poses little risk to people and things on the ground.

Intra-Cloud

A single, big thunderstorm can have multiple areas of positive and negative charges. If the charges build up enough, lightning can jump between them, inside the cloud itself. The lightning channel may be hidden from our view by the cloud, so we just see the whole cloud light up. Sometimes it's also called "sheet lightning."

"Heat Lightning"

"Heat Lightning" is a term often used to describe lightning we can see in the distance when we can't hear any thunder. The storm is far enough away that the sound of the thunder fades away before it reaches our ears. If you were closer to the storm, you'd hear the thunder.

The term was probably born because those conditions often happen during hot-weather months. People associated the heat with the storms and misinterpreted the causality.

Lightning itself is not caused by heat. It is created by opposing electrical charges. It *generates* a lot of heat. That lightning's heat is what makes the thunder. But the term "heat lightning" is a misnomer.

Ball Lightning

Pilots, passengers, and crew of some commercial airliners have reported seeing unusual phenomena that looks like lightning but is shaped like a ball. Others have reported seeing it atop power-line towers. They describe a small, sizzling sphere that appears to roll down the aisle of the aircraft or

Which way does lightning travel?

It actually goes both ways: up and down.

When opposing charges build up enough and then get near one another, an invisible channel (a "stepped leader") shoots out from the cloud toward the ground. At the same time, a similar (but oppositely-charged) channel shoots up toward the cloud. When they meet, there's a massive exchange of electricity that we see as a lightning bolt. In mere fractions of a second, there can be multiple flashes in the channel, neutralizing the charges between the cloud and the ground. Then the build-up process starts all over again.

Watch It Hit The Ground!

For a fantastic animated image of stepped-leaders moving from the cloud to the ground, visit WaitTenMinutes.com!

That's Some Serious Power!

It's estimated that the average lightning bolt could power a 100-watt incandescent light bulb for more than three months.

travel along the power lines. It can be multiple colors and reportedly disappears with no evidence of damage.

Interestingly, there have been no confirmed photographs of it and skeptics say it's not a real thing at all. So, ball lightning remains a scientific question. Kind of like UFOs.

Sprites & Elves

Sprites and elves are relatively newly-discovered forms of lightning or TLEs, transient luminous events. They've been theorized about for a long time but only recently documented.

Instead of discharging from cloud-to-cloud or cloud-to-ground, sprite flashes discharge into the upper reaches of the atmosphere, toward space, sometimes up to 60 miles above the top of their enormous parent thunderstorms. They're usually red and they seem to coincide with powerful lightning flashes in the storm below. We rarely get to see them because they tend to be fairly dim and, well, we're on the wrong side of the clouds. They've been photographed with highly-sensitive cameras aboard the International Space Station in its orbit more than 200 miles above the earth.

Elves were discovered by super-sensitive cameras on the Space Shuttle in 1992. They're huge, disk-shaped, glowing rings that can be up to 300 miles across. They tend to happen high above thunderstorms that have very active cloud-to-ground lightning. Look fast, though! They last for less than a thousandth of a second! NOAA scientists think they may be caused by an electromagnetic pulse that travels all the way up to the ionosphere!

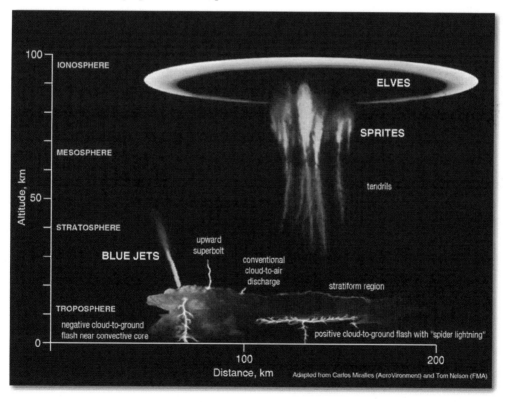

Lightning comes in many forms, happens at different altitudes, and strikes in many directions. Image courtesy: National Severe Storms Laboratory.

Lightning can strike nearly ten miles away from its parent thunderstorm. The electrical discharge can travel a long way before it finds an appropriate place to strike. When the storm itself is that far away, it may be beyond the horizon, with even the topmost part of the cloud out of view. You may see blue sky where you are. Then, BOOM! A lightning strike.

That's where the term "bolt from the blue" comes from. That seemingly random lightning bolt wasn't so random after all; it just traveled a long way from its parent storm.

In many of these cases, this is what is known as "positive lightning," lightning that starts with the positively-charged top of a large thunderstorm in the "anvil top." It reaches out to strike a negatively-charged portion of the earth that can be miles and miles away from the actual thunderstorm.

According to the National Weather Service, the Kennedy Space Center has documented anvil lightning traveling as far as 76 nautical miles (that's more than 87.5 miles)!

Lightning Dangers

The National Weather Service reports that, during the past 30 years, an average of nearly 70 Americans were killed annually by lightning. That's significantly more than the number killed by tornadoes or hurricanes. NOAA estimates that 300 to 400 Americans are injured by lightning in an average year. And lightning causes hundreds of millions of dollars in damage every year.

⚡ 10% of strike victims die

⚡ 70% suffer long-term injuries or disabilities

⚡ 85% of lightning strike victims are men

A 2013 study by Meteorologist Ron Holle, a long-time lightning researcher, found that Ohio is one of the most lightning-death-prone states in the nation; only Florida, Texas, and North Carolina are more deadly.

How Far Away is the Storm?

You can measure the distance of a storm by watching the lightning then counting the seconds until you hear the thunder.

Light travels at 670,616,629 mph (about 186,000 miles per second). By comparison, sound travels at roughly 761.21 mph (0.2114 miles per second), depending on the humidity, temperature, etc. So, the light from the lightning gets to your eyes almost instantaneously but it takes the sound of the thunder a little longer to reach your ears.

By understanding the mathematical relationship between the two, you can calculate the distance to the lightning by measuring the time between the flash and the boom.

To get a rough estimate of the number of miles between the lightning bolt and your location, count the seconds between seeing the flash and hearing the thunder, then divide by five.

Time between flash and sound	Approximate distance to the lightning
25 seconds	5 miles
20 seconds	4 miles
15 seconds	3 miles
10 seconds	2 miles
9 seconds	1.8 miles
8 seconds	1.6 miles
7 seconds	1.4 miles
6 seconds	1.2 miles
5 seconds	1 mile
4 seconds	0.8 mile
3 seconds	0.6 mile
2 seconds	0.4 mile
1 second	0.2 mile
0 seconds	It's here!

Do I have to get out of the pool?

Yes. It would be wisest to get out of the pool whenever there are storms in the area.

From: Philip
To: Marshall McPeek
Subject: When should you get out of the pool?
My 6 year old daughter Faith was at a pool oriented birthday party in Grove City, Ohio today and there was a small cell with thunder and increased wind speeds around 5 p.m. that did not last long. I told Faith she needed to get out of the water but no one else (adults and children) got out of the pool so she couldn't understand why she had to get out. The other adults said they would get out if they saw lightning but I was not going to let something happen to my daughter just because other adults weren't concerned. Can you let me know what to tell Faith about when it is time to stay away from the water or to get out of the pool?
I would appreciate a response I could share with her so she has a good understanding of this important safety issue.
Thank you for your time and consideration.
Philip

From: Marshall McPeek
To: Philip
Subject: RE: When should you get out of the pool?
Hi, Faith.
Sorry you had to jump out of the pool on Sunday... but your dad made the right decision.
Lightning can be very dangerous, especially around water. A lightning bolt can strike up to ten miles away from a thunderstorm (sometimes that's so far away that you can't even see the storm clouds). Any time you can hear thunder, you're close enough to be struck by the lightning. Always remember the 30-30 Rule: if you can count less than 30 seconds between seeing the lightning and hearing the thunder, it's time to go indoors; wait 30 minutes after the last thunderclap before going back outside.
Not to worry, there will be lots more wonderful pool days this summer! Enjoy the sunshine and be safe!
Regards,
Marshall McPeek

On a side note, since lightning frequently strikes bodies of water, you may be wondering why we don't see a lot of dead fish. That's because the positive charge that attracts the lightning to the water tends to build up only on the surface. When the strike happens, the deadly electrical current travels along the surface then dissipates. Things lurking a few feet below the water's surface are usually unaffected.

Unlike you in the pool, fish tend to stay well below the surface. When lightning strikes, they're fine. Humans tend to stay near the surface because, in general, they like to breathe air. That makes them much more susceptible to the deadly strikes.

Get out of the pool.

Odds of Being Struck

The National Weather Service reports the United States averaged 51 lightning deaths each year between 1984 and 2013. The number could be even higher because additional fatalities may not be recorded as lightning-related. Roughly 10% of lightning-strike victims die. The rest of left with varying degrees of disability. And, in the US, your odds of being struck by lightning are significantly better than winning the lottery.

Assuming an estimated US population of 318 million, here are the odds calculated by NOAA:

Odds of Becoming a Lightning Strike Victim (based on averages for 2004-2013)

Odds of being struck by lightning in a given year (reported deaths + injuries)	1/1,900,000
Odds of being struck by lightning in a given year (estimated total deaths + injuries)	1/960,000
Odds of being struck in your lifetime (est. 80 years)	1/12,000
Odds you will be affected by someone being struck (ten people affected for every one struck)	1/1,200

The National Hole-in-One Association (yes, there is one of those) says the odds of an amateur golfer acing is a hole is 12,500 to 1. So, your chances of being struck by lightning are actually slightly better!

The Ohio Lottery says, depending on the number of people playing on a particular day, the odds of winning the Mega Millions drawing is about 1 in 258,890,850, Powerball is 1 in 175,223,510 and Classic Lotto is 1 in 13,983,816. Your chances of getting struck by lightning are exponentially better.

Who Gets Struck?

Between 2006 and 2013, NWS statistics say the most likely victim of a deadly lightning strike was a man in his twenties who was fishing or playing soccer on a Saturday in July.

More than 80 percent of lightning fatalities are men. And the majority of fatal strikes happened during leisure activities, many of them on or near water.

"During this 8-year period fishermen accounted for more than three times as many fatalities as golfers, while camping and boating each accounted for almost twice as many deaths as golf," writes John S. Jensenius, Jr., a Lightning Safety Specialist for NOAA's National Weather Service who surveyed more than 260 lightning deaths.

For land-based sports, soccer players accounted for 41 percent of the fatalities, 28 percent were golfers, and 17 percent were runners. Farming and ranching made up about 37 percent of the work-related lightning-strike deaths, roofing only eight percent.

"Based on the media reports of the fatal incidents, many victims were either headed to safety at the time of the fatal strike or were just steps away from safety," Jensenius says. "For many activities, situational awareness and proper planning are essential to safety."

Stuff to Avoid

When there is lightning in the area, it's best to avoid things that conduct electricity.

⚡ Use your cell phone instead of a wired landline. The wires could become electrified if a nearby pole is stuck by lightning.

⚡ Avoid water and plumbing. Showering or washing the dishes during intense thunderstorms is not recommended because a nearby lightning strike can electrify the metal pipes, fixtures, and the water itself.

⚡ Avoid the garage. The concrete floor is likely to include steel rebar that could easily conduct electricity from a nearby lightning strike.

⚡ Unplug electronics to avoid power surges that can damage the fragile circuitry. Even high-quality surge-protectors are no match for a direct lightning strike.

30-30 Rule

"When thunder roars, go indoors," recommends NOAA's Lightning Safety slogan. It's good advice because if you can hear thunder, you're close enough to the storm to be struck by lightning. That's the basis for the 30-30 Rule:

If you count less than 30 seconds between seeing lightning and hearing the thunder, the storm is close enough to be dangerous. Take shelter.

Wait at least 30 minutes after hearing the last thunderclap before going back outside.

If You're Stuck Outside...

Don't do "the crouch" or "the squat."

For decades, if you were stuck outside, away from a safe shelter, and a lightning strike seemed imminent, the advice was: crouch down as much as possible, balancing on the balls of your feet to minimize contact with the ground, while covering your head and ears with your hands.

As of 2008, the National Weather service says, even if your hair begins to stand on end, don't crouch, just *run*. Run as fast as you can to get to a safe shelter and to minimize your chances of being hit by a second strike.

John Jensenius, NWS Lightning Safety Specialist, says the new recommendations are not "what to do in a dangerous situation" but, rather, how to avoid or get out of a dangerous situation. He says the crouch provides a false sense of safety and should be avoided, even as a last resort. Instead, plan ahead and don't get into that situation in the first place!

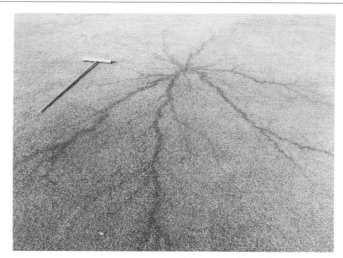

When lightning strikes the ground, it often creates a charged "zone" and you can be shocked by the current several feet from the actual strike. This image shows the burn marks where lightning struck a golf course and spread out in many directions. Photo by Ben Garbarek.

Lightning Myths

We've all seen lightning. We've all heard thunder. And we all think we know all about it. You might be surprised to find out what's fact and what's fiction!

MYTH: I'm safe from lighting in my car.

Sort of, but not completely. Being in the car is definitely better than being out in the open but it doesn't make you totally safe. If lightning hits the metal roof of the car, the electricity will travel through the shell, then into the steel belts in the tires, then into the ground. Along the way, it's likely to fry the electrical system, shatter the windows, and at least partially melt the tires. You don't want to be touching any of those things, or even leaning against the doors, while you're sitting in the vehicle. It's better to find a safe shelter.

Convertibles, motorcycles, and golf carts don't provide any protection. Neither does your fiberglass-hulled Corvette.

⚡ MYTH: My rubber-soled shoes will protect me from being struck by lightning.

Seriously? We're talking about enough electricity to power your entire house for weeks and temperatures of 50,000°F or more. A half-inch of flimsy rubber is NOT going to make any difference, nor will the tires in your car (see the myth above). Get to a decent shelter.

⚡ MYTH: Lightning-strike victims are electrified and shouldn't be touched.

On the contrary, a strike victim *should* be touched immediately. They are likely to need CPR or some other kind of significant first aid. Despite the rub-your-pajama-feet-on-the-carpet-and-shock-your-sister trick, our bodies don't store electricity efficiently and won't transfer a lightning bolt's current to a rescuer. Try to help a victim as quickly as possible.

⚡ MYTH: Lightning never strikes the same place twice.

If it's tall, pointy, and sitting by itself, it's likely to be struck over and over. New York's Empire State Building and Chicago's Willis Tower are struck dozens of times every year. Those tall broadcast towers get hit all the time, too. Heck, there are even *people* who've been struck multiple times.

Tall buildings that are likely to be struck by lightning are usually designed with protection systems that channel the electricity down the outside shell of the building and safely into the ground where it dissipates.

⚡ MYTH: If you're trapped outside when lightning is nearby, crouch in a ball or lie flat on the ground.

Actually, the crouching part was the official advice from the National Weather Service until 2008. Now, they say, it's better to sprint to the safest shelter you can find. Lying down increases your chances of being affected by the current that travels across the ground when lightning strikes the surface. The electricity can travel more than 60 feet. It can go even farther when the ground is saturated. The same is true if you curl up in a ball, balancing on the balls of your feet. Yes, you're a smaller target, but the ground current can still be deadly. Your best option is to get away from the storm before it affects the area. If you're stuck outside, keep moving and head toward shelter; the sooner you get there, the safer you'll be.

⚡ MYTH: Ben Franklin's kite was struck by lightning.

Nope. General consensus is that it didn't happen. Franklin's own account of the experiment (later published by Joseph Priestley) says there was no strike, just a collection of charges.

a) Getting struck by lightning wasn't Franklin's goal in the kite-flying experiment. His intent was to prove the hypothesis that lightning is a form of electricity and carries a charge. The ribbons and key that he is said to have used in the experiment collected a charge in a primitive capacitor called a Leiden Jar and then, when Franklin reached for the famous key, he received a small shock. That was enough to prove his point but not kill him.

b) If lightning had struck the kite's string and the attached metal wire while he was holding the apparatus, Franklin would have been electrocuted. No more Ben. No portrait on the C-note. The Discovery Channel's "MythBusters" did a whole segment on what would have happened to his body. BUSTED.

c) There are major debates about whether the experiment happened at all. Some say Franklin only wrote about the idea and that it was taken out of context and blown into an American legend. Others say he actually did it and was just lucky to survive.

Thunder

A lightning bolt almost instantly super-heats the air around its channel to nearly 50,000°F; that's five times hotter than the surface of the sun! That rapid heating (and then rapid cooling) creates the shock wave we hear as thunder.

Booms v. Rumbles

Rick posed a good question by e-mail after one of our TV segments:

> You just mentioned on the air that lightning is no wider than the thickness of a pencil... Well what causes some lightning to be SOOOOO incredibly booming and loud while others are just little "cracks and pops"?
> -Rick

Great question, Rick. To answer it, we should start with another question: "What causes thunder?"

Lightning causes thunder. Towering cumulonimbus clouds (thunderstorms) often include ice particles. Those ice particles help create an electrical charge within the cloud. In most cases, the charge separates itself out with the positive charge near the top of the cloud and the negative charge near the bottom of the cloud. The earth then builds up a positive charge under the storm cloud. When the charge builds up enough, it finds a release. The cloud sends down a negatively-charged "stepped leader" and the earth sends up a positively-charged "streamer." When they meet, we see the lightning.

The lightning channel is super-heated. It can be pencil-thin or up to two inches wide. Estimates vary, but it's somewhere between 50,000-70,000°F (28,000-39,000°C). In any case, it's much hotter than the surface of the sun — but only for a few fractions of a second. Still, that's enough time to super-heat the air around the lightning flash. When the air is heated, it expands. When it expands that much that quickly (violently), it creates a shock wave. That shock wave propagates through the molecules in the air and we hear it as thunder.

From the National Lightning Safety Institute:

> Less than 1% of lightning's energy is converted into sound and the rest released in the form of light. A sudden increase in pressure and temperature causes surrounding air to expand violently at a rate faster than the speed of sound, similar to a sonic boom. The shock wave extends outward for the first 30 feet (10 m), after which it becomes an ordinary sound wave called thunder.

When the lightning/thunder is very close to us, the sound waves don't have very far to go, so we hear it as an incredibly loud boom. When the thunder is farther away, some of the sound wave dissipates in the air before it gets to us (it attenuates, or loses some of its energy), so we hear it only as a low rumble.

Snow

It's beautiful. It creates an idyllic wintertime scene, ready for sleigh rides and holiday stories. It's fun to play in, to build snowmen and create giant backyard forts with, and to flop down and create angel shapes in.

And it's dangerous. Untreated roads are treacherous. Sidewalks turn to ice rinks. Snow and cold can take exposed limbs or even lives.

Columbus Snowfall

Snow is a fact of life in Central Ohio. We learn to deal with it and some people even say they enjoy it. And we can get a *lot* of snow.

Our deepest, one-day snowfall was on March 8, 2008, when Mother Nature dumped more than 15 inches of fluffy, white, powder on Columbus. It was fun to romp around in but not so great to shovel; even the snowblowers had trouble with *that* much snow!

Average Monthly Snowfall

Thankfully, it doesn't snow all year in Columbus! What we get in the winter is plenty, thanks. The months of May through September are our respite from the cold and snow. Occasionally, we can get an early snow in October or a late dusting in April. But most of our snowfall is concentrated in December through March.

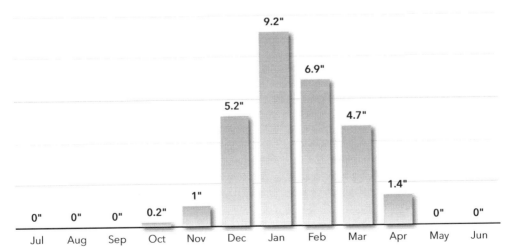

Quox and Pogonip play in the deep snowfall, March 8, 2008, the deepest one-day snow accumulation in Columbus record-keeping history.

Columbus Normal Monthly Snowfall, 1981-2010

Jul	Aug	Sep	Oct	Nov	Dec	Jan	Feb	Mar	Apr	May	Jun
0"	0"	0"	0.2"	1"	5.2"	9.2"	6.9"	4.7"	1.4"	0"	0"

January is our snowiest month with an average of more than nine inches. That's a lot of shoveling!

Most of central and southern Ohio average about 20 to 30 inches of snow every year. A small portion of Central Ohio, including Bucyrus, Mansfield, Mt. Gilead, Mt. Vernon, and parts of Licking County tend to get 30 to 40 inches.

Northern Ohio has very distinct snow belts, especially in the Cleveland area and far northeastern Ohio. Lake effect snow can bury Lake, Geauga, and Ashtabula counties in more than 100 inches of snow -- that's similar to Minnesota-style snow! Cleveland's eastern suburbs can be buried in deep snow while the western 'burbs get only a dusting.

Columbus' Top 10 Greatest Annual Snowfall Totals

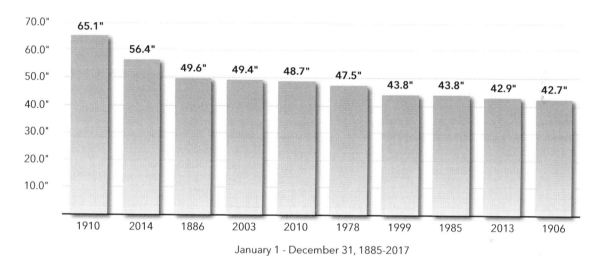

January 1 - December 31, 1885-2017

Columbus' Top 10 Greatest Seasonal Snowfall Totals

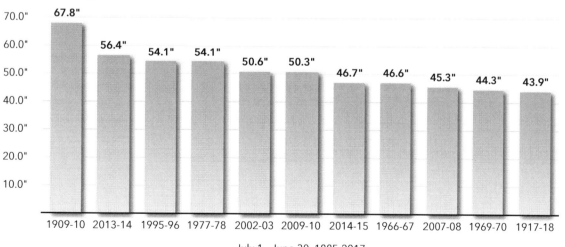

July 1 - June 30, 1885-2017

Columbus' Top 10 Lightest Annual Snowfall Totals

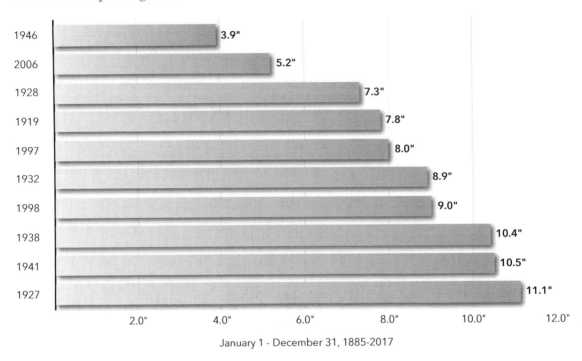

1946	3.9"
2006	5.2"
1928	7.3"
1919	7.8"
1997	8.0"
1932	8.9"
1998	9.0"
1938	10.4"
1941	10.5"
1927	11.1"

January 1 - December 31, 1885-2017

Columbus' Top 10 Greatest Daily Snowfalls

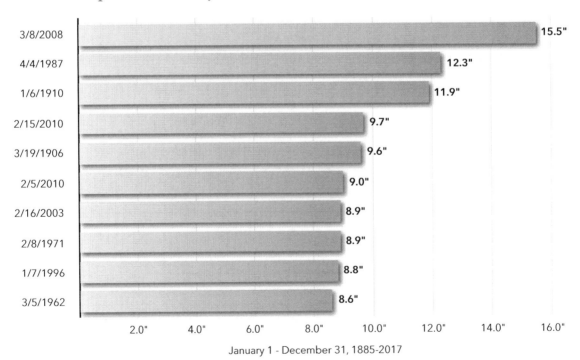

3/8/2008	15.5"
4/4/1987	12.3"
1/6/1910	11.9"
2/15/2010	9.7"
3/19/1906	9.6"
2/5/2010	9.0"
2/16/2003	8.9"
2/8/1971	8.9"
1/7/1996	8.8"
3/5/1962	8.6"

January 1 - December 31, 1885-2017

Number of Days per Season with 1" or More on the Ground in Columbus

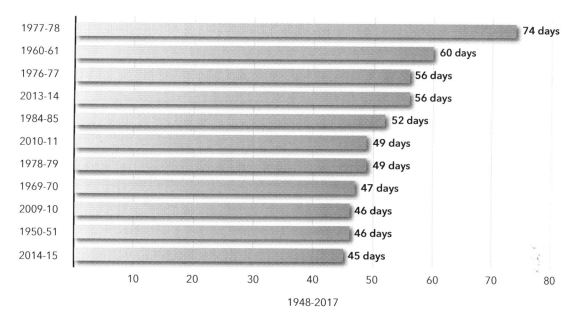

1977-78	74 days
1960-61	60 days
1976-77	56 days
2013-14	56 days
1984-85	52 days
2010-11	49 days
1978-79	49 days
1969-70	47 days
2009-10	46 days
1950-51	46 days
2014-15	45 days

1948-2017

ODOT v. Snow & Ice

When the nastiest winter weather hits, it's up to the Ohio Department of Transportation to keep the roads passable. With the help of local cities and counties, they are able to dig us out as quickly as possible and keep the Buckeye State's economy up and running.

In Franklin County alone, ODOT:

- Is responsible for 1,250 Lane miles of highways
- Keeps more than 50 trucks at 100 drivers ready to go whenever snow threatens
- Uses about 14,000 tons of salt for an average winter (480,000 tons statewide)
- Keeps 20,000 tons of salt at the ready in the salt barns (57,000 tons for the eight counties in District 6).

ODOT is responsible for clearing all the interstates across the state plus all the state and US routes outside city limits.

An ODOT snow plow battles the elements while clearing an Ohio interstate. Image courtesy the Ohio Department of Transportation.

Snow Emergencies

When snow storms roll through the area, cars slide on the roads, becoming a serious safety issue. In Ohio, your county sheriff's office may issue Snow Emergencies to encourage drivers to be safe. The sheriff can choose to close roads, too.

Blowing and drifting snow reduces visibility and can make clearing the roads difficult for plow crews. Snow and high winds create near-whiteout conditions on I-71 in Delaware County during a winter storm in February 2011.

> **Level 1 Snow Emergency**: Drivers are urged to be very cautious. The roads may be icy or covered with blowing and drifting snow.
>
> **Level 2 Snow Emergency**: Drivers should use extreme caution and only be on the roads if absolutely necessary. Roads are hazardous because of ice and snow. Check with your employer to see if you are required to report to work.
>
> **Level 3 Snow Emergency**: Roads are closed except for emergency personnel. No one else should be driving unless there is a legitimate personal emergency. Check with your employer about whether to report for work. Non-emergency travelers are subject to arrest.

Yes, you can be legally arrested under Ohio Revised Code 2917.13, "Misconduct at emergency," when your county is under a Level 3 snow emergency.

When it's that bad outside, it's safer to stay home anyway.

Bridges and Overpasses Freeze First

As the temperatures drop, you'll hear TV meteorologists and traffic reporters remind you to be extra cautious when driving over bridges and overpasses. They can become icy and slippery long before the rest of the roadway.

Most of the roadbed sits on layers of gravel and asphalt with miles and miles of earth under it. That dirt acts as an insulator and keeps the road surface a little warmer. Plus, a tiny amount of heat can radiate up from the ground.

Bridges, though, have none of that. They sit in mid air. Cold air. While the ground-insulated road can stay slightly warmer than the temperature of the overlying air a little longer, the bridges quickly drop to the temperature of the surrounding air. If that's freezing or below, there's a serious potential for ice to form. Slow down and be safe!

"Ice and Snow, Take it Slow"

ODOT's annual winter-weather campaign reminds us to take a deep breath and be safe when Mother Nature throws us a nasty day.

When the roads are covered in snow and ice, flying along at the posted speed limit may not be the best choice. You won't be able to stop (or even slow down) as quickly as you would on dry pavement. It's best to leave much more room between vehicles than usual. Slowing down helps you keep control of your car if the tires lose their grip on the road.

It's also not a great time to be texting while driving (in fact, NO TIME is a good time for that). Stay focused on the road and what's around you while you're navigating the snow and ice.

And watch out for hidden dangers. Even a road that *seems* dry may be covered with a thin sheet of ice. It blends in with the pavement, which is why it's nicknamed "black ice."

Don't Crowd the Plow

ODOT has another good wintertime reminder: "Don't Crowd the Plow."

Whether they're city, county, or state plows, they're out there in the horrible weather trying to make the roads safer. In the City of Columbus, there are more than 3,600 lane miles that need to be cleared and treated every time it snows (and that doesn't include the collector or residential streets). Those plow drivers risk their safety for us. Give them some space and let them do what they need to do.

Tailgating and passing are just asking for trouble. To do their jobs, plows need to travel below the posted speed limit. Be patient. The weather is crappy; the folks at your destination will understand why it took you a little extra time to get there (though they may ask why you didn't leave a little earlier). Slow down, listen to the radio, and calm the heck down.

Plows can make sudden turns and stops. They have limited sight lines that may prevent them from seeing you while you're riding up their backsides. Give the plows some extra space so you don't smash into the back of them. The damage to your vehicle will be much worse than the damage to that big, heavy, dump-truck-sized behemoth. Plus, it's not all about you; if you cause an accident that takes a plow out of service, you're making the situation worse for all of us. There'll be one less plow getting the snow out of the way. Don't be that guy.

How many plows?

When Old Man Winter makes an assault on Central Ohio, huge teams of "Snow Warriors" and "Snow Fighters" hit the roads and highways to do battle.

As of 2016, here is how the crews stack up:

	Plows	Drivers	Lane Miles to Clear
Franklin Co.	31	100+	766
City of Columbus	86	114	6,387
ODOT Dist. 6	171	150+	4,941

Based in Delaware, the Ohio Department of Transportation's District 6 covers eight counties: Delaware, Fayette, Franklin, Madison, Marion, Morrow, Pickaway, and Union. ODOT, Franklin County, and Columbus each have assigned routes and responsibilities so they can launch a coordinated attack each time snow covers Central Ohio roads. ODOT's mandate is to have all of its lane lines visible within two hours of the time the snow stops falling.

What is black ice?

Pure ice is clear. It's not black. It's not grey. It's clear. But you'll hear the term "black ice" fairly often in winter weather and traffic reports.

"Black ice" is a term often used to describe a layer of ice on the road that can make driving slippery and hazardous. It's difficult to see because it's transparent and takes on the appearance of whatever is underneath it, often black asphalt. An ice-covered highway can look like it's just wet and drivers can mistake it for being safer than it really is.

In many cases, the icy layer forms during a freezing-rain event. The rain falls through a warmish layer near the surface; it falls as liquid then freezes on contact with the cold surface, forming a glaze of ice. When it covers streets and sidewalks, your commute can become mildly treacherous; when it covers trees and power lines, it can become heavy enough to bring them down.

Sometimes, "grey ice" forms when the ice has tiny air bubbles trapped in it which can make it look white or grey.

When will the City of Columbus plow my street?!

A Franklin County snow plow clears a residential street near Marble Cliff in January 2016. Photo by Chris Mazivanhanga.

In general, City of Columbus crews don't plow smaller, residential streets unless the snowfall is four inches or more. In 2016, the city began assessing that policy on a snowfall-by-snowfall basis and moving crews into residential areas when they were available, even for snowfalls of less than four inches.

The city has more than 110 dedicated "Snow Warriors" ready to go, but they have their hands full with the arterial streets and freeways, so they put off the collectors and residential streets until the main roads are passable.

If it's a very light snowfall, you're probably on your own.

Shovel Your Sidewalk! Or else!

Columbus City Code Section 902.03 requires property owners to clear the snow and ice off the sidewalks on their properties. It also says you can't shovel snow into the street; so, pile it in the yard instead. Not clearing the sidewalks is a minor misdemeanor and carries a fine of up to $100!

Sleet & Freezing Rain

The terms "sleet" and "freezing rain" can sometimes be confusing because they often end up in the forecast as a pair. They are different forms of precipitation but since they have a tendency to fall near one another or to alternate back and forth, the forecast may call for both.

Sleet falls as small ice pellets. They're usually round and look like small hail. Unlike hail, they're not formed by a convective process. The pellets are created by melting-and-refreezing as they plummet toward the ground.

Freezing rain is liquid as it hits the surface but freezes on contact and creates an icy glaze. It makes the trees look pretty in the early-morning sunlight but it can be dangerous on the roads.

Snow, sleet, and freezing rain start as the same thing: snowflakes. But as they fall from high in the sky, they may transform on their way down. It's all about the local atmosphere's temperature profile.

When the snowflakes start their descent from the clouds, the air around them is really, really cold. They're frozen and they stay that way. If the air is below freezing all the way to the surface, they'll land on the ground the same way they started, as snowflakes.

Things get complicated when there's a layer of warmer air in between. Sometimes the snowflakes melt into raindrops as they fall through the warm layer. If the air is warm all the way to the surface, they'll fall as regular ol' raindrops. Those are the days with a cold rain that feels like it goes all the way to your bones.

Ice covers tree branches (and roads) in Columbus after a storm with lots of freezing rain on February 1, 2011.

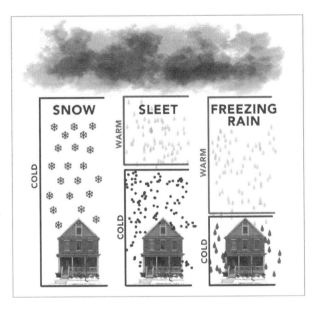

If, on the way down, the raindrops pass through another cold layer and have enough time to refreeze into ice pellets or grains, we have sleet. If the bottommost cold layer is a little thinner, the raindrops may not have time to refreeze, so they fall as liquid but turn to ice as soon as they hit the freezing cold surface, thus, freezing rain.

Graupel

Graupel is an unusual form of frozen precipitation that occasionally falls here in Central Ohio. You may hear it called "tapioca snow." It's kind of like sleet but it's bigger and softer and it tends to be white instead of clear. It can also be called "soft hail" but, unlike hail, it's not formed by a convective process. Instead, it's formed when falling raindrops join together (coalescence), then freeze and collect more ice on their way down (accretion).

Recipe for the Quintessential Snowman

Whenever the snow is just right, you'll find hundreds of us out in the cold, getting our mittens soaking wet, building armies of snowmen. It doesn't matter whether they have corn-cob pipes and button noses, they just have to be bigger than the snowperson in the neighbor's yard.

Professor Roy Pruett and his engineering class at Bluefield State College in Bluefield, West Virginia, created and published plans for building the "perfect snowman." He told the website Quartz (qz.com) that the most important thing is to have snow that is still slightly moist and about 30°F. If it's too cold, too dry-and-powdery, or too warm, your creative aspirations are doomed. And to be just right, your creation almost must have precise proportions.

Pruett says the ideal snowman is:

- ⛄ six feet tall and well proportioned with

- ⛄ a bottom snowball three-feet across (base),

- ⛄ a middle snowball two-feet across (torso), and

- ⛄ a top snowball one-foot across (head).

Pruett suggests a sturdy foundation of wet snow at least two inches deep and he recommends not building it at the base of a sledding hill where someone might knock it over!

Snow Day Rituals

Every time forecasters call for a few inches of snow, school kids (and, let's be honest, teachers, too) cross their fingers for an impromptu vacation day. Whether we spend it making snow angels, building snow men, or lounging on the couch with a blanket, a snow day is a fun, quick break from daily routines.

Sports fans have routines, rituals, and superstitions that they swear help their favorite teams bring home victories. School children have their own rituals to bring on a snow day. According to *The (Syracuse, New York) Post-Standard*, these are the Top 10 methods to encourage Mother Nature to bestow a snow day:

A tractor removes several inches of snow and ice from the sidewalks around Bucyrus Middle School on February 14, 2012; it was a great snow day for the students and the teachers!

+ wear your pajamas to bed inside out (sometimes, backward)

+ sleep with cotton balls under your pillow

+ put a pencil in the freezer

+ open the freezer door and yell, "snow day!" three times in a row

+ flush ice cubes down the toilet

+ throw ice cubes out the window

+ do a snow dance (similar to a rain dance?)

+ shake a snow globe and imagine your home town

+ put a statuette of the Virgin Mary in a window facing north

+ pray (a lot)

Good luck!

Building a Backyard Ice Rink

Legendary Central Ohio TV meteorologist Jym Ganahl is renowned for his love of winter weather, the colder and snowier the better. Nearly every winter, Jym builds an ice rink in his back yard for his grandkids and the neighborhood.

Meteorologist Jym Ganahl playing with his grandchildren and neighborhood kids on his backyard ice rink.

Jym has perfected the technique and was kind enough to share his plans:

1. Start with the flattest ground in your yard.

2. Use 4x4 pieces of wood to frame the outline of the area where you want to have the rink. 4x4 is best, but in my yard, I have to use 2x8 pieces of wood because there is a slope. 2x8s require bracing on the outside because the ice will expand and knock over the frame.

3. Place a sheet of plastic inside the frame, overlapping the wood. This is your bowl to hold the water. There will be freezing and thawing and you will alternate between ice and water during much of the winter.

Jym's Extra Tips:

+ Keep leaves out of the water. They freeze into the ice and retain heat from sun and burn holes in your ice.

+ Put rags into the four corners to soften the corners to put less pressure on the plastic liner.

+ I use 150 mil Permalon that can be cut to the size of your rink. It will be white to reflect sunlight and it will be sturdy for many years' use. It is seamless, so there are no leaks. (Jym orders it from a company in Houston, Texas, and says it takes about three weeks for delivery.) Cheaper plastic from building supply stores is called Visqueen, 6 mil or 8 mil. It tears easily and is not white.

+ Wait to put the water in the rink until there's a cold snap coming without snow. Temperatures in the teens at night will freeze one inch of ice per night, so it takes only three nights to be skating.

+ I get 30-60 days of skating in the winter with much of that time in February and March.

Follow Jym's plan and you'll be the envy of your neighborhood! Blue Jackets, eat your heart out!

Air Pressure

Every moment of every day, you're carrying an enormous weight on your shoulders. You don't feel it because you're used to it. You've been supporting it from the moment you were born.

Though we're not aware of it, air is very, very heavy and it constantly pushes down on us. When you look up at the stars, every square inch of air between you and space is pressing down on your face. We call that weight "air pressure."

Like temperature, air pressure is described with several scales. "Millibars" and "pascals" are part of the metric system, "inches of mercury" is part of the traditional, English scale that we use in the United States. (Scientists around the world, including the US, use metric measurements.) The different scales assign different numbers to the same conditions.

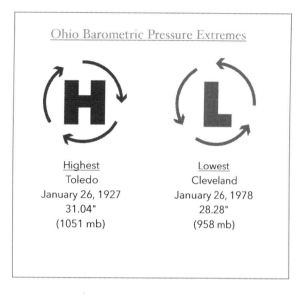

Ohio Barometric Pressure Extremes

Highest	Lowest
Toledo	Cleveland
January 26, 1927	January 26, 1978
31.04"	28.28"
(1051 mb)	(958 mb)

A "standard atmosphere" is the same as the Mean Sea Level Pressure (MSLP). It's the base from which we measure all air pressure. The average is 29.92 inches of mercury (inHg), 1013.25 millibars (mb) or hectopascals (hPa), or 101325 pascals (Pa).

Air Pressure Comparisons

	Pressure (inHg)	Pressure (mb)
Strong hurricane	26.28	890
Strong low-pressure center	28.64	970
Average low-pressure center	29.23	990
MSLP	29.92	1013.25
Average high-pressure center	30.12	1020
Strong high-pressure center	30.71	1040

When you're on top of a mountain, there's less air between you and space so there's less weight pushing down on you. That's low pressure. When you're at the bottom of the deepest valley[3], there's more air between you and space, more weight, and higher pressure.

---

[3] By "deepest valley," we mean, on land. The lowest valley on Earth is deep in the ocean and that presents a whole different set of pressure issues because of the volume of water above that point (plus the weight of the air).

Measuring Air Pressure

Knowing the air pressure can help us predict the kind of weather we're likely to have. So, meteorologists frequently measure air pressure using a gadget called a barometer.

On many barometers, you'll see weather predictions written on the scale. At one end it may say, "Fair," or "Fine," or "Sunny," and the other end may say, "Stormy" or "Rainy." That's because high pressure often creates clear skies and low pressure usually ushers in unsettled, stormy weather.

High Pressure

"High pressure" is how we refer to barometric conditions of roughly 1015 millibars or higher. You will see it depicted on weather maps as a large, bold, blue "H."

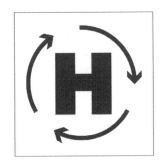

In the northern hemisphere, air circulates clockwise around high-pressure centers. And highs tend to give us clearing, sunny skies because they cause sinking air, which tends to prevent cloud formation. Yes, you can still have clouds with high pressure, but that almost always involves secondary influences.

Low Pressure

"Low Pressure" is how we refer to barometric conditions of roughly 1010 millibars or lower. You will see it depicted on weather maps as a large, bold, red "L." In the northern hemisphere, air circulates counter-clockwise around low-pressure centers.

Lows tend to be the harbingers of foul weather. They are very often surrounded by frontal boundaries and can generate very windy conditions.

Wind

Mother Nature likes things to be equal. She balances as many things as possible, including air pressure. That attempt at balance is part of what causes our weather. Without it, we'd see the same weather day after day after day (kind of like in the tropics).

When high pressure and low pressure are near one another, they'll try to equalize each other. Air will move from the high to the low, like water down a hill. The larger and steeper the difference between the high and the low, the faster the air moves.

Think of high pressure as a dome and low pressure as a bowl. Air flows out of the dome and collects in the bowl. Once the dome is flat and the bowl is full, Mother Nature is happy.

All that moving, flowing air has a name: "wind."

Air flow around a high is analogous to a clockwise-circulating dome with the air then rushing out toward a counterclockwise-circulating bowl of low pressure.

When you see isobars (lines of equal pressure) on a weather map, think of those as terraces on the sides of the low-pressure bowl. The closer together they are, the steeper the slope (the pressure gradient), and the faster the air falls into the bowl. In other words, it gets really windy!

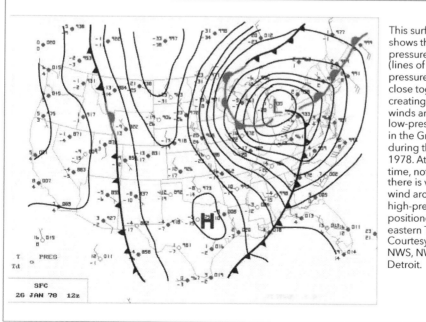

This surface map shows the tight pressure gradient (lines of equal pressure packed close together) creating very strong winds around the low-pressure center in the Great Lakes during the Blizzard of 1978. At the same time, notice that there is very little wind around the high-pressure center positioned over eastern Texas. Courtesy: NOAA/NWS, NWSFO Detroit.

"Severe Clear"

High pressure inhibits cloud formation and low humidity means there is very little water vapor in the air. That's the perfect recipe for a brilliantly blue sky with seemingly endless visibility. Where there are no clouds, not even wispy cirrus clouds, and not enough water vapor to give the sky a slightly whitish cast, we see the incredible, crystal clear, true color of the atmosphere. It's what some pilots call a "severe clear."

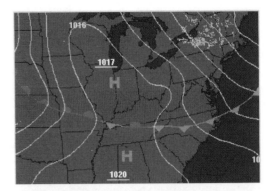

Incredible autumn colors set against a seemingly endless blue sky caused by strong high pressure and very low humidity.

NOAA NWS surface map showing high pressure almost directly over Ohio on the day the photo at left was taken.

Air Masses & Fronts

You'll hear TV meteorologists mention air masses and fronts. When explaining the forecast, we're likely to tell you about "the showers along a cold front that's passing through the area" or the "arctic air mass that's settled in for a few days."

Air Masses

An air mass is a giant blob of air, floating around the globe. Air masses can be warm, cold, moist, or dry depending on where they form and what part of the world influences their characteristics.

As air masses move around the world, they directly influence the weather under and around them.

There are six basic kinds of air masses that travel across North America.

cA: Continental Arctic

Continental Arctic (cA) air masses usually form over the dry, inland areas of far-northern Canada and the arctic ice fields. They're really cold and tend to be fairly dry because they're born away from a major source of moisture, like an open ocean.

mA: Maritime Arctic

Maritime Arctic (mA) air masses are also very, very cold but they carry slightly more humid air because they form over the open Arctic and far-northern Pacific Oceans. The catch is: since the air is so cold, they still don't carry a lot of moisture so, for practical purposes, they end up being very similar to the Continental Arctic air masses.

cP: Continental Polar

Continental Polar (cP) air masses usually get their start south of the Arctic Circle. They often form in northwestern Canada over land. They're cold and dry.

mP: Maritime Polar

Maritime Polar (mP) air masses form south of the Arctic Circle but they get their start over the open waters of the northern Atlantic or northern Pacific where they can pick up much more moisture. Even though they're still very cold, they're warmer than their arctic counterparts so they can hold more water vapor.

cT: Continental Tropical

Continental Tropical (cT) air masses are warm and dry. They form over the deserts of Mexico and the American Southwest.

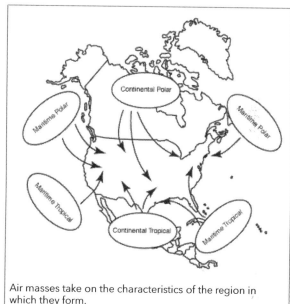

Air masses take on the characteristics of the region in which they form.

mT: Maritime Tropical

Maritime Tropical (mT) air masses are warm and humid. They form over the warm waters of the Atlantic, Pacific, and Gulf of Mexico where they pick up plenty of moisture.

Fronts

Where the edges of air masses collide, we get interesting weather. As the cold air meets the warm air or the moist air meets the dry air (or a combination of all of them), they fight for supremacy. Where they battle, we usually see showers and storms.

The edges of the air masses are depicted on weather maps as fronts. They come in four flavors: warm, cold, stationary, and occluded. Each separates a specific air mass from another.

Warm Fronts

A warm front shows warmer air moving into cooler or colder air. They're often found leading a low-pressure center and usually pivot through the region before a cold front arrives.

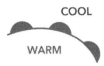

Cold Fronts

A cold front shows colder air moving into warmer air. They pivot around low-pressure centers and are often a focus for showers, thunderstorms, or unsettled weather. They act a kind of like a bulldozer as they plow through the atmosphere.

Occluded Fronts

Occluded fronts also pivot around low-pressure centers. They form when a cold front catches up to a warm front and the air masses start to combine. The air near the front is unsettled and usually triggers precipitation.

Stationary Fronts

Stationary fronts are boundaries with warm air on one side and cooler air on the other. As their name implies, they tend not to move much. They just sit there and cause the atmosphere to be tumultuous and troublesome. They're not as vigorous as cold fronts but they're more unsettling than warm fronts.

Fronts and Forecasts

Nearly any time you see a front headed for your spot on the map, you're probably going to see a change in the weather. As a front passes through the area it ushers in a new air mass, usually very different from the one that preceded it. Temperatures are likely to change. Rain or storms will often pass by with the front. Winds may become stronger as the front barrels through the region then settle quickly afterward.

Fronts are major players in forecasting. Their position, strength, and timing are huge factors in predicting the day's conditions.

The Jet Stream

The jet stream is a river of high-speed air perched about 30,000 feet above the earth's surface, about the same height where commercial jets fly. As it races along, the jet stream helps drive weather systems and patterns across the continents. It can create a separation between air masses, keeping the cooler air to the north and the warmer air to the south.

In North America, we usually deal with two versions of the jet stream: the sub-tropical jet and the polar jet.

Polar Jet

As you might guess by its name, the polar jet tends to stay relatively far north. It spends much of the year undulating across Canada and the Great Lakes. In the depths of winter, though, it can occasionally dip as far south as the Florida panhandle.

It is a driving force for weather patterns as they track across the continent.

Low pressure centers get a push as they meander into the jet stream's path — just like a boat in a river. If a low falls out of the stream, it can sit in one place for days, waiting for something else to push it along. (That's called a cut-off low.)

The jet stream can be a boundary between warm air and cold air, especially in the winter. As the jet stream undulates and twists, it can let colder air slip into normally warm areas and warm air move into areas that are usually cold.

When the jet stream takes a serious dive during the winter, we can get brutally cold weather as arctic air spills into the eastern US. When that happens, the west often gets a big dose of warmer air from the southwestern deserts.

Subtropical Jet

The subtropical jet does the same things as the polar jet, but it lives farther south. The air masses it separates tend not be as strong. The STJ isn't as vivacious as its polar counterpart.

Jet Streaks

Jet streaks are extra-fast portions of the jet stream. On a map, they often look like little eddies in the river. Where the main jet may have winds of 125 mph or faster, an embedded streak can have winds of 250 mph or faster.

So what?

Well, those increased wind speeds move more air than the surrounding jet and, since Mother Nature abhors a vacuum, that extra air has to come from somewhere to fill the void — and it's often from below. In other words, a jet streak can cause air below it to rise. (Ah, we're back to that rising air thing again.) Rising air often begets clouds which begets rain which can beget storms, etc., etc., etc.

So, in general, where you see jet streaks, expect rising air in the vicinity.

WEATHER PHENOMENA

Odd things can happen with the weather. Most of the time, it's all fairly run-of-the-mill. But now and then, there are bizarre events. If the day-to-day weather isn't interesting enough, there's always the phenomena to captivate your attention.

Do Worms Fall Out of the Sky?

One afternoon after a rainfall, a nice lady called the weather center and told us the parking lot and her driveway were covered with worms. There were so many worms, she said, they must have fallen from the sky.

"Is that possible?" she asked.

Well, umm, no.

There is no normal mechanism[4] to pull the worms up into the air, let alone drop

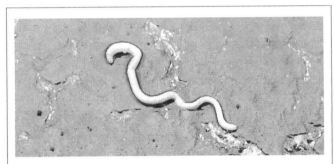

Worms often litter the sidewalk after a soaking rain.

them back to the surface. A tornado can rip things out of the ground and drop them miles away. That's not a regular occurrence and certainly not as regular as finding worms on the sidewalk after a rain. Besides, a tornado wouldn't sort the worms from other debris.

Think of it another way: When a hurricane picks up moisture from the ocean, that water vapor fuels the storm and falls later as rain. The rain is not salt water; it's just plain water. That's because the salt doesn't evaporate, it stays behind in the ocean. As luck would have it, worms don't evaporate either. So, they don't fall with the rain.

Believe it or not, though there are lots of worms uniformly distributed across the parking lot, they crawled there. On their own.

---

[4] So here's a teeny, tiny caveat: let's say there's a weak tornado, EF0, or a gustinado that is just strong enough to pick up some worms but not strong enough to do damage that would create other debris. It could, in theory, make the worms "rain" from the sky in a different location. But it would have to pick up an entire pile of those worms from a single spot; it wouldn't be able to sort the worms from anything else. Have you ever seen a two-foot high block of squirmy worms waiting to be sucked up into a vortex? Neither have we.

"Inspirational Card" Rays

You've seen them on greeting cards and inspirational posters. They're often thought of as light shining down from Heaven.

Crepuscular rays reaching down through the clouds above Broadcast Lake, April 4, 2018.

They're called crepuscular rays. We occasionally see them around sunrise or sunset and, if the conditions are just right, we can even see them in the middle of the day. It's all about shadows and particles in the air.

When the sun is blocked by broken clouds, some of the sun's rays bounce off the water vapor and dust in the atmosphere and become visible lines. Perspective gives makes them look kind of like distant railroad tracks converging toward a bright spot in the clouds.

Anti-crepuscular rays happen when sun is closer to the horizon and the rays of light appear to shine upward.

Rainbows Around the Moon

Yep. It's true. They happen. The process is exactly the same as rainbows created by the sun. Molly saw it and sent us a note:

> From: molly
> Subject: rainbow orb near moon
> Hi There! I noticed there appears to be an arc curved near the moon in the sky. I could see the color of the rainbow in it earlier and it was very vivid, just about 15 minutes ago. Now when I looked it appears to have faded some, I can't see the colors, only white. I live in Logan, Ohio, Hocking county. I don't know if you can see it up there. I have never seen anything like it.

Rainbows happen when light is refracted. You can create rainbows with a prism or a crystal. The atmosphere does it by using water vapor (or raindrops or ice crystals) in the air. Both processes, crystals or water droplets, bend the light and separate it into its component parts. When we see the spectrum in a ring around the sun, we call it a rainbow. Since we only see part of the ring, it looks like an arc across the sky.

When the moon is bright and full, its light can be refracted exactly the same way. Because the light is not as bright, the rainbow is more difficult to see and often looks like a grey ring around the moon.

Sometimes, the light is refracted by high, cirrus clouds around the sun or moon. When it's at exactly the right height above the horizon, we see small rainbow patches on either side of the sun or moon. Those colorful patches are called "sun dogs" or "moon dogs."

A sun dog appears as a rainbow-like patch to the right of the sun in this image captured in southern Franklin County by Brad Hunt on January 26, 2015. Brad says a matching sun dog appeared on the other side of the sun.

When ice in high, thin cirrus clouds refracts sunlight, it creates beautiful rainbows. This image was captured in Delaware County on a hot, July day when the sun was almost directly overhead. Photo by Elizabeth Ida (her dad, Steve, was driving).

Snow Rollers

Now and then, we get some very cool wintertime phenomena.

From: Rosetta
Subject: snow ball looking things
What are the snow ball looking things called?
Thx
Rosetta

As it turns out, Mother Nature loves making snowballs as much as we do! When the conditions are just right, she'll make "snow rollers." But the perfect recipe doesn't happen often. You need a fresh layer of moist, packable snow, a little bit of ice so the rollers don't get too deep when they start traveling, and wind strong enough to push the snowballs through the fresh snow.

Then all it needs is a little wad of snow to become a nucleus. The wind pushes it the same way you would when you start making a snowman. As the nucleus rolls through the snow, it gets bigger. Since it rolls in a straight line, in the direction of the wind, it becomes a cylinder instead of a ball.

Sometimes the inside will hollow out because the snow isn't packed tightly or isn't moist enough. Then you get a cool tube shape!

Usually, where you find one, you'll find lots of them. They can fill a whole field. They're relatively common in the Great Plains, but much less common in Central Ohio.

Enjoy them when you see them!

Snow rollers formed in the yard of Worthington Kilbourne High School after a night of very strong winds, January 27, 2014. Photos by Christopher Baggs.

Is global warming real?

We get this question almost every time we talk to a community group. It's more properly called "climate change" because it's about much more than just warming temperatures. Unfortunately, for many people, it has become a political question rather than a scientific one. Let's talk about climate change *science*; we'll leave the politics to the policy wonks.

There are actually three questions:

1. Is the planet's climate changing?
   Yes, the scientific, anecdotal, and empirical evidence is very clear on that.

2. Do we know what's causing it?
   Yes. It's combination of factors but we have a good handle on what's likely causing it. And one of the major contributors is human activity.

3. What can we do about it?
   Ugh. Ask your congressperson.

There is no scientific doubt that humans have changed the atmosphere. A couple of centuries ago, the fires that burned and the emissions we produced were small enough to be absorbed by the atmosphere and recycled by the planet's natural cycles. That was before the Industrial Revolution when enormous factories roared into existence. Before then, cars, planes, and trains weren't part of the landscape. Power stations weren't spewing tons of gasses into the air each day. Today, we're producing more emissions than the earth can deal with on its own. That's creating changes in the atmosphere including larger concentrations of carbon dioxide (CO_2), Methane (CH_4), Nitrous Oxide (N_2O), Ozone (O_3), and chlorofluorocarbons.

Here's the problem: determining the causes of climate change means placing "blame" on someone or some thing and nobody likes that. It sucks when your little sister points at you and screams to your parents, "She did it!" You're suddenly accountable for something you may not be proud of. There are going to be consequences, and fixing the situation is going to be unpleasant.

No one wants to accept responsibility for climate change or spend the money or change our way of living to fix it. This is where it becomes political. If we admit humans are a primary contributor to climate change, then folks start pointing fingers at each other. "They did it!" "No, THEY did it!" Then someone has to take the blame. It's easier to deny humans are responsible and claim climate change doesn't exist. That way we put off doing anything about it, there's no impact to the economy, and future generations get deal with the resulting mess.

Despite empirical and anecdotal evidence to the contrary, one group of climate change skeptics says the earth is simply going through a natural cycle of warming. The same group says the ban on plastic grocery bags passed by California in 2014 is "bad for the environment," there is no loss of Arctic ice leading to a reduction of the polar bear population, and ocean levels are not rising. They use a tiny fraction of available data (less than 20 years' worth) to support their argument. That particular group also wants to do away with the Environmental Protection Agency. People who live near the coastlines will show you the real-world effects that are actually happening, despite political denials.

Yes, the earth goes through hot and cold cycles with warmer spells and ice ages. Yes, sunspots run in 7- to 14-year cycles and can have a small effect on short-term temperatures. Neither of those things accounts for the enormous spikes we see today.

There's a spectrum of folks from tree-hugging alarmists to hard-core deniers. You probably fall somewhere in the middle of that spectrum and there's a good chance you've already made up your mind about climate change. Unfortunately, the partisan stalemate of the debate prevents us from agreeing on whether there *is* a real problem and whether anything needs to be done.

Science is clear. Politics are murky.

SEVERE WEATHER

In any season, Central Ohio can get some nasty weather. Damaging winds. Large hail. Tornadoes. Driving snow. Brutal wind chills. Withering heat. Understanding the alerts and having safety plans are important ways to stay safe when severe weather pummels the area. Understanding how it works makes it a little less scary!

Severe Thunderstorms

Of the nearly 100,000 thunderstorms that happen in the United States every year, only about 10 percent are classified as "severe," meaning they produce

⚡ winds of 58 mph or stronger,

⚡ hail 1" in diameter or larger,

⚡ and/or tornadoes.

Severe storms are most common during the warm, summer months but they can happen any time. Central Ohio is in good company. Nearly every location in the US is susceptible to severe weather.

TV meteorologists refer to a "categorical risk" for severe weather on a particular day. Those forecasts come from NOAA's Storm Prediction Center and are based on a thorough analysis of the upper atmosphere and surface conditions including the position of the jet stream, the position of pressure centers, the movement of moisture in the atmosphere, and a whole host of thermodynamic variables.

The risk forecast breaks into general categories to predict the possibilities for run-of-the-mill storms or severe storms with damaging winds, large hail, and/or tornadoes. The categories were updated in October 2014:

⚡ **General Thunderstorms**: just storms, nothing unusual, nothing severe.

⚡ **Marginal Risk**: severe weather could occur if the atmospheric ingredients come together just right and, if they do, severe storms are expected to be isolated.

⚡ **Slight Risk**: organized, severe

A radar image shows severe thunderstorms barreling into the Columbus metro area on July 26, 2012. Image and data provided by RadarScope.

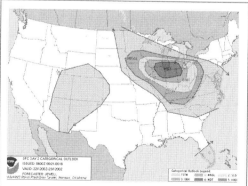

Example of a Convective Outlook map from the NOAA NWS Storm Prediction Center showing the potential for severe weather across the nation. Courtesy NOAA/NWS SPC.

thunderstorms are possible but not not expected to be widespread; the chance of a significant event exists but is relatively low.

⚡ **Enhanced Risk**: good potential for a small concentration of organized severe thunderstorms with varying levels of intensity.

⚡ **Moderate Risk**: severe thunderstorms are likely to be stronger and more widespread, the chance for significant events is higher, and there is a strong likelihood to see development of super cells with tornadoes, large hail and damaging winds.

⚡ **High Risk**: a major severe-weather outbreak is likely and includes the potential for violent tornadoes and damaging winds.

The Storm Prediction Center notes that the High Risk category "is reserved for the most extreme events with the least forecast uncertainty, and is only used a few times each year."

When there is a chance for severe weather, or while it is actually happening, the National Weather Service often will issue watches and warnings. Broadcasters are required by the Federal Communications Commission, via the Emergency Alert System, to tell you when those are issued. In many cases, you will see TV stations break into regular programming for severe weather warnings, especially active tornado warnings.

> **Severe Thunderstorm Watch**: Be prepared. Severe thunderstorms are possible in the watch area with wind gusts of 58 mph or higher or hail 1" in diameter or larger..
>
> **Severe Thunderstorm Warning**: Act now! Activate your severe weather plan and take shelter. Severe thunderstorms are occurring or imminent in the warning area that include wind gusts of 58 mph or stronger or hail 1" in diameter or larger.

Severe Thunderstorm Watches are issued by the Storm Prediction Center in Norman, Oklahoma, not by the local weather service forecast offices. Warnings are issued by the local offices and typically cover very specific areas or counties.

Watches and warnings are NOT issued by your local TV stations; they come from the National Weather Service and the the FCC requires that we broadcast them.

Doppler Radar

Doppler radar is one of the most important tools meteorologists have for tracking and forecasting severe storms. Since 1988, the United States has been covered with a system of overlapping Doppler radars that continuously monitor the atmosphere for precipitation, including severe storms.

Early radar was good at detecting rain and storms. Doppler also detects the direction that storms are moving. With Doppler, meteorologists can detect rotation in storms, which ensures earlier warnings during tornado storms.

It takes five radar installations to cover Central Ohio: Wilmington, Indianapolis, Cleveland, Pittsburgh and Charleston.

Hail

Large, powerful thunderstorms depend on rising and falling currents of air called updrafts and downdrafts. Sometimes, updrafts carry water droplets high into the cloud where they freeze into ice pellets. When the pellets move out of the updraft, they fall and pick up a layer of water on the way down. When they're grabbed by the updraft and lifted up again, the new layer of water freezes and the pellet becomes larger. The pellet goes up and down, up and down, getting larger and larger until it's too big for the updraft to lift it any more. Then it falls out of the cloud as hail. If you cut open a hailstone, you'll see the layers of ice that formed as it grew.

Large hailstones can fall at speeds faster than 100 mph and significantly damage what they hit.

The National Weather Service reports that hail causes nearly $1 billion in damage every year to property and crops.

According to the Ohio Weather Library, a weather-information site run by Ronald Hahn, hailstones "as large as 9 inches in circumference" fell in Stark County on July 6, 1817. Hail the size of "hen's eggs" fell in Franklin County in August 1825. And 5-inch-diameter hail fell in Cincinnati on June 13, 1881. Shockingly, those weren't the biggest record-setters.

The University Corporation for Atmospheric Research (UCAR) and the National Center for

Small hailstones collect after a strong storm passed through Columbus in June 2017. Small hailstones are common with strong updrafts in thunderstorms. Larger stones require a much stronger updraft.

Atmospheric Research (NCAR) report that, as of 1970, the heaviest hailstone ever documented fell in Coffeyville, Kansas. It weighed 1.67 pounds and was 5.67 inches in diameter. The largest documented hailstone fell in Aurora, Nebraska, on June 22, 2003. The Weather Service Office in Hastings verified the stone was 7 inches across and 18.75 inches around (but it weighed less than the Coffeyville stone).

Both of those records were bested by an ice ball that fell on June 23, 2010, in Vivian, South Dakota. The National Severe Storms Laboratory says the new record for the largest hailstone recovered in the

When the Sky Is Green...

When large, severe storms are in the area, you might sometimes notice a slightly greenish hue to the clouds. That's an indicator of hail. Ice refracts light differently than liquid water droplets, so the cloud can take on a slightly greenish cast.

U.S. measured 8 inches in diameter, had a circumference of 18.62 inches, and weighed 1 pound, 15 ounces.

The WMO says the world record for the heaviest hailstone is from the Gopalganj District of Bangladesh where a 2.25-pound hailstone fell on April 14, 1986. The agency also reports the same storm killed 92 people in the district.

Tornadoes

Ohio has recorded tornadoes in every month of the year. Winter tornadoes tend to be weaker, but they still can do serious damage.

The National Weather Service reports that tornadoes cause an average of 80 deaths and 1,500 injuries every year in the United States. "Most fatalities occur," the agency says, "when people do not leave mobile homes and automobiles."[5]

The remains of a mobile home are barely recognizable after a tornado struck Athens County in September 2010.

World Tornado Records

According to the World Meteorological Organization, the world's deadliest tornado touched down on April 26, 1989, in the Manikganj District of Bangladesh. It killed an estimated 1,300 people and injured more than 12,000.

Nearly all of the other worldwide tornado records are held by storms in the United States.

- **Greatest Distance Traveled:** 219 miles in 3.5 hours between Ellington, Missouri, and Princeton, Indiana, on March 18, 1925.

- **Largest Number of Tornadoes in a Single Outbreak:** 207 in the southeastern US on April 27, 2011.

- **Widest Tornado:** An F4 tornado[6] on May 22, 2004, in Hallam, Nebraska, was estimated to be nearly 2.5 miles wide.

---

[5] From a 1994 pamphlet, "Thunderstorms and Lightning... The Underrated Killers: A Preparedness Guide," by NOAA, NWS, and the American Red Cross.

[6] The Enhanced Fujita Scale wasn't in operational use until February 1, 2007.

- **Most Tornadoes in a Single Month:** In May 2003, 543 tornadoes were recorded in the United States.

- **Highest Recorded Tornadic Windspeed:** 302 mph during a storm on May 3, 1999, near Bridge Creek, Oklahoma.

- **Longest Tornado Transport:** A tornado on April 11, 1991, carried a personal check 223 miles from Stockton, Kansas, to Winnetoon, Nebraska.

Types of Vortices

Several weather phenomena look like tornado funnels or wreak tornado-like damage but they are not all tornadoes. Each type of vortex has a specific definition and is created by specific conditions.

There also are gustnadoes and eddies which are usually very small and usually do no damage.

Funnel Cloud

Funnel clouds are often the precursors to tornadoes. They look similar to tornadoes but they don't touch the ground and they don't do any damage. If a funnel evolves and DOES touch the ground, it becomes a tornado.

The best policy? Treat any funnel cloud as if it is a tornado. Take all of your tornado precautions. Find safe shelter immediately.

> NWS Definition:
> Funnel cloud: a funnel shaped cloud extending downward from a thunderstorm. It is associated with a rotating column of air that has condensed to form a cloud. It is not in contact with the ground.

Cold Air Funnel

A cold air funnel looks like a convective funnel cloud but it forms differently from a typical, supercell vortex. Cold air funnels very rarely make it to the surface to become actual tornadoes. When they do, they can cause damage similar to weak tornadoes.

Cold air funnels form behind cold fronts, in the cooler air, when there is a combination of windy conditions at the surface and very cold, upper-air winds flowing in a slightly different direction. Convection creates an updraft and the wind shear gives it some spin. If there is just enough rotation in the updraft, a small funnel can form. If there is enough moisture, some of the water vapor can condense in the vortex to make the funnel visible.

> **Tornado Outbreaks**
>
> The AMS Glossary of Meteorology suggests that a series of tornadoes is considered an "outbreak" when ten or more twisters are spawned from the same system. Some meteorologists also add the caveat that an outbreak cannot include a lull of more than six hours between active tornadoes, otherwise, the continuing series becomes a separate outbreak.

Tornado

Tornadoes are among Earth's most violent storms. They come from strong thunderstorms with very strong updrafts and significant rotation. Once they drop from the thunderstorm and touch the ground, they begin doing damage.

NWS Definition:

Tornado: a violently rotating column of air in contact with the ground and extending to the thunderstorm base. It can be a few yards across to a mile wide.

Even a small tornado has winds strong enough to do significant damage. A weak twister can fell trees and knock over garden sheds. A strong tornado can wipe a brick home from its foundation. That's why it is important to pay attention to tornado watches and warnings and to have a safety plan.

With today's Doppler radar, it is a bit easier to determine if conditions exist for a tornado to form. Strong thunderstorms can develop radar signatures that give meteorologists a heads up. Then they can send out the watches and warnings to give people time to take shelter.

A house in Millbury, Wood County, destroyed by an EF4 tornado that ravaged the area on June 5, 2010, with winds of up to 175 mph.

Tornadoes create a distinct image on radar. It's caused by the rotation in the storm and looks like a fishhook. When a "hook echo" appears on the radar screen, there is likely to be a tornado on the ground.

Water Spout

Waterspouts are tornadoes over the water. They tend to be relatively weak and often dissipate if they come ashore.

Many of them form from thunderstorms, just as tornadoes form over land. However, some of them form without the help of a convective thunderstorm; they are equivalent to cold-air funnels.

Central Ohio doesn't have bodies of water large enough to create water spouts, but you can occasionally see them on Lake Erie.

In one extreme case, one of the deadliest tornadoes in Ohio history was, technically, a waterspout for part of its life cycle. In June 1924, a massive tornado tore through Sandusky then raced out onto Lake Erie, becoming a waterspout, before coming ashore again at Lorain.

A waterspout in the Gulf of Mexico near the NOAA Ship Nancy Foster, Summer 2007. Note the "debris cloud" is simply a swirl of water. Photo by Melody Ovard, NOAA Photo Library.

Downburst

A downburst isn't a tornado but it can cause similar damage because its winds can be nearly as strong.

NWS Definition:

Downburst: a sudden rush of cool air toward the ground that can impact with speeds greater than 70 mph and produce damage similar to that of a tornado. Viewing the damage from the air does not reveal evidence of a twisting motion or convergence toward a central track, like it would for a tornado.

The downburst usually comes from the rear side of a severe thunderstorm where the air is falling instead of rising. The air races toward the ground at more than 100 mph and when it reaches the surface, it crushes things in its path and leaves a debris pattern similar to a water balloon hitting a sidewalk.

Dust Devil

While they may look like small tornadoes, dust devils form from a different process and they're usually not strong enough to do much damage. Unlike tornadoes, dust devils tend to form on hot, sunny days with clear skies and no wind.

If the hot, dry air rises quickly, it can rotate. If it spins fast enough, it can pick up dust and debris that makes the vortex visible. Dust devils are usually short-lived and travel a short distance. Interestingly, they have been seen to rotate clockwise or counterclockwise. That's odd because in the northern hemisphere, tornadoes and low-pressure centers always rotate counterclockwise.

They're sometimes also called a "dancing dervish" or "whirling dervish." In Australia, they're called "willy-willies."

Enhanced Fujita Scale

Scientists are trying to accurately measure the wind speeds and patterns inside tornadoes. The pesky problem is that the wind is so strong, it tends to destroy the monitoring equipment.

So, as an alternative, we measure the strength of a tornado by examining the damage it leaves behind.

For example, we know it takes only a 62 mph

A dust devil forms on Stock Island near Key West, Florida, in April 2006, under a clear, blue sky. Photo by James Newton via NWS Key West.

Enhanced Fujita Scale

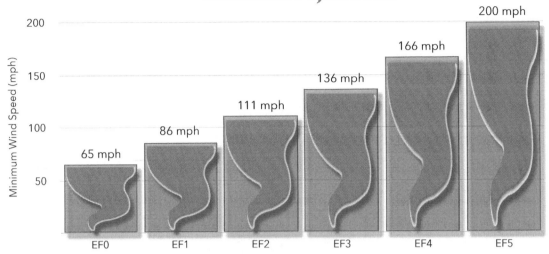

In the chart: Minimum Wind Speed (mph) on the y-axis; Enhanced Fujita Scale Number on the x-axis.

- EF0: 65 mph
- EF1: 86 mph
- EF2: 111 mph
- EF3: 136 mph
- EF4: 166 mph
- EF5: 200 mph

wind to damage a garden shed. But it takes a 121 mph wind to shift a brick home off its foundation. And it takes at least a 200 mph wind to wipe away all traces of that brick home, leaving only the foundation behind.

In 1971, Dr. Ted Fujita created an intensity scale to describe the force of different tornadoes. The Fujita Scale was adopted and used until February 1, 2007, when Dr. Fujita updated it. Now, we use the Enhanced Fujita Scale. The new version gets into more specific detail about types of damage as indicators of how strong a tornado may have been.

Today, the Enhanced Fujita Scale (EF) is the standard by which we measure and describe tornadoes.

Total Tornadoes 1950 - 2018

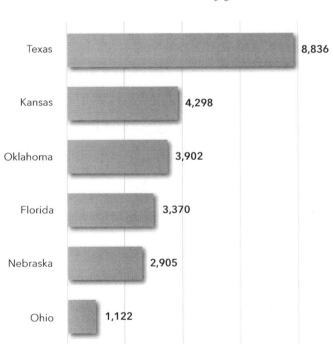

- Texas: 8,836
- Kansas: 4,298
- Oklahoma: 3,902
- Florida: 3,370
- Nebraska: 2,905
- Ohio: 1,122

Texas is, overwhelmingly, the most tornado-prone state. Ohio's tornado history ranks 22nd in the nation.
Data: Jan 1950 - Aug 2018

Ohio Tornado History

Ohio's history is replete with tornadoes. Still, many people are surprised to find out we are on the edge of tornado alley. Twisters have happened in every county in the state, including the urban areas in Franklin, Cuyahoga, Hamilton, Lucas, and Montgomery counties. Ohio has recorded tornadoes in every month of the year.

Thankfully, most storms are small. But the Buckeye State also has endured some of the strongest and most deadly tornadoes in U.S. history.

Ohio Tornadoes By Month

Between 1950 and 2013, the most Ohio tornadoes have been in June. May and July are distant second and third, respectively. You might be surprised to learn that tornadoes have been recorded in January and December. There were two in February of 2018!

On average, Ohio endures four tornadoes each June and three each in May and July. Still, we need to be prepared for tornadoes any time of the year.

Total Number of Ohio Tornadoes Per Month, 1950-2018

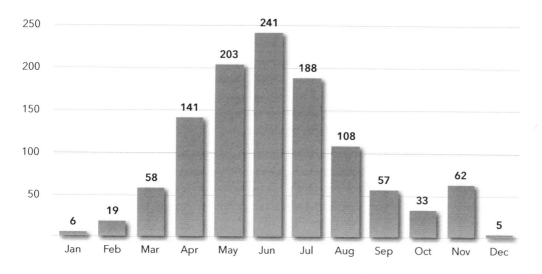

Central Ohio Tornadoes

Since our focus is on Central Ohio, let's take a closer look at some of the local twisters. Most of them, thankfully, are small but a few have reached catastrophic levels. Each time we examine the numbers, it's a good reminder of why we take tornado safety seriously.

Top Tornado-Prone Counties in Central Ohio

Franklin County leads Central Ohio in the number of tornadoes since 1950. That statistic alone should put to rest the idea that tornadoes don't hit urban areas. Obviously, they do!

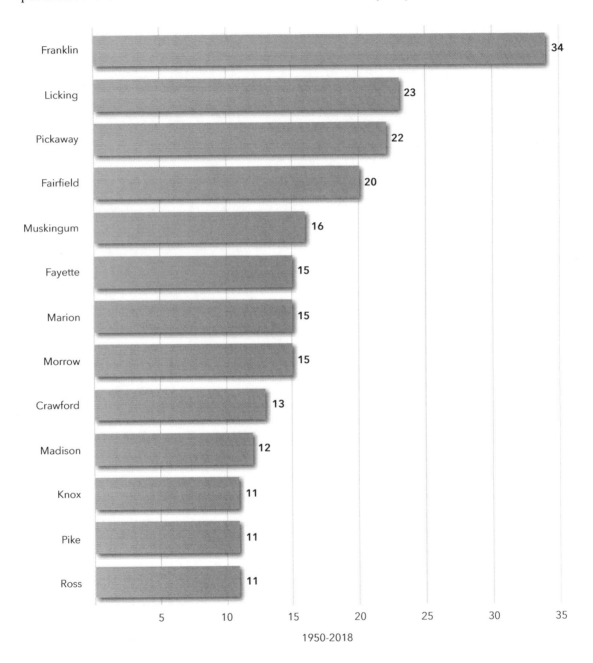

1950-2018

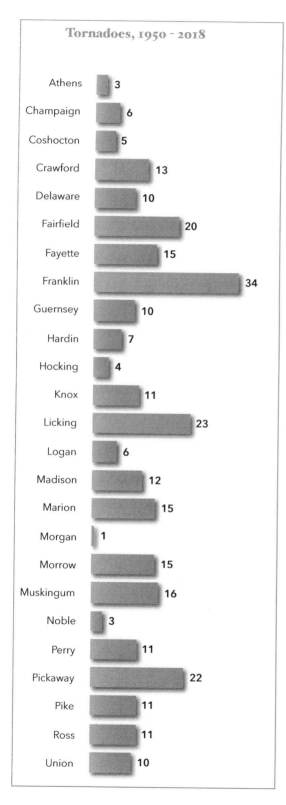

Tornadoes, 1950 - 2018

County	Tornadoes
Athens	3
Champaign	6
Coshocton	5
Crawford	13
Delaware	10
Fairfield	20
Fayette	15
Franklin	34
Guernsey	10
Hardin	7
Hocking	4
Knox	11
Licking	23
Logan	6
Madison	12
Marion	15
Morgan	1
Morrow	15
Muskingum	16
Noble	3
Perry	11
Pickaway	22
Pike	11
Ross	11
Union	10

Number of Tornadoes in Central Ohio Counties

Morgan County has had the fewest tornadoes since 1950; only one. And even that one was barely in the county! The tornado dropped out of a thunderstorm on Sept. 16, 2010, in Perry County, about three miles east of New Lexington, then traveled northeast, destroying eight houses and severely damaging more than three dozen other homes and buildings. The twister snapped or uprooted hundreds of trees and created a path of destruction 800 yards wide. After traveling nearly five miles, it finally dissipated near Rosefarm (York Township) in northwestern Morgan County. It was classified as an EF1 tornado with winds up to 110 mph.

After Morgan County, Athens and Noble have the next fewest with three each. Hocking County has recorded only four twisters since 1950.

Most Tornadoes in a Single Day

July 12, 1992, was a horrific day in Ohio. In a 24-hour period, more than two dozen twisters ravaged the state. Homes were destroyed. Cars were tossed like toys. Many people were injured. Many of the storms that day were in northern and North Central Ohio.

Top 10 Years for Ohio Tornadoes

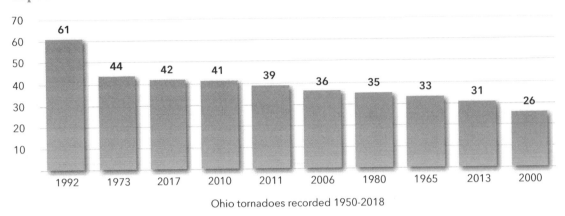

Ohio tornadoes recorded 1950-2018

Five of the Top 10 years with the most tornadoes have occurred since 2000, and three of those years are in the Top 5.

A barn was removed from its foundation and destroyed in Perry County by the same tornado that traveled into Morgan County in September 2010. Photo courtesy: NOAA/NWS

Number of Ohio Tornadoes by Fujita or Enhanced Fujita Scale

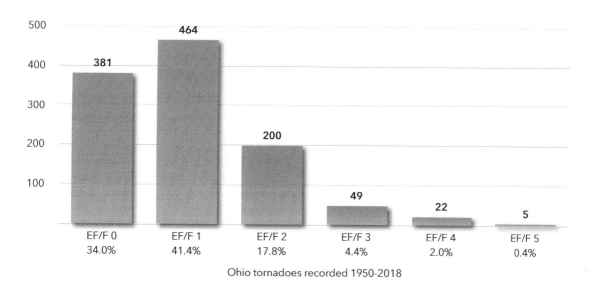

Ohio tornadoes recorded 1950-2018

The majority of tornadoes in Ohio since 1950 have been classified as F1 or EF1 on the Fujita scales. They are strong enough to do significant damage but tend not to be "devastating." Ohio has only experienced five F5 or EF5 tornadoes during that period, one of them being the enormous twister that ravaged Xenia in 1974.

Tornado Safety

Take action whenever tornado warnings are issued. Don't wait. Whether you hear it on the radio, the TV, or from the sirens in the neighborhood, activate your safety plan and take shelter.

The Ohio Committee for Severe Weather Awareness recommends using the "DUCK" method when tornado warnings are issued.

> D: Get DOWN to the lowest level
>
> U: Get UNDER something sturdy
>
> C: COVER your head
>
> K: KEEP in shelter until the storm has passed

The safest place to be when a tornado is passing nearby is in the basement. Stay away from windows. Get to the center of the building (not a corner). If there is no basement, get to the lowest level possible and take shelter in an interior room like a bathroom or a closet, away from windows.

If you're in a mobile home, a car, or outside, get to a sturdy, safe shelter as quickly as possible. If a solid building isn't available, find a low spot like a ditch and use your hands and arms to cover your head.

Don't try to outrun a tornado. It can change direction quickly and without warning.

Tornado Watches & Warnings

Tornado Watch: The Storm Prediction Center expects the potential for severe thunderstorms and tornadoes in and around the watch area. It doesn't mean that they will actually happen; it means they are possible.

Tornado Warning: A tornado is imminent, occurring, or has been detected on doppler radar. Get to a safe shelter immediately.

Tornado Emergency: A warning classification only used in the most extreme circumstances, issued when a large, dangerous tornado is bearing down on a specific area.

The criteria for Tornado Warnings has improved over the past few decades thanks to doppler radar. Doppler lets meteorologists monitor the density of the rain and the direction of the winds inside the thunderstorms. When they see a storm has enough rotation to develop a tornado, they'll issue a warning so people in that area have as much time as possible to take shelter.

Doppler-Indicated Tornado Warnings

Years ago, tornado warnings were issued only after a spotter laid eyes on a funnel cloud or an actual tornado. Today, doppler radar allows forecasters to see inside a storm, even when spotters aren't nearby. When they recognize rotation within a storm, they can issue "doppler-indicated warnings." That means warnings can be issued before a funnel actually drops from the cloud. And more lead time means safer communities.

The image to the right shows what rotation looks like on radar. In this case, as a strong storm rumbled through Clark County in April 2015, a small but distinct "signature" appeared on the radar screen. In "velocity" mode, the radar turns red, green, and purple. Red represents motion away from the radar site; green shows

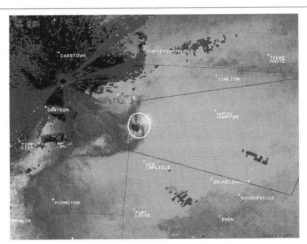

A mesocyclone couplet appears on the doppler radar unit at the Dayton Airport, April 2, 2015. A tornado warning was immediately issued for the surrounding area. Image courtesy: NWSFO Wilmington.

motion toward the radar site; and purple is motion that is either parallel to the radar or simply undetermined. The radar is the black dot on the map between Casstown and Grayson. The white circle is an added notation highlighting the rotation.

Hold your finger up to the image and trace the motion in the white circle. Red away. Green toward. Where the red and green are so close together (in a "couplet"), you'll notice your finger turning in a tight, counterclockwise circle. That's the signature of significant rotation and can be the precursor to a funnel cloud or tornado. Time to issue a tornado warning.

NWSFO Wilmington's Science and Operations Officer Seth Binau says, in this case, the rotation was about 400 feet above the ground and the couplet only lasted for about five minutes. It was enough to meet warning criteria.

The next day, after a ground survey of the path and damage, NWS confirmed an EF0 tornado with winds estimated near 80 mph had touched down near New Carlisle damaging a house, a barn, and several trees.

Tornado Sirens

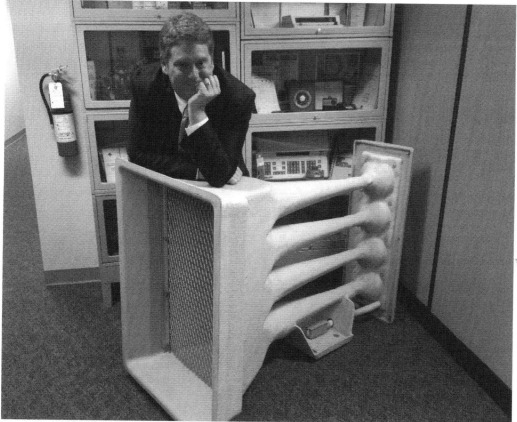

Marshall poses with an out-of-service tornado siren during a visit to the offices of Franklin County Emergency Management and Homeland Security.

While there are several ways to let you know about tornado warnings, the most high-profile method is the sirens. When they wail, it means a tornado is either on the ground in the county or a tornadic radar signature has appeared near or in the county. Whenever you hear the sirens, take action.

In the Columbus area, the sirens are installed, maintained, and operated by Franklin County Emergency Management and Homeland Security (FCEM&HS). Many of Ohio's 88 counties have a similar setup. The agency often uses state, federal, and local funding to install new sirens and keep them running. Having a centralized control center makes the system more efficient during emergency situations when minutes and seconds count.

As of 2016, Franklin County is covered by nearly 200 sirens. FCEM&HS says that's the second-highest siren density in the United States. The goal is to add at least 10 more each year. There are 16 sirens in the most-populated areas of Delaware County. The City of Dublin has an independent siren system (with 30 sirens) because the city limits include portions of three counties. Rather than dealing with separate jurisdictions, the city took on the siren responsibilities itself.

Like many other Ohio counties, FCEM&HS tests the sirens at least once a week. In the Columbus area, you'll hear them every Wednesday at noon. If there is severe weather in the area at the usual test time, they may choose to delay the test to avoid causing confusion.

Remember: Sirens Are Designed to Be Heard Outdoors

It's important to remember that the tornado sirens are an outdoor warning system. They are intended to warn people who are *outside* to seek shelter. You may not be able to hear the sirens inside your house, especially during the summer when the windows are closed and the air conditioning is on or when you are sound asleep. That's why it's important to have a secondary warning system in your home. A NOAA weather radio with an alert tone is very helpful!

Tornado Siren Fatigue

There is one significant drawback to county-wide siren systems: it's an all-or-nothing proposition. The sirens are activated for the entire county regardless of where the threat is located. That means if the tornadic cell is in the southwestern part of the county, folks 30 miles away, in the northeastern part of the county, outside the threat area, will still hear the sirens.

Unfortunately, that leads to an unintended consequence we call "siren fatigue." Even though the threat was legitimate for part of the county, other areas consider it "crying wolf." You've heard the sirens so many times, the threat has been in a different part of the county each time, and you get tired of hearing them. So, you begin to ignore them. That's dangerous. If you ignore the sirens and the threat *is* in your portion of the county, the storm can be on your doorstep before you have a chance to react.

Many counties, states, the National Weather Service, and NOAA are actively researching ways to improve the warning system. In the meantime, it's the best we have. It saves lives. Potentially yours.

In many Central Ohio counties, tornado sirens are activated countywide whenever the National Weather Service issues a Tornado Warning for the area.

With that goal in mind, Franklin County EMAHS launched a new system in the spring of 2017 that divides the county into quadrants. When Tornado Warnings are issued, managers can trigger the sirens in a more precise location. And in March 2016, Licking County began using a system that triggers the sirens based on "warning boxes" or "polygons" issued by the National Weather Service. Licking County now only tests its sirens on the first Wednesday of each month instead of weekly.

Text Notifications

In 2015, Franklin County Emergency Management and Homeland Security rolled out an opt-in text messaging system to alert residents to local

An overturned car sits in what used to be the driveway of a home in Wood County. An EF4 tornado struck the Millbury neighborhood on June 5, 2010.

hazards, warnings, and emergencies. The system includes more than 40 jurisdictions in the county and can be tailored to alert very specific populations. They can send messages to individual cell towers and those messages will go to every phone connected to that tower.

The message system works as a complement to the county's siren system. When you hear the sirens or an alert from your weather radio, the text message gives you a secondary confirmation that something's afoot. If you're inside and can't hear the sirens, the text message may be your first alert.

It's efficient. It's targeted. And it's a potential lifesaver. Sign up today at FCEMHS.org!

I Don't Have a Basement...

Here's a question from Megan:

> [W]e dont have a basement but we have a crawl space would it be safe to get into the crawl space in the event of a tornado. thanks i would really appreciate a responce especially after last night that was scary and we were concerned about weather we should go to the crawl space last night.

These questions are always difficult because everyone's home or office is different and every storm is unique. We can offer general advice and suggestions but only you can assess your specific situation.

When a tornado warning is issued, the safest place to be is in a basement, under something sturdy like a well-built staircase or a solid workbench. Try to get as close to the center of the building as possible and protect yourself from debris.

If you don't have a basement, get to the lowest floor in a central room with no windows. Interior bathrooms and closets are often good shelters. So are smaller, interior hallways. Under a lower-level stairwell may be good, too. If you get into a bathtub, cover yourself with a mattress or a sleeping bag. Don't choose a bathtub surrounded by a glass enclosure (see notes about being away from windows).

Mobile homes, cars, and trucks are not safe places. Get out and find a sturdy building for shelter. If that's not available, find a low place like a ditch (without water in it) where you can "duck and cover."

USA Today Weather Experts Bob Swanson and Doyle Rice have a great response for crawl spaces:

> A crawl space doesn't seem like a safe place. Tornadoes often shift houses on their foundations, maybe only a few feet. Imagine being between the beams in a crawl space with only a foot or two of space between the ground and the floor when a tornado shifts the house a couple of feet. Also, creatures such as snakes, that you wouldn't want to meet, have been found in crawl spaces.

The bottom line is: have a plan. When you create a plan before the storm, you'll know what to do when the warnings are issued. Your plan may not be perfect, but try to make it the best safety solution for your particular circumstances.

Tornado Myths

Tornadoes are some of the most powerful storms on Earth. They do incredible damage every year in the United States. Systems are in place to warn of their arrival and enormous agencies are ready to help clean up their mess.

But even with all the safety messages on TV, on the radio, and online, there are still a lot of myths about tornadoes and tornado safety. Let's debunk a few.

MYTH: Opening the windows will prevent the tornado's central pressure from destroying my house/school/store/office/garage.

Here's a question from Laura:

> I am wondering if I was correct in opening my front & back windows an inch or so, before I left for work, to prepare for today's bad weather.
> I have a German shepherd who has quite a problem with storms, and I thought that by opening the windows, it might equalize the pressure. And I seem to remember that opening your windows an inch was a good thing to prepare for a tornado. (I was in the Palm Sunday tornado in Radnor, Ohio, in 1965, as a child).

The idea of opening windows to "equalize the pressure" in your house is a myth. Unfortunately, it's a myth that was seared into many of our young minds during elementary-school tornado drills in the '60s, '70s, and '80s. The kids nearest the windows were tasked with opening the windows, then joining the rest of us in the tornado shelter as quickly as possible. In reality, opening the windows doesn't do anything but let in the rain.

The barometric pressure at the very center of a tornado may, indeed, be very low but the pressure surrounding the funnel is roughly the same as the rest of the region. If your house is close enough to the center of the tornado to experience a dramatic drop in the barometric pressure, then the tornado is already in your living room and the windows have already been blown out.

Opening the windows wastes precious time that would be better spent moving to a safe shelter.

MYTH: A highway overpass is a safe place to take shelter as a tornado passes by.

This very dangerous myth likely started in 1991 during a tornadic storm in Oklahoma. Some drivers (and a TV crew) decided to take shelter under an overpass as a weak tornado roared through the area. The only reason they survived was pure luck. Unfortunately, the crew's video is still running around on the web and many people misinterpret it as recommending a good shelter.

When a tornado passes through an overpass, the abutments become a dangerous wind tunnel. The area up the ramp squeezes the wind through a smaller space. It's like putting your thumb over the end of the garden hose. The wind speeds up through the smaller opening and so does the debris it's carrying.

If you're sitting under the bridge, you become a stationary target with no protection. Don't shelter there. Get out of the way of the storm or get to a legitimate shelter.

MYTH: The safest place to shelter in the basement is the southwest corner.

The original rationale for this myth comes from the direction in which storms often travel. In many cases, storms travel west to east or southwest to northeast. Not always, but lots of times. So, people reasoned, the tornadoes dropping from those storms would likely travel in a similar direction.

If a tornado hit your house while tracking from the southwest toward the northeast, it might push the house in the same direction. So, the thinking went, a lot of the debris would end up in the opposite corner from the original strike: the northwest. Therefore, staying in the southwest corner would keep you away from most of the debris.

Unfortunately, that's not the scenario that often plays out.

In the real world, most tornadoes aren't strong enough to push your house to the opposite side of the foundation. Instead, they end up shifting the house on the foundation just enough for it to topple into the basement right there. That could be on any side of the house.

The safest place to be is closest to the center of the basement, under a sturdy table or staircase that can support the weight of falling debris.

MYTH: Tornadoes don't hit cities.

Of course they do. Just ask the City of St. Louis. It's been hit dozens of times. Tornadoes have ravaged downtown Dallas, Memphis, Miami, and Oklahoma City. A twister can cut a path through a busy metropolitan area just as easily as it can ravage a rural corn field.

The only reason we rarely hear about tornadoes in cities is pure statistics.

Think of it this way: put a big map of Ohio on the wall. Take a good look at it. Notice how little area is covered by the cities compared to how much rural area fills the state. Now, throw a dart at the map. Statistically speaking, your dart is much more likely to land in a rural area than to hit a bullseye in a city's downtown business district. But both are possible. Tornadoes are just like that dart.

 MYTH: Tornadoes don't hit my town (hill, neighborhood, lake, etc.).

Yes, they do. They hit any place they want.

There is no "heat island" creating a protective bubble for your city. There is no protection provided by the "Great Divide." The old cemetery doesn't route tornadoes around your neighborhood. The river is not a force field. No, as a resolute viewer once suggested, the cars driving around Columbus' outer belt do not create a counteractive, swirling vortex that destroys tornadoes (not even if they all went very, very fast in the same direction).

Tornadoes can drop out of any supercell thunderstorm with the necessary updrafts, downdrafts and shear. Having a safety plan is a better idea than depending on the protection of old wives' tales.

Dogs and Storms

Pogonip is very comfortable in her crate and often sleeps in it with the door open.

For dogs who are afraid of storms, many trainers recommend conditioning and crate training. A crate becomes a dog's "safe space." You can even drape thick cloth around three sides to make it cave-like and create a den. The dog can retreat to the crate to feel more protected and relieve some anxiety. (Our dogs are comfortable enough in their crates that they sometimes sleep in them with the doors open.)

For some dogs, a compression suit is helpful for anxiety. They wear it like a very, very snug jacket. The tight fit, somehow, makes them feel less anxious, like they're being held.

Strong Wind

The wind doesn't have to be tornadic to cause serious problems. Straight-line winds can do significant damage, too. Strong thunderstorms can produce downdrafts that create winds nearly hurricane strength.

When extreme wind events are in the forecast, it's a good idea to take the same precautions as when there are tornadoes in the forecast. Listen for watches, warnings, and advisories and be prepared.

Wind Advisory: Non-convective sustained winds of 31 to 39 mph are expected to last for an hour or more or wind gusts of 46 to 57 mph.

High Wind Watch: Non-convective sustained winds of 40 mph or higher are expected to last for an hour or more or wind gusts of 58 mph or stronger.

High Wind Warning: Non-convective sustained winds of 40 mph or stronger for an hour or more or wind gusts of 58 mph are imminent or occurring.

Extreme Wind Warning: Winds of 115 mph or higher, associated with non-convective, downslope, derecho (NOT associated with a tornado), or sustained hurricane winds are expected to occur within one hour.

Derecho

A bow-shaped line of strong thunderstorms that marches across several states producing dangerously high winds for hours at a time may be classified as a "derecho."

They're usually lines of storms hundreds of miles long, often in a bow shape, that race across the region at freeway speeds or faster. They produce large hail and straight-line winds of 75-100 mph that can cause significant damage.

From the AMS Glossary:

derecho

A widespread convectively induced straight-line windstorm. Specifically, the term is defined as any family of downburst clusters produced by an extratropical mesoscale convective system. Derechos may or may not be accompanied by tornadoes.

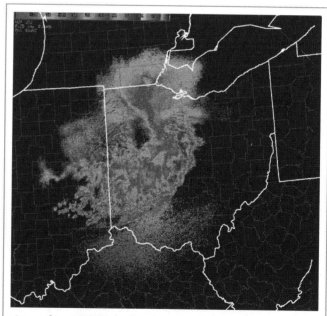

Image from NWS Radar from June 29, 2012, shows the huge, bow-shaped echo as the storms raced across Ohio. Image courtesy: NOAA/NWS

Such events were first recognized in the Corn Belt region of the United States, but have since been observed in many other areas of the midlatitudes.

The wind damage from derechos can look similar to the damage caused by tornadoes except there's no twisting. The debris path is a straight line laid out in the direction the storms are moving.

The good news is that we can often see them coming hours before they arrive. That gives meteorologists plenty of time to put out the warnings so we can batten down the hatches and be ready.

Central Ohio endured a massive derecho event on June 29, 2012.

In typical derecho fashion, it slammed through the area at more than 60 mph and churned out wind gusts of more than 80 mph. There was some significant damage reported across the region. Hailstones up to three-quarters of an inch in diameter were reported in Licking County.

Flooding

Flash flooding kills more Americans every year than any other weather-related disaster. According to NOAA's National Weather Service, more than 140 fatalities happen every year and most of those are either at night when the flood waters are difficult to see or when people get trapped in their vehicles. That's why the NWS vigorously promotes its flooding-safety campaign, "Turn Around. Don't Drown."

Six inches of rushing water is enough to knock down an adult. It takes much less for children. A car can be carried away by only 12 to 15 inches of water. Hold a ruler next to your leg and measure 12 inches from the floor. You'll probably be surprised by how low that is. Fast-moving water packs quite a wallop. A gallon of water weighs 8.34 pounds. Imagine tens of thousands of gallons of water rushing at

Flash flooding swamped the underpass, stranded several cars, and halted traffic on State Route 315 under Broad Street in Columbus on June 12, 2008. It only takes a few inches to stall out your car in those conditions.

you at 30 mph, hitting you with thousands of pounds of force. It can knock you down quickly. Avoid being in that situation.

Hydrology is the study of the water, including the way it moves and behaves on Earth and in the atmosphere. For weather watchers, it includes rain, runoff, rivers, lakes, flooding, and the full water cycle. Hydrology is important when forecasters want to give people a heads-up about potential flooding. For example, they'll try to determine how much rain is going to fall from a day's worth of thunderstorms then attempt to predict how that water will behave once it hits the ground. Running off into a farm field or a rural stream has a very different impact than overflowing the sewers in an urban area.

Types of Flooding

When the meteorologists at the National Weather Service issue watches, warnings, and advisories, they'll usually mention a specific type of flooding.

> **Urban Flooding**: as its name would imply, Urban Flooding happens in densely populated, urban areas and cities. It is usually caused when heavy rainfall overwhelms the local storm sewers. The water backs up and begins filling streets, intersections, and basements. It can happen very, very quickly because large expanses of concrete and asphalt keep the water from sinking into the ground and, instead, it runs off.

> **River Flooding**: when large amounts of rain fall in a particular area much of that water runs toward streams and rivers. They tend to be in low-lying areas. If there is more water than the stream can handle, The water level begins to rise. It, too, can happen quickly. River Flooding Warnings tend to happen around those valley areas and at specific river-forecast points.

> **Flash Floods**: Flash Floods also happen after quick, heavy rainfall. When storm sewers and streams are unable to keep up with the runoff, the excess water can run into unexpected places. Hillsides and even streets can become channels for the raging water as it attempts to escape.

> **Areal Flooding**: these watches and warnings are often issued for large areas that radar indicates may experience longer-term high water; the situation may not be associated with a particular watershed.

Flood Safety

Watches, warnings, and advisories can help us avoid flooded areas. They're issued whenever there's a chance for high water to inundate a particular area.

The National Weather Service has created a simple rule for flood safety: "Turn Around. Don't Drown." When you see high water, avoid it. Don't drive through it. Don't try to walk through it.

Here are a few recommendations for flood safety:

    ◌ Have an evacuation plan and practice it.

- Keep a disaster kit stocked and ready to take with you.

- Fill a bathtub with clean drinking water before flooding contaminates the common water supply.

- If the water threatens to get into your house, turn off the main power and the natural gas.

- Move valuables to higher floors, if there is time to do it safely.

Avoid walking through flood water. It may be deeper, swifter and more contaminated than expected. It may be hiding debris or holes under the surface. For example, manholes may be open under the surface of the water when their covers are blown off or moved by the force of the rushing water in the sewer system; you can step into one and disappear under the water, likely to be swept away in the sewer's accelerated current.

This manhole cover was thrown out of place by the force of the water during a heavy-rain event in Grandview Heights. (The photo was taken as the water was receding.) While the water is still high, the open hole may be hidden, and you could accidentally step into it.

Flood Watches and Warnings

Flash Flood Watch: Conditions are favorable for flash flooding. It does not mean that flash flooding will occur, but it is possible.

Flash Flood Warning: Flash flooding is imminent or occurring.

Flood Watch: Conditions are favorable for flooding. It does not mean flooding will occur, but it is possible.

Flood Warning: Flooding is imminent or occurring.

River Flood Watch: River flooding is possible at one or more forecast points along a river.

River Flood Warning: River flooding is occurring or imminent at one or more forecast points along a river.

Ohio Flooding History

Ohio has seen some vicious floods. The Great Flood of 1913 inundated most of the state, including Columbus and Central Ohio, and killed nearly 500 people. In late March, a series of storms dumped nearly 10 inches of rain across the region. Water rose as high as 15 to 20 feet with a strong current smashing through levees and tearing houses away from their foundations. An estimated 4,000 homes were damaged. Survivors told stories of watching helplessly as people screamed for help from houses that were being carried down the river. The bridges were washed away at Broad, State, and Town Streets. It's been called the "most-catastrophic weather disaster to afflict Ohio."

The Ohio River floods of January 1937 flooded everything from Pittsburgh to Cairo, Illinois, and practically wiped Portsmouth off the map, even with a massive flood wall in place. The water crested nearly 14 feet above Portsmouth's wall, after city officials opened the flood gates, intentionally flooding the downtown business district but preventing the crushing onslaught of a breach. Water levels in Cincinnati reportedly reached 80 feet, nearly 30 feet above flood stage.

On June 14, 1990, after nearly 5.5 inches of rain fell in less than three hours, a flash flood sent a wall of water and mud more than 20 feet high and 300 feet wide (the size of a football field with bleachers) crashing downstream near Shadyside in Belmont County. Twenty-six people were killed, 80 homes were destroyed, and more than 250 were damaged. The aftermath from that disaster inspired changes to the National Weather Service's methodology for issuing flood watches and warnings.

Flood Insurance

Homeowners are often surprised to discover that most flooding losses are not covered by standard insurance. Tragically, they often find out when it's too late. You need a flood-specific rider or policy. Check with your agent to see what coverage is available. In some particularly flood-prone areas, the only option may be policies provided by the National Flood Insurance Program (NFIP) which is administered by FEMA.

"As of September 2005, the average Ohio premium for a NFIP policy was $592 annually, compared to $450 per year, nationally," says a booklet from the Ohio Severe Weather Committee.

Extreme Cold

Even though Ohio is in a temperate zone, we can get some very cold air. Every once in a while, a blast of arctic air will make its way into the state. When it does, our temperatures plummet. The cold air is especially dangerous when it is accompanied by a snow or ice storm that knocks out power. In some cases, communities open warming shelters to help people stay warm until the power comes back on. The cold can be very dangerous for livestock and pets.

Hypothermia sets in when your core body temperature drops to 95°F or lower. It becomes "severe" when your body gets to 86°F or colder. Shivering is your body's way of warming up in small increments, but that's not enough when you're hypothermic. Other symptoms include

* shallow breathing,

* numbness in your hands and feet,

* drowsiness or exhaustion,

* confusion and memory loss, and

* slurred speech.

In extreme cases, you might even pass out.

If you are stuck out in the cold, you may develop frostbite. Frostbite can lead to amputations if it is severe enough.

Coldest Temperature Ever Recorded in Ohio

The village is long gone but the record still stands. The late Milligan, Ohio, in Perry County, is the site of the coldest temperature ever recorded in Ohio.

As a severe blast of arctic air poured into Ohio during the "Great Blizzard of 1899," the temperatures plummeted beyond the scales of average thermometers. Steve Eveland was the on-duty observer for the US Weather Bureau's station in Milligan on February 10th. He noted a temperature of -39°F, the lowest temperature officially reported in the Buckeye State. Ever.

It was likely caused by "cold air drainage" into the valley around the Moxahala Creek (Jonathan's Creek).

Kind of like water, cold air often flows downhill. It's more dense than warm air and so it tends to sink instead of rise. The cold air runs down the hillsides and into valleys where it pools, creating pockets of very cold temperatures. (This is the same reason why you'll often see fog in valleys and low-lying areas when it's clear on the hilltops.) That cold pool happened to surround the village and they recorded Ohio's coldest-ever temperature.

The area where Milligan once stood is now part of the village of McLuney, in Harrison Township, just south of Crooksville.

Winter Driving Tips from AAA

When winter weather looms, it's always a good idea to brush up on how to drive in the ice and snow. AAA Ohio has some good suggestions:

Keep the gas tank at least half full, slow down to give yourself an extra gap between vehicles, and, if you start skidding, take your foot off the pedals, keep looking where you want to go, and steer the car that way.

Have a pre-packed emergency kit in your car with blankets, jumper cables, flares, and extra clothes.

Replace your windshield wipers and fluid, make sure the battery is fully charged, and check your tires for tread and adequate pressure.

If you get stranded, save gas by only running the heater for 10 minutes per hour and leave the window open a crack for ventilation; use the blankets from your emergency kit to stay warm.

Consecutive Days at -10° or Colder

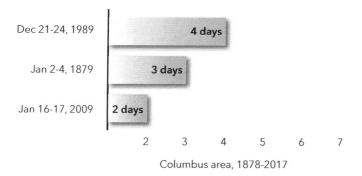

Dec 21-24, 1989 — 4 days
Jan 2-4, 1879 — 3 days
Jan 16-17, 2009 — 2 days

Columbus area, 1878-2017

Plus another 15 years between 1880 and 1994 with consecutive runs of two days at or below -10°F.

Consecutive Days at -5° or Colder

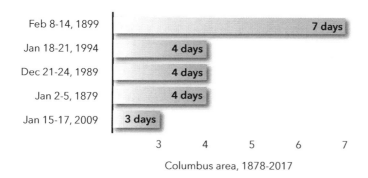

Feb 8-14, 1899 — 7 days
Jan 18-21, 1994 — 4 days
Dec 21-24, 1989 — 4 days
Jan 2-5, 1879 — 4 days
Jan 15-17, 2009 — 3 days

Columbus area, 1878-2017

Plus another 13 years between 1884 and 1989 with consecutive three-day runs at or below -5°F. And 36 more years with two-day runs.

Consecutive Days at 0° or Colder

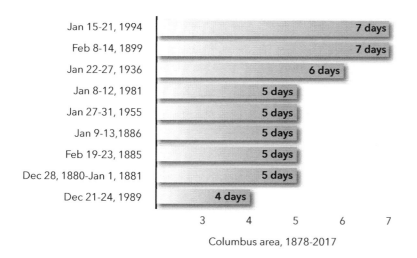

Jan 15-21, 1994 — 7 days
Feb 8-14, 1899 — 7 days
Jan 22-27, 1936 — 6 days
Jan 8-12, 1981 — 5 days
Jan 27-31, 1955 — 5 days
Jan 9-13, 1886 — 5 days
Feb 19-23, 1885 — 5 days
Dec 28, 1880-Jan 1, 1881 — 5 days
Dec 21-24, 1989 — 4 days

Columbus area, 1878-2017

Plus another 13 years between 1879 and 1989 with consecutive four-day runs at or below 0°F. And 30 years with three-day runs.

115

Winter Storms

A blanket of fresh, deep snow is beautiful. It also can be a nightmare. When it falls during a busy commute or brings down power lines, it has the potential to be deadly. When the snow is combined with ice, it can be devastating to infrastructure and the economy.

Most Ohio towns and cities are prepared to handle an occasional heavy snowfall. Now and then, though, Mother Nature sends a storm that overwhelms the system. That's when schools and businesses close.

It's always a good idea to be prepared before the storm arrives!

Watches and warnings are issued for very specific sets of criteria. The criteria varies in different parts of central and southern Ohio.

Winter Storm Warning: A combination of hazardous winter weather is occurring or imminent for Franklin County including:

* 6 inches or more of snow or 1/2 inch of sleet within a 12-hour period or
* 8 inches or more of snow within a 24-hour period and/or
* Enough ice accumulation to cause damage to trees or power lines and/or
* A life-threatening or damaging combination of snow and/or ice accumulation with wind

South of Columbus and east of I-71 (including Pickaway, Ross and Fayette counties), the criteria are different; it takes less snow and ice to trigger a warning. Other Central Ohio counties have different criteria based on the NWS office that issues local watches and warnings.

Pets & Cold

Imagine being stuck out in the cold, barefooted, with only a light jacket. That's what it's like for our pets.

Sure, they have fur, but, for most of them, it's not thick enough to truly protect them from the bitter cold we get during Ohio winters. (Yes, your Husky may be a special case.) They need shelter and warmth, just like us.

When it gets really cold, bring them inside. Even if they live outdoors most of the year, give them a warm break as often as possible. Make sure they have a well-insulated shelter that protects them from the wind, rain, and snow and dry bedding where they can save some body heat. Keep the water dish from freezing over and their food from becoming an icy rock.

If you see an animal stranded outdoors in the brutal elements, call Columbus Humane at 614.777.7387. One of their agents can make a visit to help the animal and its owner.

Legend:
- two or more simultaneous freezing/frozen precip events
- 6" or more in 12 hours; 8" or more in 24 hours
- 4" or more in 12 hours; 6" or more in 24 hours
- 4"-6" or more in 12 hours; 6"-8" or more in 24 hours

Since each NWS forecast office establishes its own criteria for issuing Winter Storm Warnings, Central Ohio counties may experience very different conditions under the same warning category.

Winter Weather Advisory: 3 inches of snow, or less than a 1/2 inch of sleet in 12 hours, or falling/blowing snow with winds of 34 mph or less that reduce visibility to 1/4 mile or less, or significant black ice conditions; in essence, any winter weather conditions that could be hazardous or inconvenient but that aren't serious enough to warrant the issuance of a Warning. Travel on foot or by vehicle may be difficult or dangerous.

Blizzards

Blizzards are the most notorious winter storms. They close schools, block roads, bring down power lines, and shut down entire states for days. Some blizzards are so strong they make it into history books. Thankfully, true blizzards are rare occurrences in Ohio.

One of the most memorable features of any blizzard is the snow. But, by definition, blizzards involve much more than heavy snowfall. A blizzard includes high wind and low visibility for specific amounts of time. What goes in the history books, though, is the aftermath with power out for days, schools out of session, and, in at least one case, activation of the National Guard.

Blizzard: A winter storm which produces the following conditions for at least 3 hours:

- sustained winds or frequent gusts to 35 mph or greater, and
- considerable falling and/or blowing snow reducing visibility to less than 1/4 mile.

Blizzard Warning: This product is issued by the National Weather Service when blizzard conditions are life threatening. It is issued in Central Ohio when forecasters expect sustained winds of 35 mph or stronger and visibility reduced to 1/4 mile or less for at least three hours..

IMPORTANT NOTE: There is no temperature requirement or specific snowfall rate (or depth) that must be met to achieve blizzard conditions. Instead, it's all about the strength of the wind, reduced visibility, and duration of the conditions.

Ice Storms

Ice storms can be some of the most beautiful storms in Ohio. They leave behind a sparkling, gorgeous coating on every outdoor surface. While it may be fantastic for photographs, ice storms wreak havoc across the region. The ice is exceedingly dangerous to drive on, it can destroy trees and power lines are no match for its weight.

Unfortunately, when an ice storm approaches, there's not much you can do but hunker down, be prepared, and wait it out.

The ice usually arrives in one of two forms: freezing rain or sleet. Sometimes they come together. The ice can also form during a cold overnight after a rain while everything is wet and the rain freezes in the cold temperatures.

Freezing rain is rain that freezes on contact with a cold surface. Sleet falls as small ice pellets. Graupel is very similar to sleet.

Ice Storm Warning: 1/4 inch or more of ice accumulation is expected in the next 12 to 24 hours.

Freezing Rain Advisory: Ice accumulations of up to 1/4 inch are expected in the next 12 to 24 hours.

Jan 2009 Ice Storm

When a massive storm moved into Ohio Jan. 26-28, 2009, 8" to 10" of snow fell in Columbus with 10" to 12" of snow in Marion and Bucyrus. But the snow was, surprisingly, not the biggest problem. A thick coating of ice had the most impact and did the most damage.

As the storm progressed, a layer of warmer air moved into the region aloft, just warm enough for some of the snow to melt as it fell toward the surface. The ground (and cars, and trees, and power lines) was still below freezing, though, and so the rain turned to ice as soon as it landed on the surface. It was a textbook freezing rain scenario.

Much of central and north-central Ohio was covered in a 1/4" to 1/2" of ice. Southern Ohio was coated with 1/2" to 1" of ice. All of that on top of heavy, wet snow. The trees and power lines didn't stand a chance. The Ohio Public Utilities Commission reported nearly 172,000 Ohioans were without electricity because of the snow and ice.

Naming Winter Storms

Hurricanes are the only storms that get names. The National Weather Service does not name winter storms, nor does your local TV weather person. Naming a winter storm is a marketing thing, not a meteorology thing.

In 2012, The Weather Channel, on its own, began assigning names to large winter storms. Like the National Hurricane Center, it uses an alphabetical sequence of names and uses those names for coverage and promotions.

TWC claims there is plenty of science that precedes the naming of a winter storm. A committee of three winter-weather experts looks through all of the data, the forecasts, and the potential impacts, then decides whether a storm should be named. During the 2012-2013 season, 27 storms earned names. According to TWC's website, weather.com, the three major factors for naming a winter storm are:

- Winter Storm Warnings affecting 2 million people or 400,000 square kilometers
- Winter Weather Advisories affecting 8 million people or 600,000 square kilometers
- Winter Weather Advisories + Winter Storm Warnings affecting 10 million people or 1 million square kilometers

In some ways, naming a winter storm might make a modicum of sense. When you are simultaneously tracking multiple hurricanes in the vast, featureless ocean, it is helpful to have names as references. That way, Hurricane Cornelius is quickly differentiated from Hurricane Bartholomew or Hurricane Delbert. So, when you are tracking a couple of cool-season low-pressure centers as they wander across the well-mapped continent, one could make the argument that names may be of similar benefit.

In practical, realistic, day-to-day terms, though, all it does is contribute to hype and hysteria.

- "Winter Storm Fifi is wreaking havoc up the east coast... at five!"
- "Winter Storm Jebbodiah dumps three feet of snow on the Rockies... at six!"
- "Winter Storm Twiggy blamed for shutting down thousands of schools... at eleven!"

As it is, TV weather folks already get blamed for over-playing stormy conditions. Naming winter storms only makes that worse.

Extreme Heat

Ohio summers can produce high temperatures near 100°F and, when it's humid, the Heat Index can make it feel much hotter. It only takes a few minutes in that kind of heat to begin to feel the health effects. The Ohio Department of Health says extreme heat kills an average of 675 Americans every year.

The warmest it's ever been in Columbus is 106°F. Other parts of Ohio have seen temperatures climb to 113°F with a heat index even higher.

Heat exhaustion and heat stroke can develop very quickly at those temperatures.

When it's hot...

- Reduce strenuous activities,

- Wear lightweight, light-colored clothing,

- Eat less,

- Drink more water, avoid alcohol,

- Stay in the air conditioning,

- Avoid too much sun (sunburn makes it more difficult for your body to dissipate the heat), and

- Do not take salt tablets unless directed by a doctor.

Slip, Slap, Slop

During the summer, ultraviolet radiation from the sun can do serious damage to your skin. Melanomas can develop rapidly and can be deadly if they're not treated quickly. Protecting your largest organ (your skin) is essential!

In New Zealand, where they have some of the highest ultraviolet readings on the planet, the government's Health Promotion Agency developed a catchy "SunSmart" slogan to remind us all to be sun-aware: "Slip, slap, slop."

It reminds us to

- Slip on a shirt to block the sun's rays,

- Slap on a hat to give your head and neck some shade, and

- Slop on some high-SPF sunscreen to protect all that exposed skin.

Recently, they also added "Wrap" to the slogan to include wrap-around sunglasses with UV protection to shield your eyes.

If you have sick or elderly neighbors, take a few minutes to check on them. Make sure they have a way to stay cool and plenty of water to drink. With a quick visit, you could save a life.

Columbus Area Heat Waves

One of the warmest years in recent memory was the Summer of 2012 with a total of four dozen days at 90°F or warmer, 11 of them consecutively. It was a scorcher of a summer! It lands in the history books in the Top 3 years with the most 90-degree days, only shy of tying the all-time record by a single day.

Consecutive Days at 90° or Warmer

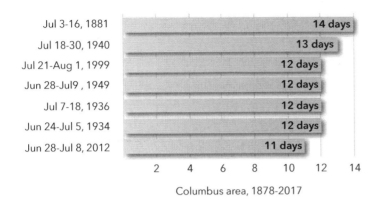

Jul 3-16, 1881 — 14 days
Jul 18-30, 1940 — 13 days
Jul 21-Aug 1, 1999 — 12 days
Jun 28-Jul9 , 1949 — 12 days
Jul 7-18, 1936 — 12 days
Jun 24-Jul 5, 1934 — 12 days
Jun 28-Jul 8, 2012 — 11 days

Columbus area, 1878-2017

Plus another 4 years between 1901 and 1988 with consecutive 11-day runs at or above 90°F.

Consecutive Days at 95° or Warmer

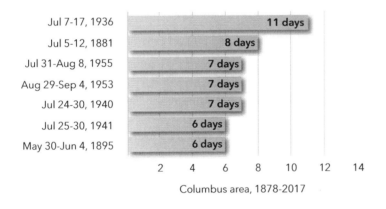

Jul 7-17, 1936 — 11 days
Jul 5-12, 1881 — 8 days
Jul 31-Aug 8, 1955 — 7 days
Aug 29-Sep 4, 1953 — 7 days
Jul 24-30, 1940 — 7 days
Jul 25-30, 1941 — 6 days
May 30-Jun 4, 1895 — 6 days

Columbus area, 1878-2017

Plus another 9 years between 1895 and 2012 with consecutive five-day runs at or above 95°F.

Consecutive Days at 100° or Warmer

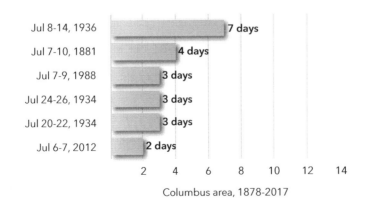

Jul 8-14, 1936 — 7 days
Jul 7-10, 1881 — 4 days
Jul 7-9, 1988 — 3 days
Jul 24-26, 1934 — 3 days
Jul 20-22, 1934 — 3 days
Jul 6-7, 2012 — 2 days

Columbus area, 1878-2017

Plus another 7 years between 1897 and 1988 with consecutive two-day runs at or above 100°F.

Heat-Related Disorders

Your body gets rid of heat by sweating and increasing blood flow near the surface of your skin. When the Heat Index is high, it means there's lots of humidity. All that moisture in the air makes it more difficult for your sweat to evaporate, cooling your body. You can overheat much faster.

	Heat Index	Effect on the body
Caution	80°F - 90°F	Fatigue is possible after prolonged exposure and/or strenuous physical activity.
Extreme Caution	90°F - 105°F	Sunstroke, heat stroke, heat cramps, and heat exhaustion are possible after prolonged exposure or strenuous physical activity.
Danger	105°F - 130°F	Sunstroke, heat cramps, or heat exhaustion are likely, and heatstroke is very possible.
Extreme Danger	130°F or higher	Heatstroke and sunstroke are very likely.

Heat disorder symptoms

Heat cramps: painful twitches and charley horses, usually in muscles of your legs and abdomen. You sweat a lot.

Heat exhaustion: heavy sweating, weakness, cold skin, pale, and clammy. Vomiting. Irregular pulse. You may still have a normal temperature though.

Heatstroke (or sunstroke): high body temperature (106°F or warmer). Hot, dry skin. Rapid and strong pulse. Possible unconsciousness.

Annual Box Fan Drive

Every summer, Life Care Alliance (the fantastic folks who run Central Ohio's Meals On Wheels program) launches its annual fan drive. They collect hundreds of box fans and give them to seniors who, otherwise, don't have a way to stay cool.

Many homes don't have central air-conditioning and many seniors are apprehensive about leaving their doors or windows open. So, their homes get warmer and warmer until they are stiflingly hot and potentially deadly.

A simple fan can circulate enough air to cool a room by ten degrees. That difference can be life-saving.

To donate a fan (or cash) to the cause, contact Life Care Alliance at 614.278.3130 or visit their website at LifeCareAlliance.org.

Drought

In general terms, a drought happens when an area doesn't get enough precipitation for an extended period of time and the water supplies in the atmosphere, on the surface, and underground become deficient.

A "meteorological drought" happens first; it's when there is a prolonged period with below-average precipitation. There's not enough rain to supply crops, fill reservoirs, or maintain the underground aquifers. In some cases, there's not enough snowfall to create the spring melt necessary to replenish the water table.

An "agricultural drought" is related to the soil conditions when below-average precipitation or artificial water depletion means there's not enough moisture to hold the dirt in place (wind erosion becomes a problem) and crops don't have enough water to thrive. Even if there's plenty of rain, an agricultural drought can happen if growers siphon off all the water or use it up in poorly-planned farming ventures.

A "hydrological drought" happens when the water reserves begin to fall below average. Lakes, reservoirs, and aquifers start to run low because the stored water is being drained faster than it can be replenished. It can be caused by a lack of precipitation or a manmade issue (as has happened in Asia) when one country diverts a water source and leaves another country dry.

Droughts can cause enormous economic and even social problems. Mass migrations push populations toward water sources when their homelands dry out. Droughts can cause hunger and famine when crops fail season after season. They can even cause energy shortages for areas that depend on hydroelectric power.

Drought Monitor

The US Drought Monitor was created in 1999 to track the climatic, hydrologic, and soil conditions. Every Thursday morning, the Drought Monitor releases a detailed map depicting the conditions across the country. It is jointly produced by the National Drought Mitigation Center at the University of Nebraska-Lincoln, the USDA, and NOAA.

With the help of more than 350 observers, hydrologists classify each portion of the country into five categories from "abnormally dry" to "exceptional drought." Federal, state, and local planners can then use the information to allocate water resources.

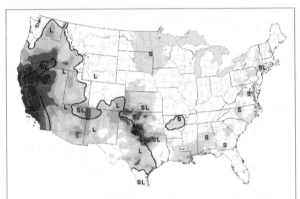

An example of the US Drought Monitor map. "The U.S. Drought Monitor is jointly produced by the National Drought Mitigation Center at the University of Nebraska-Lincoln, the United States Department of Agriculture, and the National Oceanic and Atmospheric Administration. Map courtesy of NDMC-UNL."

Central Ohio Droughts

Even in a very dry year, Central Ohio still gets some rain. We've never recorded a year with less than 20" of precipitation (that includes rain and snowfall). So, while we may see our lawns turn brown and even have a disastrous year for farming, we still get enough moisture to avoid being an arid desert.

Columbus Area Top 10 Driest Years

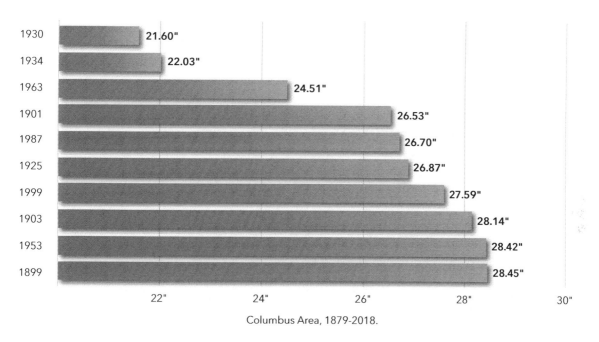

Columbus Area, 1879-2018.

Columbus Area Top 10 Driest Months

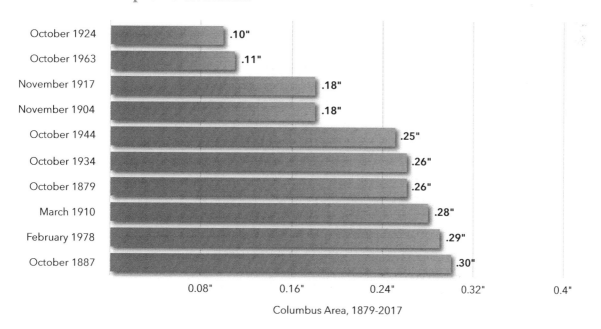

Columbus Area, 1879-2017

Hurricanes

Hurricanes. Cyclones. Typhoons. They're all names for the same kind of big, nasty, tropical storms.

What you call it depends on the part of the world you live in. In the Western Atlantic, Caribbean, and Eastern Pacific, we call them hurricanes. Southeast Asia refers to the same type of storm as a typhoon. Australia calls them cyclones.

Can Hurricanes Form in the Great Lakes?

As an historic typhoon (Nesat) pummeled The Philippines in September 2011, some people began to wonder whether the same kind of storm could happen in Central Ohio.

> Matt Manee via Facebook:
> "Is it possible for a hurricane to form in lake Erie and cause damage?"

The answer is "no, but kinda."

Hurricanes are a tropical phenomenon. They are deep low-pressure centers that generate an organized blob of thunderstorms circulating around the low. They use the warm ocean water as "fuel" and are sustained by some specific upper-level winds.

Once the system begins generating sustained winds of 39 mph or more, it becomes a "tropical storm" and is assigned a name by the National Hurricane Center. When the winds reach 74 mph or higher, the system is upgraded to "hurricane."

Here's the definition of "hurricane" from the AMS Glossary:

> A tropical cyclone with one-minute average surface (10 m) winds in excess of 32 meters per second (64 knots) in the Western Hemisphere (North Atlantic Ocean, Caribbean Sea, Gulf of Mexico, and in the eastern and central North Pacific east of the date line).

The Great Lakes don't provide the appropriate conditions for hurricane formation. While they're very big bodies of water, they aren't extensive enough (or warm enough, even in the summer) to provide the kind of fuel a hurricane requires. Plus, the jet stream and upper-level winds often move those low-pressure centers across the continent relatively quickly, too fast to benefit from the lakes' warmer water; tropical storms tend to move very slowly and take advantage the huge expanse of warm ocean water.

There's also the issue of cyclogenesis, the formation of the initial low-pressure center. Many tropical storms take days or even weeks to spin up enough strength to start generating strong winds. The storms that barrel through the Caribbean, Gulf of Mexico, and western Atlantic often form off the African coast or in the southern Caribbean where the water is warmest and where they're less likely to get sheared off by the upper-level winds. Many of the low-pressure centers that blast through the Great Lakes form in the cool, dry areas of western Canada.

One of the hallmarks of a tropical system is that it doesn't have warm or cold fronts; it's warm all the way around. The extra-tropical (outside the tropics) systems that pass through the Great Lakes feature fronts and are surrounded by distinct air masses.

Now, with all of that said, the Great Lakes can endure some very deep low-pressure centers that create hurricane-strength winds. And those winds can do some serious damage. Whether it's a warm, tropical wind or a cold, arctic blast, 74+ mph winds can severely damage people and property.

One of the all-time worst Great Lakes storms was the storm of 1913. Even though it was called the "Great Lakes Hurricane," it wasn't actually a hurricane. It was an incredibly strong, deep, low-pressure center that dropped out of Canada. The winds were strong enough that they were likened to a hurricane, thus the nickname. Huge ships sank, lives were lost, and the damage was terrible.

So, no, hurricanes cannot form in the Great Lakes. But, yes, very strong systems that pass through the Great Lakes can have damaging, hurricane-strength winds. Still, they are very different types of systems.

The Saffir-Simpson Scale

All hurricanes are dangerous but some are more dangerous than others.

Wind is only a portion of a hurricane's destructive combination. Many of these storms also produce a significant storm surge, the heavy rain can cause major flooding, and they can even spawn tornadoes.

In the early-1970s, wind engineer Herb Saffir and meteorologist Bob Simpson began looking at the impact and damage potential of hurricanes. They studied the big ones and the smaller ones, assessing the storms' destructive power. And they developed a wind scale that we now use to describe classes of hurricanes.

The Saffir-Simpson scale only examines wind speeds. It doesn't consider the effects of flooding, tornadoes, or storm surge. In general, though, the stronger a storm's Saffir-Simpson category, the more likely it is also to produce other kinds of damage.

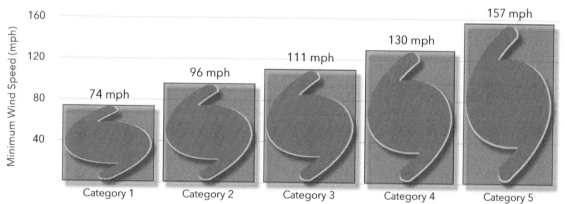

Category 1 storms are strong enough to create deadly flying debris. That debris can smash windows and the wind can topple chimneys. The wind is strong enough to demolish older mobile homes. Some roof materials or vinyl siding may come loose.

Category 2 hurricanes will destroy most mobile homes and do significant damage to poorly-constructed frame homes. Unsecured roofs can be lifted and torn away. Masonry walls that aren't reinforced may collapse.

Category 3 events are considered "major hurricanes." Poorly-constructed homes are likely to be destroyed when the wind removes the roof and the walls fall down. Wood- and even steel-framed buildings may have structural damage. Trees will be snapped or torn from the ground. Expect electricity and water services to be damaged and unavailable for days or weeks.

Category 4 hurricanes with winds up to 156 mph create "catastrophic" damage. Nearly all mobile homes will be destroyed. Well-built homes can expect severe damage. Windows and roofs will be destroyed. Trees and power poles will be snapped or destroyed, blocking roads where they fall. Power outages could last for weeks or months and water shortages are inevitable.

Category 5 storms can create flying debris that is deadly even if you're inside a building. Most frame homes will lose their roofs and walls. Older metal buildings will collapse. Industrial and low-rise apartment buildings are not likely to endure. Most trees and power poles will be torn down, utilities will be unavailable for months, and a large portion of the area will be uninhabitable for weeks or months.

Hurricane Names

The National Hurricane Center began naming tropical storms in 1953. Before that, storms were referred to by the Saint's Day on which they occurred or when and where they made landfall, as in "Hurricane Santa Ana" (Puerto Rico, July 26, 1825), "The Florida Keys Labor Day Hurricane of 1935" (September 2) or "The Galveston Hurricane of 1900" (September 8). Anthropomorphic names make it a little easier for meteorologists to track multiple storms at the same time, especially when they're issuing lots of watches, warnings, and updates.

Today, the names are overseen by a committee at the World Meteorological Organization (WMO). Originally, all the storms were given women's names. Then in 1979, in the spirit of inclusion and equality, men's names were added to the lists.

For the Atlantic basin, the WMO keeps several lists of 21 alphabetical names (they don't use names starting with the letters Q, U, X, Y, or Z). The lists are recycled every six years so, for example, the names being used in 2015 won't come around again until 2021. There's a different list of names for the eastern-Pacific basin which keeps us from using the same name twice in the same season, once in the Atlantic and once in the Pacific.

If a season has more than 21 named storms, the WMO starts using the Greek alphabet: Hurricane Alpha, Hurricane Beta, Hurricane Gamma, etc.

And, no, you cannot have a tropical cyclone named for you (or your ex).

Atlantic Cyclone Names

2019	2020	2021	2022	2023	2024	Extras
Andrea	Arthur	Ana	Alex	Arlene	Alberto	Alpha
Barry	Bertha	Bill	Bonnie	Bret	Beryl	Beta
Chantal	Cristobal	Claudette	Colin	Cindy	Chris	Gamma
Dorian	Dolly	Danny	Danielle	Don	Debby	Delta
Erin	Edouard	Elsa	Earl	Emily	Ernesto	Epsilon
Fernand	Fay	Fred	Fiona	Franklin	Florence	Zeta
Gabrielle	Gonzalo	Grace	Gaston	Gert	Gordon	Eta
Humberto	Hanna	Henri	Hermine	Harold	Helene	Theta
Imelda	Isaias	Ida	Ian	Idalia	Isaac	Iota
Jerry	Josephine	Julian	Julia	Jose	Joyce	Kappa
Karen	Kyle	Kate	Karl	Katia	Kirk	Lambda
Lorenzo	Laura	Larry	Lisa	Lee	Leslie	Mu
Melissa	Marco	Mindy	Martin	Margot	Michael	Nu
Nestor	Nana	Nicholas	Nichole	Nigel	Nadine	Xi
Olga	Omar	Odette	Owen	Ophelia	Oscar	Omicron
Pablo	Paulette	Peter	Paula	Philippe	Patty	Pi
Rebekah	Rene	Rose	Richard	Rina	Rafael	Rho
Sebastien	Sally	Sam	Shary	Sean	Sara	Sigma
Tanya	Teddy	Teresa	Tobias	Tammy	Tony	Tau
Van	Vicky	Victor	Virginie	Vince	Valerie	Upsilon
Wendy	Wilfred	Wanda	Walter	Whitney	William	Phi
						Chi
						Psi
						Omega

Retiring Cyclone Names

Names are removed from the lists if their associated storms were particularly deadly, costly, or if using the name again would be insensitive to their victims. Dozens of names have been retired since 1954. Andrew, Donna, Gilbert, Hugo, Katrina, Rita, Sandy, and Wilma are a few that will never be used again.

After the devastation caused to the US east coast by Hurricane Sandy in 2012, NOAA decided to retire the name. No more Atlantic-basin storms will be given the name Sandy. She's done. She was replaced by "Sara" in 2018.

They do this, now and then, when a storm is particularly bad or memorable.

Retired Cyclone Names, 1954-2017

Agnes	Connie	Frances	Irene	Marilyn
Alicia	David	Frederic	Iris	Matthew
Allen	Dean	Georges	Irma	Michelle
Allison	Dennis	Gilbert	Isabel	Mitch
Andrew	Diana	Gloria	Isidore	Nate
Anita	Diane	Greta	Ivan	Noel
Audrey	Donna	Gustav	Janet	Opal
Betsy	Dora	Harvey	Jeanne	Otto
Beulah	Edna	Hattie	Joan	Paloma
Bob	Elena	Hazel	Joaquin	Rita
Camille	Eloise	Hilda	Juan	Roxanne
Carla	Erika	Hortense	Katrina	Sandy
Carmen	Fabian	Hugo	Keith	Stan
Carol	Felix	Igor	Klaus	Tomas
Celia	Fifi	Ike	Lenny	Wilma
Cesar	Flora	Inez	Lili	
Charley	Floyd	Ingrid	Luis	
Cleo	Fran	Ione	Maria	

Earthquakes

Ohio is lucky not to experience *big* earthquakes very often but we do get tremors from time to time. Thankfully, it's nothing like the building-leveling temblors they can get in California or Mexico!

Even so, Ohio is riddled with fault lines. They run in all directions, all over the state. Most of them are buried far below the surface.

Ohio sits in the middle of a tectonic plate, instead of on the edge of one. We float along on the North American plate without feeling much of anything. Usually.

The Ohio Seismic Network (OhioSeis) keeps track of it all with the help of the Ohio Department of Natural Resources. OSN Senior Geologist and Network Coordinator Mike Hansen writes that "at least 200 earthquakes with epicenters in Ohio have been felt since 1776." There are often a dozen or more Ohio quakes every year.

Visit OhioSeis' offices in Delaware sometime to check out their displays and data!

Cryoseism

The seemingly never-ending winter of 2014 produced some very, very cold nights. And, in the process, created a rare phenomenon that got people talking on Facebook.

> Valerie: Is there such a thing as ice or snow quakes? I keep hearing these loud popping sounds similar to the house settling but its much louder then normal. Maybe I need to hear from the professional weather guy, Marshall McPeek to help settle this mystery.
>
> Teresa: Funny you would say that we heard a noise the other night when it wass so cold and my grandaughter said what was that I also said house settling lol
>
> Brenda: I have heard them too

They're called "ice quakes" or "frost quakes." Technically, it's called cryoseism. It happens when the water in the ground freezes and expands, putting pressure on the ground and the rocks around it. It's like putting a full bottle of water in your freezer; it'll split the plastic bottle as it turns to ice and expands. As the ice pushes on the ground, you may hear popping and snapping as the frozen dirt and rocks suddenly shift to release some of the pressure. It's fascinating and creepy at the same time!

Tsunamis

Tsunami (soo-NAH-mee) is the official name for what we generically call a "tidal wave." We are lucky not to have them here in Central Ohio. As far as geologists can tell, the bed of Lake Erie (or Buckeye Lake or Indian Lake or Grand Lake St. Mary's) is not geologically unstable enough to develop such a wave.

That said, if an earthquake were to shift the bottom of Lake Erie by 10 to 20 feet, a large wave could develop. Going east, it would go relatively unnoticed as it slammed into the bluffs of western New York. But going west or south, it could inundate the islands, Cleveland, and parts of the Toledo area. Thankfully, as far as we know, there are no tectonic boundaries in the Lake Erie basin large enough to create that situation.

Large earthquakes in the Pacific and Indian Ocean basins can create significant tsunamis. As the floor of the ocean shifts up, down, or sideways in an earthquake, the water is displaced, and a surface wave is instantly created. In the middle of the ocean, the wave doesn't look like much. But the wave and its energy race across the ocean at speeds of 500 to 600 mph, as fast as a jetliner. As it approaches land and shallower water, the wave becomes visible. Then, as it comes ashore, the power of the water can destroy everything in its path. It is the ultimate flash flood.

There is no protection other than to head for the highest ground possible and to wait for the water to recede.

Volcanoes

Volcanoes are not exactly top of mind in Central Ohio. Not a lot of mountains or other tectonic activity here.

However, massive eruptions in other parts of the world can have a direct effect on our local weather. Time and time again, we have seen volcanoes temporarily change the climate across the globe.

Eruptions can throw enormous amounts of dust and ash into the atmosphere. As it is carried into the troposphere (and even the stratosphere), it mixes with the air currents and is spread worldwide. If is thick enough, it can have disastrous effects.

When Mount Pinatubo erupted in the Philippines in 1991, it blasted rock and ash 34 km (more than 21 miles) into the sky, about two-thirds the height of the stratosphere. That summer, average global temperatures dropped by half a degree and the dust, suspended in the atmosphere, refracted light more than usual to create some of the most spectacular, purple and pink sunrises and sunsets seen in generations.

The Year Without A Summer

The weather turned chilly in the spring of 1816. Very chilly. Temperatures were pushed well-below normal.

Sunlight was reduced enough that year that crops failed across the US and Canada. Snow fell on June 6 in New York and Maine. Ice "as thick as window panes" was reported in Ohio as late as July 5. Frost returned to the northeast as early as August 23. Ice was seen in lakes and rivers in Pennsylvania in July and August.

The weather aberrations likely were caused by a combination of factors. The sun was in the midst of the Dalton Minimum, a 40-year period of unusually low solar activity, sending less energy toward the earth than normal. But the main cause was a "volcanic winter" caused by the enormous eruption of Mount Tambora in Indonesia on April 5-15, 1815. It was one of the largest eruptions recorded in more than 1,300 years and killed nearly 12,000 people on the nearby islands. In 2018, a British researcher[7] even suggested that the Tambora eruption and the resulting changes in the weather may have led to Napoleon's defeat at Waterloo!

It blew an estimated 19 cubic miles of debris into the atmosphere, enough that the earth was blanketed in what was described as a "dry fog." It turned the atmosphere reddish and further dimmed the sunlight. Average global temperatures dropped by more than a full degree (that's a lot). It took another year for enough dust to settle out of the atmosphere that the weather returned to something close to normal.

---

[7] Genge, M.J., 2018, Electrostatic levitation of volcanic ash into the ionosphere and its abrupt effect on climate: Geology, v. 46, p. 835–838, https://doi.org/10.1130/G45092.1

Watches & Warnings

When watches and warnings are issued for approaching severe weather, it really helps to know the difference. One means "be ready for some nasty weather" and the other means "it's here! Take cover!"

Watches and warnings are issued by the National Weather Service (not your local TV stations). We will track storms and tell you where the trouble is likely to be but the NWS is officially charged with issuing the warnings.

The Federal Communications Commission requires broadcast license holders to distribute that information. When we break into the your favorite shows to tell you about severe weather, it's because the government requires stations to pass that information along to you.

ADVISORY	WATCH	WARNING
Significant and potentially hazardous weather is imminent or happening and you should proceed with caution.	Severe weather is possible. It may not be happening yet but it's possible. Have a plan and be prepared to take shelter when necessary.	Severe weather is either happening right now or it's eminent. It's time to take shelter immediately.

Top Risks in Franklin County

Franklin County Emergency Management and Homeland Security occasionally conducts risk assessments for the area. They look at dozens of emergency scenarios to figure out what the potential damage might be, how many lives could be lost, what first-responders would have to do, how a disaster would impact the region, and what the after-effects might be once the immediate danger subsided. Here are the top potential worst-case disasters as ranked by FCEM&HS:

1. Tornadoes
2. Cyber Threat
3. Infectious Disease
4. Flooding
5. Lone Wolf Terrorist Attack
6. Dam Failure
7. Utility/Energy Interruption or Failure
8. CBRNE Terrorist Incident
9. Severe Winter Weather
10. Hazardous Materials Incidents
11. Civil Disturbance
12. Severe Summer Weather
13. Aircraft Accident
14. Space Weather
15. Extreme Heat
16. Earthquakes
17. Invasive Species
18. Air & Water Pollution/ Contamination
19. Drought

NOAA Weather Radio

NOAA Weather Radio is "The Voice of the National Weather Service." The system includes more than 800 transmitters covering all 50 states, Puerto Rico, the US Virgin Islands, and US-controlled islands and territories in the Pacific.

The broadcasts are created by local NWS Forecast Offices and include specific forecasts and weather information for that area. In Central Ohio, depending on where you live, you'll hear broadcasts from the offices in Wilmington, Cleveland, Northern Indiana, Pittsburgh, or Charleston.

Anywhere you go in the US, you'll find the 24-hour broadcast on at least one of these seven frequencies:

- ✦ 162.400 MHz
- ✦ 162.425 MHz
- ✦ 162.450 MHz
- ✦ 162.475 MHz

- ✦ 162.500 MHz
- ✦ 162.525 MHz
- ✦ 162.550 MHz

There tends to be a little bit of overlap in the coverage areas, so you might be able to pick up the broadcast on more than one frequency.

When severe weather moves through the area, the regular broadcasts are replaced by minute-by-minute updates to help you stay safe. As watches and warnings are issued by the local forecast office, you'll hear tones on the radio followed by information about the storms affecting your area.

If you have a newer weather radio, your device may have its own alarm that goes off when watches and warnings are issued. For the hearing impaired, weather radios can activate special alerting devices such as strobe lights, bed shakers, or pillow vibrators.

Choosing and Using a Weather Radio

Weather radios are fairly easy to find. You can almost always find them at an electronics store and they are often available at other locations (like grocery stores) leading up to severe weather season. The Red Cross often sells them and sometimes they are even given away as premiums for NPR donors. And, of course, you can always find them online.

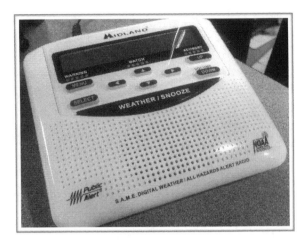

Generally, they cost about $10-$20, depending on the features. Fancy ones can cost much more. Some are available with flashlights or beacons, cell phone chargers, and standard AM-FM receivers. Others have built in-solar panels or hand cranks for power. (Those are especially helpful when the power is out for a long time and your supply of batteries runs low.)

Most of the newer radios are programmable. You can save yourself a lot of headache by customizing the messages and broadcasts and alarms you receive.

In most cases, programming your radio will involve (gasp!) using the instruction manual. Each brand is slightly different and the menus behave slightly differently. But it is worth the time and effort to get it done.

If your timing is just right, you might even find an event where a local meteorologist shows up at a grocery store and will program your radio for you!

SAME Codes

Most newer models of weather radios can be programmed with SAME codes to save you a lot of aggravation. SAME stands for "Specific Area Message Encoder."

Every county is assigned a number. Watches and warnings are issued with those numbers and that allows you program your weather radio to only alert you to messages targeted to the counties in which you are interested.

Get More Batteries

Even if you keep your weather radio plugged in, make sure you have extra batteries. Once the electricity goes out, the power outlet won't do much good. Batteries will keep your radio on keep you informed while you're waiting out the storm using a flashlight.

In other words, by using same codes, you'll get warnings for Marion County without having to listen to warnings for Franklin County and vice versa.

Here are the codes for Central Ohio. Use these when you are programming your radio. Find your county and then the transmitter frequency closest to where you live.

County	SAME #	Transmitter Location	Frequency
Athens	39009	Athens	162.425
Athens	39009	Garfield	162.500
Champaign	39021	Columbus	162.550
Champaign	39021	Dayton	162.475
Coshocton	39031	Bridgeport	162.525
Coshocton	39031	High Hill	162.475
Coshocton	39031	New Philadelphia	162.425
Crawford	39033	Carey	162.525
Crawford	39033	Mansfield	162.450
Crawford	39033	Sandusky	162.400
Delaware	39041	Columbus	162.550
Fairfield	39045	Chillicothe	162.500
Fairfield	39045	Columbus	162.550
Fayette	39047	Chillicothe	162.500
Fayette	39047	Columbus	162.550
Franklin	39049	Columbus	162.550
Guernsey	39059	Bridgeport	162.525
Guernsey	39059	High Hill	162.475
Guernsey	39059	New Philadelphia	162.425
Hardin	39065	Carey	162.525
Hardin	39065	Lima	162.400
Hocking	39073	Athens	162.425
Hocking	39073	Chillicothe	162.500
Hocking	39073	Columbus	162.550
Knox	39083	Columbus	162.550
Knox	39083	Mansfield	162.450
Licking	39089	Columbus	162.550
Licking	39089	High Hill	162.475
Licking	39089	Mansfield	162.450
Logan	39091	Dayton	162.475
Logan	39091	Lima	162.400
Madison	39097	Columbus	162.550

Marion	39101	Carey	162.525
Marion	39101	Columbus	162.550
Marion	39101	Mansfield	162.450
Morgan	39115	Athens	162.425
Morgan	39115	Bridgeport	162.525
Morgan	39115	High Hill	162.475
Morrow	39117	Columbus	162.550
Morrow	39117	Mansfield	162.450
Muskingum	39119	Bridgeport	162.525
Muskingum	39119	Columbus	162.550
Muskingum	39119	High Hill	162.475
Noble	39121	Bridgeport	162.525
Noble	39121	High Hill	162.475
Noble	39121	Marietta	162.400
Perry	39127	Athens	162.425
Perry	39127	Bridgeport	162.525
Perry	39127	Columbus	162.550
Perry	39127	High Hill	162.475
Pickaway	39129	Chillicothe	162.500
Pickaway	39129	Columbus	162.550
Pike	39131	Chillicothe	162.500
Pike	39131	Otway	162.525
Richland	39139	Mansfield	162.450
Richland	39139	Sandusky	162.400
Ross	39141	Chillicothe	162.500
Ross	39141	Otway	162.525
Scioto	39145	Ashland	162.550
Scioto	39145	Otway	162.525
Union	39159	Columbus	162.550
Wyandot	39175	Carey	162.525
Wyandot	39175	Lima	162.400
Wyandot	39175	Mansfield	162.450
Wyandot	39175	Sandusky	162.400

EAS System

The Emergency Alert System was created by the Federal Communications Commission in 1996. It replaced the Emergency Broadcast System. It uses digital technology to send targeted messages to specific areas that may be at risk for severe weather or other emergencies.

The EAS is the system that occasionally takes over your radio or TV with a series of super-irritating beeps and a pre-recorded message that says "this is just a test." On your television, it also crawls a message across the screen.

While it may be annoying, it's vital to test the system because, in a real emergency, it may be the first place you get life-saving information or instructions.

Safety Weeks

State and national agencies want all of us to be mindful of the dangers of severe weather. We don't have to be afraid of the weather; we just need to be smart about safety.

Certain weeks of the year are designated as "awareness weeks." They're a good time to think about the plans we have for dealing with severe weather. Where will we go if a tornado threatens our school, home, or office? What's the best safety plan when severe thunderstorms are in the area? What local dangers are there for flooding?

It's always good to have a plan in place before you need it.

National Severe Weather Preparedness Week

Every year, in early March, the National Weather Service teams up with state and local emergency management agencies to remind us to be ready for some of the nasty weather we get here in the US. It's a great time to brush up on your severe-weather knowledge and to make sure you have action plans ready to activate at a moment's notice.

From tornadoes, to earthquakes, to floods, to extreme heat waves, it's wise to be prepared. Update your emergency kits with fresh supplies and practice your action plan with your family.

Ohio Spring Severe Weather Awareness Week

Spring is when severe weather tends to be top of mind. It is the beginning of (what we often think of as) severe-weather season even though severe weather can happen all year.

In early March, the Ohio Committee for Severe Weather Awareness (www.weathersafety.ohio.gov) works with the National Weather Service and local emergency management agencies to sponsor a week of school programs and media campaigns to help everyone be prepared.

Statewide Tornado Drill

In most counties, you will hear the tornado sirens at a specific time each week. Local emergency management agency's test them frequently to make sure they are working properly. The goal is to make sure they are ready when they are truly needed. Franklin County Emergency Management and

Homeland Security tests the sirens every Wednesday at noon. Your county may have a similar schedule.

Each year, at 9:50 a.m., on the Wednesday of Ohio Severe Weather Awareness Week, the sirens are simultaneously tested in all 88 counties. The state wide tornado drill is an opportunity for schools, businesses, and other citizens to practice their tornado preparedness plans. It's also a chance to make sure you know what the sirens sound like!

National Flood Safety Awareness Week

Flooding is one of the leading weather-related killers in the US. What would you do if the water started rising around your house? What about at your workplace? Do you know what to do if the water surrounds your car?

Flood Safety Awareness Week, in mid-March, is when you should review your safety plan and your skills so you are ready, just in case.

Heat Awareness Day

Heat Awareness Day is in late-May, just as the weather starts to really warm up here in Central Ohio.

Heat waves can be deadly. In July 1995, more than 700 people in 10 midwest states died (including 6 in Ohio and more than 520 in the City of Chicago) during a brutal hot-and-humid spell. On July 13, 1995, the heat index at Chicago's Midway Airport hit 125°F.

Especially for the elderly and the frail, heat can cause health problems very quickly.

This week is a good time to make note of who lives around you and who might need help during extremely-hot weather.

National Lightning Safety Awareness Week

As we noted earlier, lightning kills several hundred people in the US every year. It may be spectacular to see and fascinating to study, but it can be seriously injurious and deadly.

This awareness week, in late June, is when we take some time to remember its victims and to think about our own safety.

Great Central US Shakeout

While we may not have a lot of earthquakes in Ohio, portions of the Midwest are still at risk for some serious shaking.

The Shakeout is usually scheduled for a day in October. It helps first responders, emergency managers, and residents prepare for the possibility of significant temblors.

Ohio Winter Safety Awareness Week

Man, it gets cold here in Ohio! We need to be ready every year. Winter storms, ice, and brutal cold can make conditions hazardous or even dangerous. When a big snow storm bashes the area, electricity (and heat) can go out for days. Ice can bring down tree limbs and power lines, leaving us in the cold and dark. And, when the wind chills drop well-below zero, it can be downright dangerous to be outdoors.

Use this week in mid-November to think about and prepare for what you would do if the power goes out for a few days and your house starts to get very, very cold. Double-check the emergency kit in your car so you are prepared if you get stuck in the snow.

Create an Emergency Plan

- ✦ Talk with your family and create plans for different kinds of severe weather events. Write them down and be sure everyone understands the arrangements. Don't forget to include provisions for your pets!

- ✦ Practice your plans a few times a year so the whole family remembers what to do.

- ✦ Have your disaster preparedness kit(s) updated and ready.

Build a Disaster Kit

When a natural disaster strikes, it could be a few days before help arrives. It's smart to prepare ahead of time and have what you might need. Once a tornado or flood takes out the grocery store, you may not be able to get new supplies for a while. So, build an emergency kit, keep it near your shelter, and update it with fresh supplies now and then.

Emergency planners recommend having enough supplies to last each member of your family (and each pet) for at least three days.

At Home

Once you assemble your supplies, store your kit in an inexpensive, plastic bin with a lid.

TIP: Put the bins in a place that will be accessible quickly, preferably near the place where you plan to take shelter during storms. The emergency bins won't be very helpful if you can't pull them out from the back of a collapsed closet.

- ✦ NOAA Weather Radio (battery-operated, solar, or hand crank)
- ✦ Flashlight (with extra batteries)
- ✦ Canned or non-perishable foods (and a manual can opener)
- ✦ A gallon of water for each person for each day
- ✦ First aid kit

- ✦ Sleeping bags
- ✦ Copies of important documents and phone numbers
- ✦ Prescriptions
- ✦ Toothbrushes and toiletries
- ✦ Extra socks, hats, gloves and coats for winter emergencies

In the Car

- Fire extinguisher
- Basic tool set including a tire-repair kit
- Booster cables
- First aid kit
- Road flares
- Bottled water

- Non-perishable high-energy snacks (granola bars, energy bars, raisins, peanut butter crackers)
- Flashlight (with extra batteries)
- Battery-operated radio (with batteries)
- Blankets
- Ice scraper, brush, and small shovel
- Sand or non-clumping kitty litter and a tow rope

Pet Supplies

- Food and water for three days
- Leash and collar

- ID tags
- Medications and copies of vet records (including vaccination tags)

If your family has special needs, make sure to plan for that! Does someone need an extra tank of oxygen, a wheelchair, or special medications? Keep extras with your emergency supplies.

If you don't have time to assemble a disaster kit, you can buy pre-made kits online or in some sporting goods stores. They're pricey but can save you time.

Protecting Your Stuff

Insurance experts recommend taking lots of pictures or video in each room of your house to document your stuff. Get close-ups of the expensive things like TVs, computers, and jewelry. Whenever possible, narrate the video with the purchase dates and costs. And it helps to include the serial numbers and model numbers for appliances and electronics.

TECHNOLOGY

Whether you're doing it professionally or as a home hobby, monitoring the weather requires gadgets. Lots of gadgets. Some of them are inexpensive. Some you can even make at home. Others eat up big portions of government-sized budgets.

Many of the basic instruments have been around for hundreds of years and the principles by which they operate are still exactly the same. Conveniently, most of them have evolved into electronic versions that let us easily collect, store, and share the data.

NWS Technology

The National Oceanic and Atmospheric Administration's (NOAA) National Weather Service (NWS) is, by necessity, a technology-driven agency. It uses millions of hours of computing time every year to run the environmental models we use for everyday and long-range forecasting. Enormous radomes continuously scan the sky for signs of threatening weather. Balloons and rawinsondes measure the condition of the atmosphere, meter by meter. Highly-equipped airplanes fly directly into hurricanes to study them and measure their power.

Great technology makes it possible for us more accurately to predict the future. As it continues to improve, so does our understanding of atmospheric processes and forecasting.

Radar

By the 1880s, scientists had discovered that radio waves bounce off solid objects. It wasn't until the 1930s that a crude-but-workable tracking system was created. Regular use of radar ("RAdio Detection And Ranging") wasn't implemented until World War II.

Radar uses radio waves to detect objects around it. The antenna sends out a beam at specific strengths. When the beam hits an object, like a plane or a raindrop, part of the beam is reflected back to the antenna. The radar array is able to measure the strength of the return signal and determine how far away the object is.

Doppler radar adds a second dimension to the data: it can measure an object's speed as it travels toward or away from the radar site. That helps forecasters determine the direction of a storm or even to find rotation inside a particular storm.

National Weather Service Forecast Offices in more than 120 locations across the United States and its territories use NEXRAD (Next Generation Radar) to track thousands of storm systems every year. Doppler makes it possible for meteorologists to see threatening weather more than 80 miles away and provide the appropriate warnings to the surrounding area.

Weather Balloons

Every day, twice a day, 365 days a year, National Weather Service forecasters in 102 locations send enormous hydrogen-filled (it's less expensive than helium) balloons into the sky. Sensors are attached to each balloon to record atmospheric data from the surface all the way to the stratosphere where the balloon finally pops and the equipment falls back to the earth. The information is vital to understanding the conditions in the atmosphere and how the thermodynamics are set up at that moment. Knowing the temperatures at different levels of the atmosphere helps determine whether strong storms may form, whether an inversion is in place, how humid it is and whether the winds are twisting at different levels.

Each balloon's data is transferred to a chart called a "Skew-T Log-P" that shows temperature, pressure, dew point, pressure, wind speed and wind direction. The chart to the right shows the conditions from the surface to about 20 miles above Wilmington, Ohio.

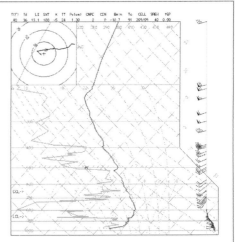

A Skew-T Log-P chart generated by the National Weather Service depicting the condition of the atmosphere at a specific location including wind, temperature, and dew point, from the surface to more than 50,000 feet (100 mb).

NCEP & The Computer Models

The National Centers for Environmental Prediction (NCEP) are a division of the National Weather Service (NWS) which is an agency of the National Oceanic and Atmospheric Administration (NOAA) which is a division of the Department Of Commerce (DoC).

NCEP's Centers produce forecasts for a bunch of subsets:

+ AWC: Aviation Weather Center
+ CPC: Climate Prediction Center
+ EMC: Environmental Modeling Center
+ NHC: National Hurricane Center
+ OPC: Ocean Prediction Center
+ SWPC: Space Weather Prediction Center
+ WPC: Weather Prediction Center

NCEP is in charge of the computers. Enormous supercomputers spend every hour of every day crunching data and churning out model forecasts. The models begin with current data and then use algorithms to predict how weather systems will evolve over time.

Each model covers a specific area and time. Some are global, others are hemispheric, others are more localized. Some only predict a few hours into the future and some attempt to look nearly two weeks ahead. There are multiple models produced by the United States, Canada and Europe. The US Navy has its own model. There are also corporate, for-profit, proprietary models.

No model is perfect. They all have their own eccentricities and biases. Humans have yet to create an exact replica of the Earth's atmosphere inside a computer. There are so many variables, it may be decades before technology evolves enough to make it happen. In the meantime, humans can use the model output (or "guidance") to create forecasts based on our own understanding of weather and the atmosphere. That's the part where forecasting becomes "an art."

Ganahl's Law

"Garbage in, garbage out."

Remember that from the 1980s? The phrase came up over and over to describe what was put into and what, subsequently, came out of computers.

It still holds true today. If the initial conditions in the computer models aren't the same, the results won't be either. In the extended forecasts, the models are projecting the formation and evolution of storms and systems that don't yet exist. If they don't start the process with reliable or identical data, they will produce wildly different results. They didn't start with the same butterflies, so they don't end up with the same tornadoes.

The shorter the forecast period, the less opportunity there is for the errors to compound. In other words, the farther you go out in the forecast, the less accurate it can be... because the errors feed on each other.

This is one of the reasons the National Hurricane Center's path forecasts come out as cones instead of lines. There's a larger and larger margin of error as the forecast moves farther into the future.

That leads us to what I call "Ganahl's Law."

During a week in late December 2010, as we were carefully tracking the potential for a big, Christmas storm, the models and their forecasts continued to pivot and change wildly. In our forecasting frustration, Jym reminded us that we can't really know what a system is going to do until it (a) forms in real time and (b) moves east of the Rocky Mountains. Once it's past the Rockies, he noted, then we can get a better handle on its projected track because, by then, the system actually exists, has real properties and characteristics, and it is finally interacting with known atmospheric dynamics. Only then can we (and the models) get a good handle on it.

Meteorologist Jym Ganahl at a local grocery store during a weather-radio-programming event.

Sometimes, that's less than 48-hours into the future. Before that, it's some pretty serious guesswork. And he was absolutely right.

Therefore, what I've dubbed as "Ganahl's Law" states:

"The path of a synoptic-scale cyclone may not be accurately forecast in the eastern two-thirds of the United States prior to the physical storm moving east of the Rocky Mountains."

Sure, I'm willing to accept some minor modifications to the new law's wording. But you get the idea. Our meteorological crystal balls may be good, but they have very real limits. It takes a storm like that Christmas' to remind us that the computer models are not infallible and that extended forecasts, even five to seven days out, really are just a well-educated guess.

Hurricane Hunters

During hurricane season, brave pilots and researchers climb into specially-outfitted aircraft to explore areas outside, around, and inside hurricanes. Hurricane Hunters fly above and directly into some of the most powerful storms on Earth. Their death-defying research and data have vastly improved our knowledge of hurricane formation, life cycle and behavior.

NOAA Hurricane Hunter WP-3D Orion turboprop and Gulfstream IV jet aircraft in flight. The Gulfstream flies above and around hurricanes, dropping sensors into the storms; the P-3 flies into the the storms to gather lower-level data. Photo courtesy NOAA.

Hurricane Hunters sometimes are the only reconnaissance available during major storms. While satellite images can provide enormous amounts of reliable information from a safe distance, firsthand data is often the best, the most accurate, and the most current.

Can you imagine the turbulence and thrashing the Hurricane Hunters must endure during each flight? Aaaaaargh!

ASOS & AWIPS

The National Weather Service has a network of hundreds of automated weather-reporting stations around the country. They collect readings of the current conditions at each location every hour of the day, 24 hours a day. The readings include temperature, humidity, wind, and often sky cover.

The data they collect not only helps assess current conditions, but it also helps feed accurate, initial data to the predictive computer models.

You can find a lot of the hourly data, including for your area, online. It is a fantastic tool when you are creating your own nowcast or forecast.

NWS Co-op Program

The National Weather Service runs a Co-Op Program that collects data from professional and amateur observers. Your data becomes part of the official records for the area.

It's a commitment. You'll be responsible for taking readings at least once, sometimes twice day. Every day. 365 days per year. You'll need to measure and log the daily rain and snow, high and low temps and get that data to the NWS. And your site will be inspected annually to make sure it continues to meet the quality standards.

The NWS says, to become a co-op observer, you'll need:

+ Dedication to public service
+ Attention to detail
+ Ability to learn and perform daily duties
+ Willingness to allow NWS to place measuring instruments on your property
+ Willingness to allow at least one visit per year from a NWS representative.

Readings are usually taken at 7 a.m. and 7 p.m. every day.

NOAA's National Weather Service manages hundreds of Automated Surface Observing System (ASOS) installations around the country to continually collect weather data. The data is used for assessing the current status of the atmosphere as well as initialization data for the forecast models. Photo from NOAA and NWS Collection.

There are rules and regulations to follow in order to assure quality data and reliability. Equipment must meet specific parameters and be carefully located. In some cases, you may even be required to take one of the NWS's specific training courses. If you're willing to make the commitment, it's free to join and the NWS is always happy to have more data.

Technology At Home

Many of us like to keep track of the weather we experience at home. We may use the data in diaries, blogs, or even to predict when the tomatoes will be ripe in the garden. There are dozens of home weather stations available in electronics stores and online.

Most home weather stations will include basic monitoring equipment for temperature and humidity. Slightly more advanced systems may also include a rain gauge and anemometer. High-end models may also include wi-fi, logging and transmission capabilities.

Most of them are fine for keeping track of the rudimentary weather in your neighborhood. They may not, however, be suitable for official record keeping. The National Weather Service has some specific guidelines for data collection that help make sure readings are accurate and reliable.

Personal Weather Systems (PWS)

You can buy a personal Personal Weather System (PWS) at almost any hardware store, department store, electronics store or hundreds of places online. Depending on the level of sophistication, they can run from $50 to more than $400. The simple ones will tell you the current temperature and humidity.

More advanced ones, will also include barometric pressure, dew point, windspeed, and rainfall amounts. The really cool ones will even do it wirelessly and save the data directly to your computer, ready to upload to your website, a commercial website, or the NWS co-op program.

WiFi Weather Stations

Some of the fancy PWS systems make collecting and sharing the data super easy. They are solar-powered and send the data to a monitoring device via wi-fi. The monitor can then be attached to your computer to save or share the data. Some models will even send the data directly to an app on your phone and then it can be shared from there or automatically uploaded.

It's all a matter of how much you're willing to spend on the equipment.

MADIS Data

If you want to share your data with the world, you can use your internet-connected PWS to send your readings to a personal website or to the National Weather Service and your local TV meteorologists!

The Meteorological Assimilation Data Ingest System (MADIS) is a network of more than 6,000 local weather stations that automatically provide data through the Citizen Weather Observer Program (CWOP).

Local NWS Offices

National Weather Service
Wilmington, OH
1901 South State Route 134
Wilmington, Oh 45177
937-383-0031

National Weather Service
Cleveland, OH
Federal Facilities Building
Cleveland Hopkins Airport
Cleveland, OH 44135
216-265-2370

National Weather Service
Charleston, WV
400 Parkway Rd.
Charleston, WV 25309
(304) 746-0180

National Weather Service
Pittsburgh, PA
192 Shafer Road
Moon Township, PA 15108
412-262-1591

The siting requirements aren't quite as rigid for MADIS as they are for the Co-Op program, but they're still very important. And there's a pretty solid quality-control system for the incoming data; if your data seems off compared to the surrounding stations, expect someone to check up on you!

To join CWOP, contact your local NWS Forecast Office.

Thermometer

A thermometer is probably the first weather-related instrument you learned about as a kid. As simple as it sounds, temperature is one of the most important pieces of weather data you can collect. Temperature differences can have an enormous effect on the weather and how it evolves over time.

Galileo had created an early thermometer (actually, a thermoscope[8]) by around 1600. His device used a large glass ball, a thin vertical pipe, and a vase filled with water. The water went up and down in the pipe as the temperature rose and fell. The thermometer evolved over the next several hundred years to include various scales (°F, °C, °K, °Rø, etc.), some with mercury, others, eventually, with electronic sensors.

To get accurate temperature readings at home, be sure your thermometer is in an open area with adequate ventilation, away from buildings, away from heat-radiating sources like pavement, and protected from direct sunlight.

"Temperature Readings of -0°?"

All thermometers have a scale. In the US, we usually use the Fahrenheit scale (°F). Most of the world, including the scientific community, uses the Celsius or centigrade scale (°C). But you'll also find Kelvin (°K), Delisle (°De), Newton (°N), and Rømer (°Rø) scales, among others. Each has a very specific use.

The key to using a thermometer, though, is being able to read that scale... and figuring out what to do when the device gives you what seems like a funky reading.

> Linda via Facebook:
> Hey Marshall I live close to Fresno Ohio and my temp gage says -0. Is there such a thing as -0? Just saying!!!!!

As odd as it seems, that can really happen. But it's more of a math and technology issue than an actual temperature reading.

Some of today's electronic thermometers are able to measure in half- or tenth-degrees, even if they don't display it. So what's happening is that the reading is actually something like -0.4°F and we have a rounding issue.

- -0.50° would round down to -1°
- -0.49° would round up to "-0°"
- +0.49° would round down to 0°
- +0.50° would round up to 1°

In any case, it's really cold outside! Bundle up!

---

[8] A thermoscope provides a visual representation of changes in temperature. A thermometer does the same thing but has a calibrated scale.

Barometer

The uneven heating of the earth leads to pockets of high and low pressure across the planet's surface. Those highs and lows are major drivers of our local weather. High pressure often leads to sunny days, clear nights, and calm conditions. Low pressure usually leads to unsettled weather, showers and thunderstorms, or or even potentially severe weather. A barometer measures – and partially predicts – it all.

And old-school barometer with a needle and a dial, shows a scale from low to high pressure. The face usually says something like, "Stormy," on the low end of the scale and, "Sunny," on the high end of the scale. It may not be perfectly accurate every day, but it is often in the ballpark. It's usually an okay "nowcast." Your electronic barometer may have a similar predictive system that displays weather icons.

Rain Gauge

You can find an inexpensive rain gauge at almost any hardware or department store. It is easy to attach one of the graduated, plastic tubes to a fence post in the middle of the yard, away from buildings and trees. Rainwater will collect in it with each precipitation event. Don't forget to record the amount and dump the gauge every day!

In many automated home weather systems, hydrometers are small buckets that collect rainwater. Using either cups on a vertical wheel or an electronic sensor, they measure the amount of rain that falls into the bucket. The mouth of the collector is calibrated with the size of the measuring device.

Anemometer

An anemometer is a goofy-looking device that measures wind speed and direction. It includes a small wind vane and a horizontal wheel of spinning cups. The cups are pushed by the wind and their speed indicates the speed of the wind.

When installing one at home, be sure that your anemometer is in an open area, not blocked by buildings or in a man-made wind tunnel.

Smartphone apps

Your smartphone is an amazing piece of technology. You have an entire world's worth of data at your fingertips. New apps are released all the time that show the forecast, local radar, temperatures, humidity and current warnings. Almost any piece of weather data is available with just a few taps.

Most of the TV stations, newspapers, and other media outlets provide free apps that include a forecast. There are no-cost apps from WeatherUnderground and the Weather Channel. Some mobile operating systems even have a built-in weather app.

Here's just one piece of advice when choosing an app: pick one with a forecast that includes human intervention. In other words, make sure the forecast is updated by a real, live meteorologist who spent time with multiple forecast models, understands the local microclimates, and customized the results for your area. It's likely to have a better chance of being accurate than app that only shows you the results of a single computer model.

You can also use your smartphone's web browser to surf over to the National Weather Service's local forecasts; those have plenty of human intervention and are updated regularly by NWS meteorologists.

Search your smartphone's app store for the latest and greatest weather apps. Many of them are FREE!

FORECASTING

"The trouble with weather forecasting is that it's right too often for us to ignore it and wrong too often for us to rely on it."

-Patrick L. Young, Author & Entrepreneur

By definition, meteorology is "the study of the weather."

Or, as the American Meteorological Society puts it:

> The study of the physics, chemistry, and dynamics of the Earth's atmosphere, including the related effects at the air-earth boundary over both land and the oceans. Fundamental topics include the composition, structure, and motion of the atmosphere. The goals ascribed to meteorology are the complete understanding and accurate prediction of atmospheric phenomena.

Blah, blah, blah. It's the study of weather.

For most people, though, meteorology is synonymous with forecasting. They are not interested in the painstaking research, the minutia of the thermodynamic processes, or the mind-numbing math. They just want to know whether it is going to rain on their newly-fertilized lawn, snow during the Buckeyes' game, or delay their vacation flight. To be sure, forecasting is the most publicly-visible aspect of the weather business.

Good forecasting can make or break events or businesses. When the forecast calls for rain, festivals and outdoor businesses see lower attendance. Forecasts are vital to airlines as they try to maintain on-time departure rates. Power companies use forecasts to position cleanup crews in advance of severe weather. And Lake Erie boaters know firsthand how quickly the water can become dangerous and why it's so important to check the forecast before venturing out. Forecasts help people to be prepared and can save lives and money.

We Use a Lot of Forecasts

The researchers at the National Center for Atmospheric Research (NCAR) and the University Corporation for Atmospheric Research (UCAR) did a survey in 2006 and found that (even back then) nearly 90% of us look for weather forecasts on a daily basis and many people seek out two or three forecasts every day.

The report says, when extrapolated out to the US adult population, "Americans receive a yearly total of about 300 billion forecasts."

Honestly, we do our best to get it right. Meteorologists study the atmosphere, learning about the thermodynamics and the patterns; we pore over the model data every day, looking for the anomalies; and we create forecasts based on the best computer model guidance available as well as our own knowledge and experience of the area.

Despite the myriad pitfalls, our accuracy rate is very good, especially through the first three days. Sometimes, though, Mother Nature reminds you that she is in control and full of surprises. She loves nothing more than to keep a forecaster humble.

NWS Forecast Offices

Every portion of the United States and its territories is covered by at least one National Weather Service Forecast Office (NWSFO). Each office provides local forecasts, regional radar monitoring, and issues warnings and advisories for the surrounding area. From Key West (EYW) to Seattle (SEW), and San Diego (SGX) to Portland, Maine (GYX), it's all covered. Even Guam (GUM) has its own forecast office.

The closest NWSFO to Columbus is in Wilmington, Ohio (ILN[9]). It opened in February 1994 when the Columbus and Cincinnati offices were shut down. The consolidated office in Wilmington serves an area that includes the Columbus metro, Cincinnati, southern Ohio, portions of southern Indiana, and parts of northern Kentucky. The Cincinnati (CVG) and Columbus (CMH) airports, though, still have local radar antenna (Terminal Doppler Radars) that supplement the larger, more powerful radar in Wilmington.

CWAs in Ohio

Sometimes we forget just how big Ohio really is. It's huge. With 88 counties and nearly 45,000 square miles, that's a lot of area for which to forecast. The forecast in Toledo is likely to be completely different from the forecast in Portsmouth. Lima's conditions probably aren't the same as Steubenville's. So the Buckeye State is divided into forecast zones and each zone is handled by the closest National Weather Service Forecast Office.

Each office is responsible for a County Warning Area (CWA). The local meteorologists create forecasts and issue watches and warnings only for their office's assigned counties. It takes five NWS offices to cover all of Ohio: Wilmington (ILN), Cleveland (CLE), Charleston (RLX), Pittsburgh (PBZ), and Northern Indiana (IWX).

Computer Models

Meteorologists around the world rely on incredibly-fast, number-crunching, supercomputers to assist in creating the forecasts you see online, on TV, and hear on the radio. The computers take in the raw data, churn it through massive algorithms, and spit out their best guess at how the atmosphere will behave in the future. Think of it kind of like a super-complex video game that, instead of predicting how football players will react on the gridiron, it predicts how the clouds will move, the jet stream will kink, highs will shift and hurricanes will form.

There are thousands of pieces of data and tens of millions of calculations.

---

[9] In many cases, you'll see the office code preceded by the letter K to indicate it's a United States mainland site. For example, products from Wilmington, Ohio, will often be labeled "KILN," and products from Cleveland will show "KCLE" in the product header.

Even with the same data to start with, different models will come to different solutions. With so much data and since there's no all-encompassing, perfect algorithm, they all have their own biases. Each one tends to make its own judgement calls each time it runs, some right, some wrong. Sometimes the model solutions agree. Many times, they don't. That's why the models are often called "guidance." The final forecast comes down to human decision making.

The models are just one of the tools meteorologists use to create the forecast. We look at each model's solution and, tapping in to our own education and experience, try to decide whether it might be right, in the ballpark or just plain wrong.

National Centers for Environmental Prediction (NCEP)

Dozens of models are produced by the National Centers for Environmental Prediction (NCEP) in College Park, Maryland, every day. Depending on the model, solutions are churned out or refreshed every hour to every 12 hours. And many of the models have multiple versions.

Here's a short sample:

+ GFS: Global Forecast System

+ HRW: High Resolution Window Model

+ NAM: North American Mesoscale Model

+ RAP: Rapid Refresh Model

+ SREF: Short-Range Ensemble Forecast Model

+ WW3: Wave Watch 3 Model

Other models track sea surface temperatures, hurricanes, air quality, tides and surges.

The US Navy has its own model, the NCOM, to predict coastal ocean conditions. The Canada Meteorological Center produces the CMCE. The United Kingdom's Met Office provides the UKMET. And the European Center for Medium-range Weather Forecasting shares the ECMWF with forecasters around the world.

Each model produces graphical and numerical versions. It's usually a good idea to look at both versions when you're assembling your forecast.

Some of the graphic versions look like a familiar weather map with predicted precipitation and barometric pressure lines (isobars).

Other maps show how the atmosphere is expected to look at different levels and how the wind and vorticity may behave as they interact with surface highs and lows or the jet stream.

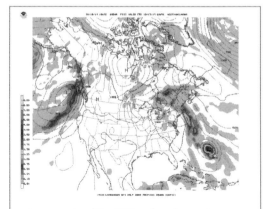

An example of the GFS surface forecast showing lines of pressure and expected precipitation. Courtesy NOAA/NCEP.

The numerical models are a great way to see the specific forecast conditions at a specific location. The maps give you a much better sense of the forecast's synoptic scale features.

Partly Cloudy v. Mostly Sunny

Meteorologists aren't being optimists or pessimists when they create the forecast. There are specific definitions and quantifications for nearly every term they use.

The Weather Service Operations Manual (issued July 11, 1984) divided the sky into tenths. While much of the WSOM is still valid and in use, today's forecasters divide the sky into eighths or oktas.

"Partly Cloudy" and "Partly Sunny" only differ because you can't see the sun at night. But "Partly Cloudy" and "Mostly Sunny" actually differ by several "oktas."

Day Sky Condition	Night Sky Condition	Opaque Cloud Coverage
Sunny	Clear	1/8 or less
Mostly Sunny	Mostly Clear	1/8 to 3/8
Partly Sunny	Partly Cloudy	3/8 to 5/8
Mostly Cloudy	Mostly Cloudy	5/8 to 7/8
Cloudy	Cloudy	7/8 to 8/8

NWS forecasters are allowed to use other terms as well. According to the WSOM, "The terms [and phrases] listed below are viewed as hedge terms and should be used sparingly and with great discretion."

+ Clear to partly cloudy
+ Partly cloudy to cloudy
+ Fair to partly cloudy
+ Scattered clouds
+ Variable cloudiness
+ Variable high clouds

The word "fair" is fair game (though not encouraged) as long as the sky cover is "less than 4/10 opaque clouds, no precipitation, and no extreme conditions of visibility, wind, or temperature (generally pleasant weather conditions)." The WSOM also recommends against using "specialized terms" such as "broken clouds."

Probability of Precipitation (POP)

POP stands for "Probability of Precipitation." It's the percentage you often see included with the forecast. It represents the forecaster's best estimate for the chance of rain or snow at a given location. For example, a 30% POP for Columbus means that the city has a 30% chance of getting wet and a 70% chance of staying dry.

Wind Descriptions

In the forecast, we describe the prevailing direction from which the wind is blowing. For example, we might say, "The wind is out of the northwest at 5 to 10 miles per hour."

Here's how the NWS quantifies the descriptions:

Sustained Wind	Descriptive Term
0-5 mph	Light Light and variable wind
5-10 mph, 10-15 mph	None
15-25 mph	Breezy (mild weather) Brisk or Blustery (cold weather)
20-30 mph	Windy
30-40 mph	Very Windy
40 mph or greater	Strong, dangerous, high, damaging (High Wind Warning Criteria)

What's it going to be like this winter?

"There is no way that we can predict the weather six months ahead beyond giving the seasonal average."

— Stephen Hawking, *Black Holes and Baby Universes*

We are asked for ultra-long-range forecasts all the time.

- "What's it going to be like this winter?"
- "What will the weather be for my wedding in six months?"
- "Will my outdoor graduation be rained out next year?"

Unfortunately, even though humans know a lot about the weather, we can only accurately predict so far into the future. We do a great job three days out. Day 5 becomes a little iffy. Day 7 is a very highly-educated guess. But one month, three months, nine months, or a year is simply farther than our current science can handle.

Still, long-range forecasting is a constant goal. When it is right, it can be very helpful. When it's wrong, it can be devastatingly expensive for businesses, industries, and governments. Companies would like to know whether to stockpile extra supplies or have additional crews ready for severe seasons. City and county leaders need to know whether to order extra road salt in places that could have snowy winters. Utility providers like having a heads up in case unusual amounts of electricity, gas or propane use are expected for the season.

So, the National Center for Environmental Prediction's (NCEP) Climate Prediction Center (CPC) creates monthly and seasonal forecasts. They look at dozens of factors including jet stream patterns, sea surface temperatures (including El Niño and La Niña events), and large-scale climatology attempting to predict a few weeks to a year into the future.

CPC's long-range maps show general chances for above-average (A), average or equal chances (EC), or below-average (B) temperatures and precipitation.

Like The Old Farmers Almanac, sometimes the long-range forecasts are spot on and sometimes they're a miss. The difference is, CPC is able to update the maps and outlooks on a regular basis as new information becomes available.

So, will it be colder than usual this winter? I can give you an answer right now and have a 50-50 shot at being right. Ready to flip a coin?

So, About This Winter...

Local TV legend Jym Ganahl has discovered a pattern during his more than 30 years of forecasting in Central Ohio: the general conditions during the first week of December often predict the conditions for the rest of the winter. His experience shows that the local pattern is often established by then. Of course, there will be extremes throughout the season, but the general conditions will persist.

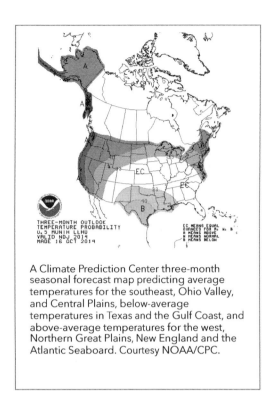

A Climate Prediction Center three-month seasonal forecast map predicting average temperatures for the southeast, Ohio Valley, and Central Plains, below-average temperatures in Texas and the Gulf Coast, and above-average temperatures for the west, Northern Great Plains, New England and the Atlantic Seaboard. Courtesy NOAA/CPC.

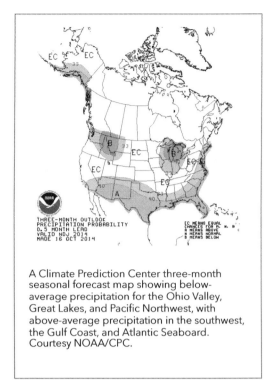

A Climate Prediction Center three-month seasonal forecast map showing below-average precipitation for the Ohio Valley, Great Lakes, and Pacific Northwest, with above-average precipitation in the southwest, the Gulf Coast, and Atlantic Seaboard. Courtesy NOAA/CPC.

Creating the Forecast

Whether it's from the National Weather Service or from your favorite TV weatherperson, there are a gazillion variables that have to be considered when creating the forecast. It takes time and experience to assemble all the pieces.

> "Imagine a rotating sphere that is 8,000 miles in diameter, with a bumpy surface, surrounded by a 25-mile-deep mixture of different gases whose concentrations vary both spatially and over time, and heated, along with its surrounding gases, by a nuclear reactor 93 million miles away. Imagine also that this sphere is revolving around the nuclear reactor and that some locations are heated more during parts of the revolution. And imagine that this mixture of gases receives continually inputs from the surface below, generally calmly but sometimes through violent and highly localized injections. Then, imagine that after watching the gaseous mixture you are expected to predict its state at one location on the sphere one, two, or more days into the future. This is essentially the task encountered day by day by a weather forecaster."
>
> Bob Ryan, (Ret.)
> Longtime Washington, DC, broadcast meteorologist

Once you have assembled the data and assessed the current conditions, it's time to put the pieces together to create the forecast. You look at the models, see how they agree and how they differ. Tap into your meteorological knowledge and experience to judge how weather patterns typically behave. You can even draw the maps by hand to help wrap your brain around the situation.

There is an "art" to forecasting. The computer models don't always have a good handle on the current situation. And they all have their own biases. So, human judgment and experience are essential to the process.

The Bowling Alley Analogy

This is a fantastic analogy dreamed up by ABC6 & FOX28 Meteorologist Andrew Buck Michael. Think of creating a forecast like a game of bowling where each day is equivalent to half the length of an alley. On the first day of the forecast, only half a length from the pins, you have a fantastic shot at a strike. Victory!

On the second day of the forecast, you're at the full length of the bowling alley. You still have a great shot a a strike but you might be off a little and have to pick up the spare.

By three days out, you're a length and half... four days is two alleys away... and at five days, you're two-and-a-half alley lengths away from the pins. You can still pull off a strike but there's a lot of alley between here and there and a lot more room for something to go awry. There are more bumps in the surface, differences in the wax, variances in the way the slats were laid, all having a subtle influence on the ball and the way it rolls. Your chances of hitting those pins dead-on start to get a little iffy.

Day six is three lengths. Day eight is four lengths. Day 10 takes you to five lengths. At that distance, just avoiding the gutter and hitting any of the pins is a mild victory.

The point is, the farther out the forecast, the more difficult it becomes to be accurate.

"Must Be Nice..."

We hear it all the time. Everyone is always ready to remind the meteorologist about the times he or she got it wrong.

"Must be nice to have a job where you can be wrong half the time and still keep your job," says the guy in the checkout line.

"How come you guys can never get it right?" asks the lady who has just interrupted your dinner at a restaurant.

They're right. We sometimes blow it. Sometimes we REALLY blow it. Now and then, Mother Nature throws a giant wrench in the forecast. It's humbling, to be sure. And we take our lumps for it.

No excuses. No point in being defensive. Sometimes the forecast is just plain wrong. Forecasters do their best to get it right but occasionally missing it is one of the hazards of the job.

Forecasts have become much more accurate over the years. With better data and better models, we are able to get it right more often than not. In general, our accuracy rate is better than 90% for the first three days. So, when it's right, it's routine – and no one notices. But when the forecast goes afoul, that's what everyone remembers.

Even the best major-league pitchers don't throw a perfect game each time they step up to the mound. NFL (and Buckeye) quarterbacks throw the occasional bad pass. The Jamaican Olympic bobsled team has a bad run now and then. Despite missteps once in a while, we still think of them all as very good at what they do. Most forecasters are, too.

CENTRAL OHIO SEVERE WEATHER HISTORY

Ohio weather is far from being the most vicious on Earth, or even in the country for that matter, but the Buckeye State certainly gets plenty of inconvenient and disruptive weather. We have a chance for some type of severe weather in every season. The state's history is replete with giant storms, devastating floods, horrific tornadoes, and paralyzing blizzards. Mother Nature has claimed thousands of Ohio lives over the years. While we may not be able to prevent her wrath, we do usually learn from each storm and that makes us better-prepared for the next one.

Here's a look at a few of the weather events that have earned a place in Central Ohio history.

The Great Flood of 1913

"The flood was second only to Noah's."

--Bishop Milton Wright, Dayton flood survivor and father of Orville and Wilbur Wright

March 23-27, 1913.

When more than 10 inches of rain fall in less than four days, the results are destined to be disastrous. In March 1913, nearly the entire state of Ohio was inundated as the runoff pushed rivers to record levels. Estimates say, statewide, more than 40,000 homes were flooded. More than 450 people died.

In the five days between March 23 and 27, 1913, Columbus recorded nearly four inches more rain than the average for the entire month. The city ended with a total of nearly five inches more rain than usual by the end of that March.

Bellefontaine collected more than 11 inches of rain and Upper Sandusky recorded 10.41". Both cities were pushed at least 8 inches above the monthly average in just five days.

In Columbus, the Olentangy River rose more than 20 feet in a day. Newly-raised levees were breached. The Scioto River invaded normally-dry neighborhoods, sweeping away houses, and leaving some victims trapped in treetops, desperately screaming to be rescued. The homes that remained had flood water halfway up the walls of second-floor bedrooms.

Chillicothe, Zanesville, and Bucyrus were all under water. In Tiffin, the Sandusky River broke previous high-water records by more than 10 feet. The Ohio River poured over the levees at Portsmouth and inundated more than 4,000 homes. Dozens of bridges were simply washed away.

Weather Bureau Meteorologist Alfred Henry filed a comprehensive report summarizing the events and the damage caused by the incredible rain and flooding.

"Some of the small towns on the Ohio River were completely submerged by the water," he wrote, "not a house showing above the water line."

Even Henry seemed awed by the volume and power of the water. "It is stated that when the Scioto flood was at its height [at Portsmouth] it carried a current of water clear across the Ohio River that was 5 or 6 feet higher than the level of the Ohio above the current," he wrote.

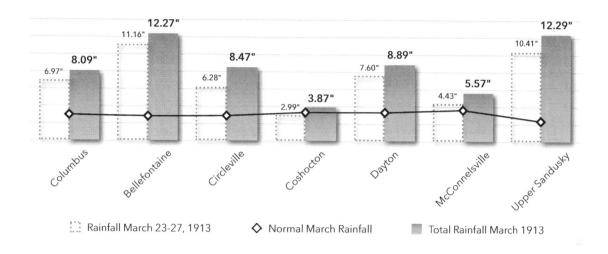

Rainfall March 23-27, 1913 ◇ Normal March Rainfall ▨ Total Rainfall March 1913

Given the enormous amount of destruction statewide and the tragic number of deaths, it's been called "Ohio's Greatest Weather Disaster."

The damage estimates were staggering. Bridges and roads were washed away. Homes disappeared. Livestock vanished downstream. Henry estimated the costs statewide to be more than $113 million (that's in 1913 dollars; equivalent to about $2.7 billion in 2015 dollars). Central Ohio was saddled with more than $25 million (more than $599 million) in clean up. Dayton alone suffered more than $73 million in losses (about $1.8 billion in 2015 dollars).

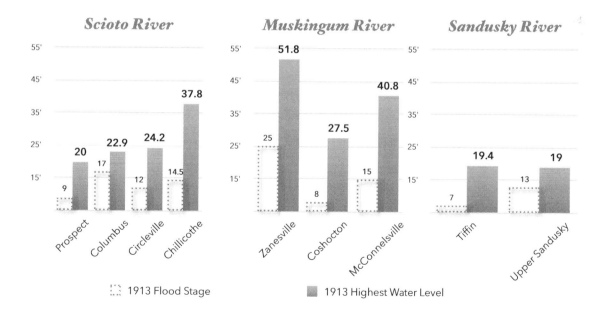

⬚ 1913 Flood Stage   ▨ 1913 Highest Water Level

Statewide Blizzard & Cold Snap of 1918

January 10-15, 1918.

There were two very distinct, very separate storms between Jan. 11 and Jan. 15, 1918. One brought in the brutally cold air and some moderate snow (3"-5"). The second brought heavy snow (8"-12") and ferocious winds for a one-two punch.

Newspaper reports from the time indicate that 48-mile-per-hour winds caused blowing and drifting snow to get so deep that railroads crews couldn't keep the tracks clear. Coal deliveries were interrupted across the state. Thousands were without heat and businesses were forced to close. A headline in *The Ohio State Journal* reads, "Newsies' Store Turned Into a Lodging House for Families Without Fuel in Their Homes."

Falling Temperatures and Snow of January 11-15, 1918

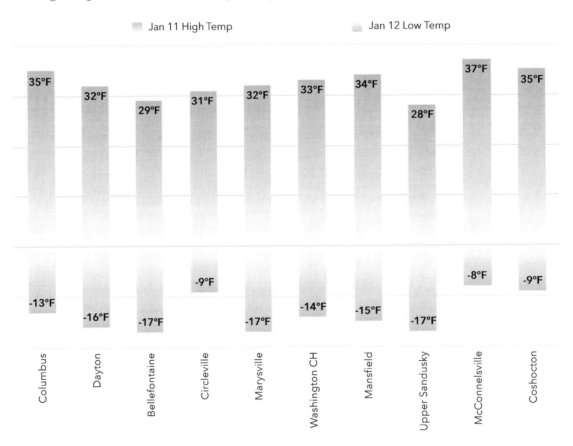

Jan 11 High Temp   Jan 12 Low Temp

City	Jan 11 High Temp	Jan 12 Low Temp
Columbus	35°F	-13°F
Dayton	32°F	-16°F
Bellefontaine	29°F	-17°F
Circleville	31°F	-9°F
Marysville	32°F	-17°F
Washington CH	33°F	-14°F
Mansfield	34°F	-15°F
Upper Sandusky	28°F	-17°F
McConnelsville	37°F	-8°F
Coshocton	35°F	-9°F

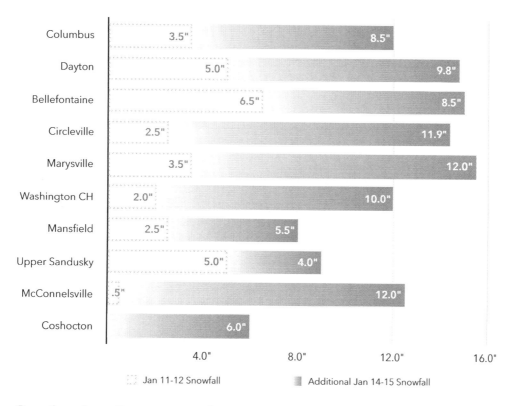

Columbus	3.5" ··· 8.5"
Dayton	5.0" ··· 9.8"
Bellefontaine	6.5" ··· 8.5"
Circleville	2.5" ··· 11.9"
Marysville	3.5" ··· 12.0"
Washington CH	2.0" ··· 10.0"
Mansfield	2.5" ··· 5.5"
Upper Sandusky	5.0" ··· 4.0"
McConnelsville	.5" ··· 12.0"
Coshocton	6.0"

4.0"   8.0"   12.0"   16.0"

▫ Jan 11-12 Snowfall   ▪ Additional Jan 14-15 Snowfall

Sweltering Summer of 1934

Summers in the early- and mid-1930s are remembered for being brutally hot. It was the time of the Dust Bowl. And Central Ohio suffered through it with much of the rest of the midwest. The hot, arid conditions destroyed crops and left the soil so dry it blew away in the wind.

It was miserable. There was no central air conditioning yet. All you could do was open the windows and hope the breeze didn't feel like it was coming from an oven. People who could afford them used fans and ice blocks, hoping cool down a little bit. Homes became hot boxes nonetheless. In some cases, people reportedly slept on their roofs and lawns, desperately trying to get cooler.

In a single week in late July 1934, at least 160 people are reported to have died because of the extreme heat.

All-time temperature records were broken around the state on July 21, 1934. The warmest temperature ever recorded in Ohio happened that afternoon in Gallipolis where the thermometer jumped to 113°F. Columbus' record still stands at 106°F. Circleville and Marysville reached 108°F. Coshocton set a record of 104°F on both July 21 and 22.

The Columbus Sunday Dispatch reported that a street-level thermometer at its downtown building "showed pedestrians to be wading through a temperature of 112 degrees at 5:30 p.m. This temperature fell to 100 at 8:30 p.m."

Many of the daily records around the state were broken again in July 1936 but the summer of '34 still had the hotter overall average for June, July and August. The average temperature for July 1934 makes it the hottest month ever recorded in Ohio.

In 1936, Columbus had more days at 95° or warmer, and more days at 100° or warmer, but 1934's overall average was pushed higher because the overnight lows tended to stay slightly warmer. Either way, they were both sweltering-hot summers! The summer of 2012 comes in a very close third!

July 21, 1934 v. All-Time Records

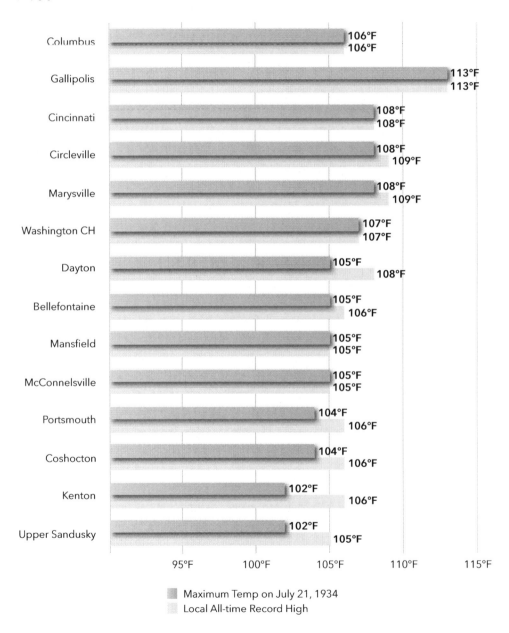

Sweltering Summer of 1936

Record heat again overtook the region in July 1936. The all-time record high was tied on July 14 at 106.1°F.

On July 14, 1936, the *Columbus Evening Dispatch* reported, "a death each hour in Ohio has been recorded during the heat wave, with the total now 183. Toledo continues to lead the state with 42. Cleveland reported 31 and Cincinnati, 25. These figures include drownings." The paper noted that at least four deaths had been reported in Columbus. The next day that figure had grown to 11.

Ohio River Flooding of 1937

January 1937 was a turbulent weather month, to be sure. There were wild fluctuations in temperatures and copious amounts of precipitation changed back and forth between rain and snow then melted and ran off. The combination left the ground saturated and the water quickly began to fill the rivers. There was flooding along many tributaries but the worst was along the Ohio River. The Ohio reached some of its highest levels in recorded history.

It began with a warm spell. Marysville set a daily record high of 64°F on Jan. 8. It seemed like it was going to be a very pleasant January with mild temperatures. Then Mother Nature turned on us.

Between Jan. 13 and 25, some areas of Ohio recorded more than 10 inches of precipitation. During those 12 days, daily rainfall records were set across the state. And the water kept rising. It was one of the wettest months recorded in Ohio.

With more than half a dozen inches of rain already saturating the ground, a cold front swept through Ohio on Jan. 20 and the temperatures plummeted. The rain turned to snow. Daily snowfall records were set in many areas on Jan. 22. And by Jan. 23, record low temperatures were being set across the state. The very next day, temperatures recovered into the 40s and all that snow began to melt and run off. The rivers continued to rise.

Between January 13 and January 25, 1937, ten of the 13 days experienced significant amounts of precipitation. The ground was fully saturated and/or frozen so the additional water started running off and generated raging floods.

In those two weeks, Columbus collected 8.99" of precipitation. Dayton measured 9.96" of precip, 10.79" in Circleville, 8.81" in Marysville, and 8.66" in Marion.

By Jan. 26, the Ohio River at Cincinnati crested 28 feet over flood stage. In Portsmouth, city officials deliberately flooded the downtown area with 10 feet of water after opening the floodgates to keep the river from breeching and destroying the flood wall. By controlling the water as it came in, they prevented a catastrophic flash flood that would have destroyed buildings with a massive wall of water instead of just flooding them. The water eventually crested 14 feet above the flood wall.

It's estimated that the high water left more than 50,000 people homeless in the wet, winter cold.

The Great Anna Earthquake

March 1937.

So, technically, the Anna earthquakes may not have been severe-weather events, but they were a minor "natural disaster."

On March 2, 1937, a series of tremors shook the area from Anna to Wapakoneta to Bellefontaine. It was enough to crack plaster, topple chimneys and rotate cemetery headstones. One schoolhouse was damaged enough to be declared unsafe.

Early the next morning, on March 3, people were shaken out of bed and the windows rattled as another tremor jolted the same region.

But the biggest temblor came on March 8, just before midday. The quake measured a healthy 5.4 magnitude on the newly-implemented Richter Scale and an intensity of VIII on the Modified Mercalli (MM) scale[10], making it one of the strongest earthquakes to ever rattle the state. Chimneys that had just been repaired from the previous week's shock were felled again; it's been estimated that nearly every chimney in the city was damaged or destroyed. Cans and boxes were rattled off store shelves. More tombstones were twisted on their foundations. There were even reports that organ pipes were twisted in a local church. And many of the area's wells and springs changed their behavior as groundwater shifted in subsurface aqueducts.

According to the US Geological Survey report of the incident, the "shock was felt in upper stories of multistory buildings in Chicago and Milwaukee and in Toronto, Canada."

The Thanksgiving Snow Storm of 1950 & The Blizzard Bowl

Nov. 23-27, 1950.

This one gave us the infamous "Blizzard Bowl" between Ohio State and Michigan. The two teams faced off in Columbus while enduring single-digit temperatures and 40 mph winds. The snow caused white-out conditions on the field. Despite the miserable conditions, the Wolverines won 9-3, wrested the Big Ten Championship from the Buckeyes, and moved on to the Rose Bowl.

In the meantime, the rest of the state was in the midst of a massive snow storm. Some portions of Ohio were buried under 20 to 30 inches of snow and drifts that reached second-story windows. Winds of up to 60 mph brought down trees and power lines and buildings collapsed under the weight of the snow. The Ohio National Guard was called out to deliver food and get victims to hospitals.

---

[10] While somewhat problematic, the Modified Mercalli (MM) scale, created in 1931, uses damage to estimate the strength of earthquakes. Without instruments to accurately measure a tremor's intensity and location, the best estimate comes from the physical aftermath.

The Blizzard of '78

As the anniversary of the Blizzard of 1978 comes and goes on Jan. 26, many of us think about where we were and how we survived one of the biggest winter storms in our memories.

On TV, I mentioned that the storm itself only left four inches of new snow in Columbus. It's true. Only four inches.

That prompted a blizzard of its own; dozens of emails reminding me that I'm a total idiot who has no idea what he's talking about.

"Four inches of snow???" wrote David Keeton from Lancaster. "What..are you sure on your facts." [sic]

David's was one of the nicer messages. He mentioned that he remembered living through the storm as a fifth grader. I remember it, too, as an elementary-school-aged kid who was sent home with days and days worth of homework to do during the time away from the classroom. Multiplication tables, as I recall.

January 1978 was the snowiest month ever recorded in Columbus... but *not* because of The Blizzard.

The Blizzard itself only dropped 4.7 inches of snow in Columbus. That's right. Less than five inches. That's it. The western and southwestern parts of Ohio, including Dayton and Cincinnati, had *much* more.

So why did we have 10-15-foot snow drifts? Why was the state shut down for days? And why did Governor Rhodes have to call out the National Guard?

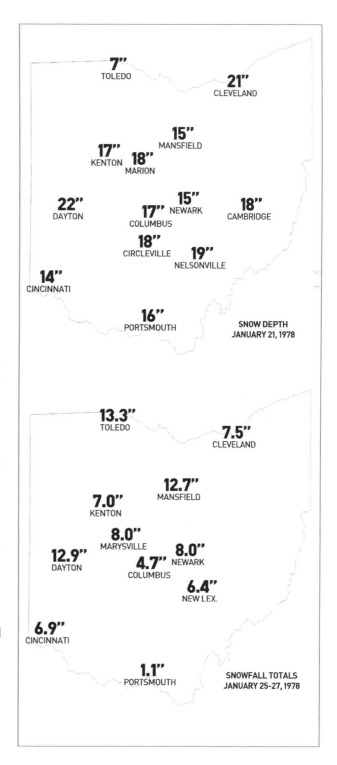

7" TOLEDO
21" CLEVELAND
15" MANSFIELD
17" KENTON
18" MARION
22" DAYTON
17" COLUMBUS
15" NEWARK
18" CAMBRIDGE
18" CIRCLEVILLE
19" NELSONVILLE
14" CINCINNATI
16" PORTSMOUTH

SNOW DEPTH
JANUARY 21, 1978

13.3" TOLEDO
7.5" CLEVELAND
12.7" MANSFIELD
7.0" KENTON
8.0" MARYSVILLE
8.0" NEWARK
12.9" DAYTON
4.7" COLUMBUS
6.4" NEW LEX.
6.9" CINCINNATI
1.1" PORTSMOUTH

SNOWFALL TOTALS
JANUARY 25-27, 1978

There are two components to the answer:

❄ There were already 15-20 inches of snow on the ground before the Blizzard struck, slowly accumulating throughout the month.

❄ The wind was absolutely ferocious.

The storm center had amazingly low pressure, setting an all-time record in Columbus of 28.47 in/Hg (964.10 mb). Cleveland dropped to 28.28 in/Hg (957.66 mb), the lowest non-hurricane-related pressure ever recorded on the US mainland (at the time).[11] Those conditions produce incredibly strong winds. The Blizzard's 60-75 mph gusts whipped the new and existing snow around to create the enormous drifts we all remember.

In Columbus, those huge drifts were mostly from the existing snow, not the new storm. Elsewhere in the state, it was a combination of old and new snow.

Columbus' Top 10 Snowiest Months

1. 34.4" in January 1978
2. 30.1" in February 2010
3. 29.2" in February 1910
4. 26.3" in February 2003
5. 25.4" in January 1918
6. 25.3" in March 1906
7. 24.5" in January 1996
8. 24.3" in January 1910
9. 21.9" in January 1985
10. 21.8" in March 2008

Where were you?

Where were you during the Blizzard of 1978? What do you remember about the storm and how you and your family survived it?

Share your story at WaitTenMinutes.com!

---

[11] The United States' mid-continent, record-low barometric pressure was surpassed by another storm that ravaged the Upper Great Lakes on October 26, 2010, dropping to a new record low of 955.2 mb at Bigfork, Minnesota. According to a 2004 American Meteorological Society article by Kocin and Uccellini called "Northeast Snowstorms," the lowest non-hurricane barometric pressure reading ever recorded in the continental US was 28.10" (952 mb) measured on March 1, 1914, at Bridgehampton, New York (Long Island) during an extraordinary nor'easter.

The Cardington Tornado

June 13, 1981

The tornado sirens wail every Wednesday at noon. It's just a regular test. But it still makes many Cardington residents jump. Even after more than 30 years, the memories from The Tornado are still very fresh in many people's minds.

The storm rolled into Central Ohio on June 13, 1981. Some Cardington residents say they remember tornado warnings being issued for Delaware County that day but not for their area in Morrow County.

A freight train rumbled through the village that afternoon. A few minutes after it cleared the tracks in the middle of town, residents and business owners heard a similar noise again. Many assumed it was just another train.

At 2:23 p.m., an F3 tornado shredded the village.

"It was unbelievable," said former mayor Cecil Maxwell. He was 88 years old at the time of our interview in 2011 and said he still remembered that day vividly. He was visiting his daughter, Janice, in Delaware when the storm ravaged his hometown. They heard the news from a neighbor's police scanner and Maxwell immediately called Cardington's police station. He says he was surprised to get a dispatcher on the phone.

"I hate to tell you, mayor, but there's been a bad tornado that's hurt your town," he recalled her saying. "I said, 'Can you tell me about it?' and just then she lost the connection."

The devastation was horrific. Four people were killed including a nine-month-old boy. Another 56 were injured. Damage was estimated to be at least $25 million.

Maxwell raced back to Cardington via some country roads. He says his first priority was to find survivors. By then, many people were already beginning to help one another.

"If they hadn't told me it was a tornado, I would have probably have assumed that Cardington had been bombed," says Tom Harden who was the County Sheriff at the time. "In 24 years as the Morrow County Sheriff, I've never seen anything similar to this or even close to it."

Poles were snapped. Dozens of buildings were destroyed. Hundreds more were damaged. All three of the city's fire trucks were crushed when the fire station's roof collapsed. Harden says he remembers the solid steel frame of a mobile home was wrapped around a tree so it touched itself on the other side.

"I couldn't really realize how vast this devastation was," Harden says of standing in the village center. Then he flew over the area in the governor's plane with the Ohio Highway Patrol. From there he saw the tornado's path and the widespread damage.

Just hours after the storm, Harden said to the *Columbus Dispatch*, "I saw Xenia and this is probably worse than Xenia." Governor James A. Rhodes called it the worst he had ever seen.

"Governor Rhodes called the armory and told us to get to Cardington," remembers Tom George. He was on weekend drill duty with the Ohio National Guard in Marion. His unit, A Battery, 134th Field Artillery (now called the 37th Brigade), was assigned to security detail for the village.

"When we got here, I was totally amazed at how much damage there was," he says. His unit spent nine days living in the Vocational Agriculture building at the local high school. He remembers turning away "tourists" from Michigan who had traveled all the way to Cardington to see the damage in person.

George specifically remembers the storm's bizarre ferocity. He says he saw blades of grass thrown with such force that they were embedded in the steel hood of a car. And a glass bottle that punched through a solid piece of plywood. The bottle was still in tact. On both sides of the panel.

The American Red Cross estimated that at least 120 homes and 42 businesses had been "heavily damaged."

The twister was categorized on the Fujita Scale as an F3 with winds between 158-206 mph. The Fujita Scale estimates the strength of a tornado's winds based on the damage and debris left behind. In 2007, the scale was updated and is now referred to as the Enhanced Fujita Scale. By the updated measure, the Cardington storm would likely be classified as an EF4.

Evelyn Long was a reporter for the *Marion Star* and covered the storm's aftermath. She says the news traveled as far as Colombia where a former exchange student heard the story and spent nearly a week trying to contact friends in Cardington.

Many of the village's businesses were damaged. Most were able to survive but several disappeared and so did the jobs they provided for the community.

"Clement's Furniture never reopened," says Harden, the former sheriff. He says the Walter-Long car dealership closed, the Cardington Mill shut down, and Sherman's Hardware "only lasted a little while" after the storm.

Other survivors say Stahl's Manufacturing, with nearly a hundred employees, struggled for years and eventually closed after slowly dismissing its workforce. Some of the former Cardington workers were reportedly absorbed by a companion plant in Wooster.

In 2011, the village established the Cardington Heritage Festival to honor the tornado's anniversary and to pay tribute to the leadership of then-Mayor Maxwell. The festival helped raise funds for a park named in Maxwell's honor. He donated more than 30 acres of land near Whetstone Creek that had been used for decades as pasture for his family's business, the Riverside Dairy.

Maxwell is very humble about his role in helping rebuild the village. He makes a point of using the word "we" and reminding people that it was a joint effort involving the entire community.

"People are willing to step forward and go that extra mile to help their neighbors and that really happened here in Cardington, Ohio," Harden notes proudly.

"I was glad I wasn't mayor at the time!" says Mills Poorman, glancing across the room at Maxwell with an understanding smile. Poorman has served multiple terms as Cardington's mayor including a stint in the late-1970s, before Maxwell.

Like many, Poorman is not convinced that Cardington, or any community demolished by a massive tornado, can ever fully recover. Even after three decades.

"Life goes on," Poorman says. "Our objective now is to get as many businesses into the community as possible. We're proud of Cardington. We hope to get things rebuilt and, hopefully, the economy will pick up and we'll be back, better than what we were."

The Big Freeze of 1994

Jan. 19, 1994

The coldest snap in Ohio history descended on the Buckeye State on Jan. 19, 1994. Record lows were set across the state. Temperatures were below zero for more than two days (50 consecutive hours). As Kent State University researchers Thomas and Jeanne Schmidlin chronicle in their book, *Thunder in the Heartland*, at least 35 counties reported temperatures of -30° or colder including a -37°F reading in Logan.

Flying Over the Aftermath

My dad was a pilot. We had a four-seater Cessna hangared at the Bucyrus airport. One afternoon, he suggested we go for a ride. At the time, I didn't realize we were going sightseeing.

After a few minutes in the air, he began to circle. Then he started pointing out a debris field on the ground. From up there, it looked like a model had been crushed into match sticks. We were flying over the aftermath of the Cardington tornado.

All-time records were set across the state and the wind chills, at times, dipped to -50°F and colder.

In Columbus, an eighth-floor window at Central Police Headquarters cracked, reportedly, because of the bitter cold and eventually sent shards of glass crashing to the pavement below. Water lines ruptured around the city and the cold slowed repair efforts to about a third of their usual speed.

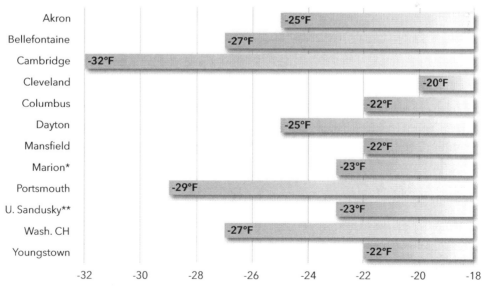

All-Time Record Lows Set Jan. 19, 1994

Akron	-25°F
Bellefontaine	-27°F
Cambridge	-32°F
Cleveland	-20°F
Columbus	-22°F
Dayton	-25°F
Mansfield	-22°F
Marion*	-23°F
Portsmouth	-29°F
U. Sandusky**	-23°F
Wash. CH	-27°F
Youngstown	-22°F

* Marion recorded lows of -23°F on Jan 19 & 20, 1994, as well as on Feb 26, 1963.
** Upper Sandusky dropped to -23°F on January 19 & 20, 1994.

Circleville EF3 Tornado

October 1999.

They saw it coming on the radar screen. The storm was barreling toward the city at nearly 60 mph. The warning was issued and, with 15 minutes to spare, Pickaway County Sheriff Dwight E. Radcliff gave the order to set off the city's tornado sirens.

At almost 5 p.m., the tornado ravaged portions of Circleville with winds of up to 206 mph, damaging more than a dozen buildings including several homes. It was classified as an F3 twister.

Because of the advanced warning, only four people were injured.

Sheriff's Communications Officer Sgt. Linda Welsh told the *Columbus Dispatch* that weekly tornado-siren tests often prompted complaints, specifically from one man who lived near a siren. "I wonder what he's thinking today," she said.

Union Co. & Van Wert Tornadoes

Nov. 10, 2002.

The weather was unusually warm in the afternoon of Sunday, Nov. 10, 2002. Columbus set a daily record high of 71°F. But with that warm, moist air, came very heavy rain and strong thunderstorms. (Columbus set a daily precipitation record with 1.52 inches of rain that day.) Some of those storms developed extremely strong convective currents and the National Weather Service was issuing watches and warnings all afternoon.

One particularly strong thunderstorm traveled from western Indiana into northwestern Ohio and produced an F4 tornado that ravaged the city of Van Wert. Infamously, a movie theater there was destroyed but patrons managed to escape just before the walls collapsed onto the auditorium seats.

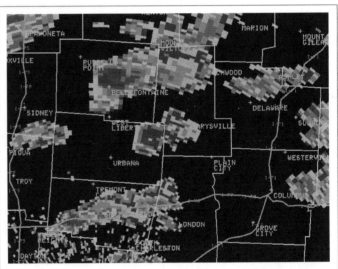

An archived image of National Weather Service radar shows the supercell storm that produced an F3 tornado in Logan and Union Counties on November 10, 2002. Image courtesy: NOAA/NWS

In Central Ohio, another large storm developed in Logan County and reached severe parameters as it came through Bellefontaine. Tornado Warnings were issued for Logan and Union Counties as worrisome radar returns began to develop. Around 4:30 p.m., an F3 tornado dropped out of the clouds in Logan County. It traveled more than 10 miles and, along the way, created a damage path nearly 300 yards wide.

More than a dozen homes were damaged or destroyed in Union County. Serendipity Stables, a non-profit horse farm providing therapy for special needs children, was heavily damaged and several horses were killed; one survived after being hurled the length of three farm fields. A huge, high-tension power line tower was brought down and turned into a heap of twisted metal. At least two people were injured.

For the day, northwestern and central Ohio endured 19 tornadoes. Five people were killed.

Christmas Snow & Ice Storm of 2004

Two days before Christmas 2004, a massive winter storm plowed through Ohio. A swath from Dayton to Marion and Bucyrus picked up 16-20" of snow. Columbus had 6-10" of snow and was covered in a layer of ice.

Southern and southeastern Ohio were coated in thick sheets of glistening, deadly ice. The ice storm knocked out power to tens of thousands of homes, brought down thousands of trees, and was blamed for at least four deaths. The Ohio Insurance Institute says the storm resulted in at least $85 million of insured losses. And then-Governor Bob Taft declared emergencies in at least 20 counties.

Remnants of Hurricane Ike

September 14, 2008.

It was a beautiful, late-summer day in Central Ohio. The sky was a gorgeous blue, the sun was shining, and Columbus was buzzing with activity. The storm came in suddenly, within minutes. It left just as quickly.

Hurricane Ike battered the Gulf Coast with 110 mph sustained winds, deadly storm surges, and enormous amounts of rain. It was a Category 2 hurricane as it made landfall in Galveston, Texas. But it didn't stop there.

This massive tree was one of several blown over in Columbus' Goodale Park by the ferocious winds of former-hurricane Ike.

Most hurricanes lose energy as they move ashore, away from the warm waters of the Gulf of Mexico. The warm water provides fuel for the thunderstorms that swirl around a deep low-pressure center. When they drift away from the moisture, they become more stable, and the storm begins to weaken. Eventually, they develop fronts and become "extratropical."

Ike was having none of it.

The low-pressure center continued to spin at incredible strength. Even though it turned extratropical on Sept. 14, it still had a central pressure similar to a Category 1 hurricane with winds to match, as it wandered up the Mississippi River Valley. By the time the storm made it to St. Louis, it met up with the jet stream and took a hard-right turn, heading directly toward the lower Great Lakes.

Enormous amounts of rain continued to fall on the west side of the storm's track. Ohio was on the dry side of the system. As it slammed into Ohio, the skies were bright. It certainly didn't seem like much of a hurricane any more. But the winds turned out to still be incredible.

The storm arrived in Columbus early in the afternoon of Sept. 14, 2008. In moments, the winds went from light to fierce. Port Columbus reported a gust of 75 mph. Trees came down. Power poles fell. Roofs were torn apart. Not a drop of rain fell.

A mulch fire at a Groveport landscape supply business was fanned high into the sky as firefighters continued their battle against it from day into night. Gas station canopies were peeled back and road signs were ripped away. The Delaware County Fair and a chalk-drawing festival in Columbus were both shut down.

At least three people reportedly were killed by falling trees. More than a million homes were left in the dark.

The cleanup took weeks. Many Columbus-area residents were without electricity for nearly two weeks. Some even longer. In all, the National Hurricane Center estimates Ike did nearly $30 billion in damage, making it the third-costliest hurricane in US history, right behind Sandy and Katrina.

CALENDAR OF OHIO
SEVERE WEATHER ANNIVERSARIES

Here is a selected list of significant events in Ohio's long and distinguished history of severe-weather.

January

Coldest Month and Winter: January 1977, Winter 1976-'77

According to *Thunder in the Heartland* author Tom Schmidlin, the average temperature in Ohio in January 1977 was 11.9°F, about 17 degrees below average. Most reporting sites, he writes, were below freezing for the entire month. It was the coldest winter on record with deep snows and widespread fuel shortages.

Statewide Cold Snap and Blizzard: Jan. 12-15, 1918

On Jan. 12, several inches of snow fell, temperatures dropped to -10°F to -20°F, winds kicked up to 40-60 mph, and wind chills plummeted to nearly -80°F.[12] Bellefontaine, Upper Sandusky, and Marysville reported air temperatures of -17°F.

Then, on Jan. 14, many areas of Ohio collected an additional 10-15 inches of snow that, combined with another round of high winds, pushed snow into drifts taller than houses. Circleville, Marysville, and McConnelsville all reported up to 12 inches of new snow.

Nastiest Cold Snap: Jan. 19, 1994

Record lows were set across the state as arctic air plunged into the state. Much of Ohio stayed below zero for 50 hours or more. Thirty-five counties reported temperatures of -30°F or colder. All-time records were set at Logan (-37°F), Cambridge (-32°F), Portsmouth (-29°F), Washington Court House (-27°F), Akron (-25°F), Marion (-23°F), Columbus (-22°F), Youngstown (-22°F), and Cleveland (-20°F).

Ohio's Coldest Daytime: Jan. 20, 1985

As an arctic air mass settled into the state, record-low temperatures gripped the state during the early morning hours. By midday, temperatures still hovered at -19°F in Dayton, -15°F in Columbus and Cincinnati, and -11°F in Toledo and Cleveland. Strong winds of 20-30 mph drove the wind chills to -60°F and colder.[13]

---

[12] As calculated by the Wind Chill formula in use at the time. The formula has since been updated in hopes of being more accurate.

[13] This wind chill calculation uses an old version of the formula. Using the revised WCI formula adopted by the National Weather Service in 2001, the wind chill would be -42 to -48°F. That still qualifies as one of the coldest wind chills ever recorded in Columbus.

Even the postal service gave up. It was just too cold for the intrepid couriers to make their appointed rounds. Deliveries were cancelled for the day. Several people were reportedly treated for frostbite including a man who walked nearly three miles in the cold after his car broke down.

Highest Flood on the Ohio River: Jan. 26, 1937

After nearly two weeks of rain, runoff caused one of the most widespread and deepest floods ever to plague the Ohio River Valley. At Cincinnati, the water reached a record of 28 feet above flood stage inundating an estimated 10-percent of the city. Portsmouth was left with 10 feet of water in its downtown buildings after city officials deliberately opened the floodgates, saving the flood wall, and avoiding an even larger, flash-flood disaster.

The Blizzard of '78: Jan. 26, 1978

This was one of the strongest storms in Ohio history. The low-pressure center that ravaged the Great Lakes brought with it a then-record-low barometer reading, temperatures that plunged as much as 50 degrees in less than 24 hours, hurricane-force winds of more than 70 mph, and more than a foot of snow in some parts of the state. The winds created drifts more than 10 feet high and shut down the state for more than two days. More than 50 people were killed. The governor mobilized nearly 5,000 National Guard troops to help with cleanup.

Southern Ohio Ice Storm: Jan 26-28, 2009

Along with 8" to 12" of snow, central and north-central Ohio were covered in a 1/4" to 1/2" of ice. Southern Ohio was coated with 1/2" to 1" of ice. All of that on top of heavy, wet snow. The trees and power lines didn't stand a chance. The Ohio Public Utilities Commission reported nearly 172,000 Ohioans were without electricity because of the snow and ice.

February

National Weatherperson's Day

From the National Weather Service Forecast Office in St. Louis:

Feb. 5 is National Weatherperson's Day, commemorating the birth of John Jeffries in 1744. Jeffries, one of America's first weather observers, began taking daily weather observations in Boston in 1774 and he took the first balloon observation in 1784. This is a day to recognize the men and women who collectively provide Americans with the best weather, water, and climate forecasts and warning services of any nation.

March

The Great Anna Earthquake: March 8, 1937

The tremors began on March 2, cracking plaster, toppling chimneys, and shifting headstones. But the largest shake came around midday on March 8. By some reports, every chimney in the city was brought down, including the ones that had just been repaired. Wells and springs changed their behavior as underground aquifers were shifted. Richter: 5.40 magnitude. Modified Mercalli: VIII intensity.

The Great Flood of '13: March 23-27, 1913

More than 460 Ohioans died as flood waters rose across the state from Toledo to Cincinnati. The water was highest at Dayton, Hamilton, and Columbus. More than 10 inches of rain fell in less than four days. The Olentangy River reportedly rose more than 20 feet in a single day, flooding thousands of homes and businesses and leaving survivors clinging to trees.

Palm Sunday Tornadoes: March 28, 1920

Four tornadoes ravaged northwestern Ohio on a warm spring afternoon and evening. Wood, Ottawa, Lucas, Paulding, Henry, Darke, Mercer, and Van Wert counties were the most devastated. Ohio's four twisters were part of a violent outbreak of at least 30 in eight states. More than 150 people were killed including 29 Ohioans. It has been ranked as one of the deadliest tornado outbreaks in American history.

April

The Xenia Tornadoes - Part 2: April 3, 1974

The day's super-outbreak spawned 148 tornadoes in 13 states. The Xenia Tornado was the most devastating and deadly of the lot. A dozen tornadoes struck Ohio that day killing three dozen people, 32 of them in Xenia. The F5 twister in Greene County wiped entire neighborhoods from their foundations and destroyed much of the central city including seven of twelve schools. It created a 32-mile path of destruction from Xenia to Wilberforce where it leveled portions of Central State University. Nationwide, "Xenia" instantly became an adjective used to describe incredible tornado damage. Other tornadoes from the same family touched down in Clark, Madison, and Franklin Counties.

Palm Sunday Tornadoes v 2.0: April 11,1965

Fifty-five Ohioans were killed in a violent outbreak that became the second-deadliest day in the state's history. Multiple "families" of tornadoes crossed the northwestern part of the state including several violent, long-track twisters. One F4 tornado cut a six-mile path across the north side of Toledo. Another cluster of tornadoes killed 34 as they slashed a swath through Mercer and Van Wert counties, destroyed homes near Bluffton, cut a 20-mile path near Tiffin, and cut a half-mile-wide path all the way from Oberlin to Strongsville. Another twister created a path of destruction through Shelby County. Just after 11 p.m., parts of Delaware and Morrow counties were leveled as a tornado destroyed homes in Radnor, killing three people. Then, around midnight, another tornado wrought a 28-mile path of destruction from Ashville to Lancaster.

Deepest Snow on Record: April 19-20, 1901

Heavy, wet snow fell across the eastern half of Ohio with many areas reporting between 25" and 35" of accumulation. At Gratiot, west of Zanesville, a total of 42" was reported, one of the deepest ever recorded in Ohio. Drifts were more than 10 feet high because of the strong winds. Hundreds of roofs collapsed under the excessive weight.

The Xenia Tornadoes - Part 3: April 25, 1989

Yet another tornado (F2) trashed part of Xenia when it dropped down in the Shawnee Village neighborhood on North Monroe Street. Six homes were destroyed and about 100 were damaged. Sixteen people were injured.

May

The Xenia Tornadoes - Part 1: May 13, 1933

Just before dawn, a tornado ripped across the east side of Xenia leveling more than 50 homes and killing two people. Another 25 were injured. It was the at least the second time the city had been struck directly; according to the Xenia Area Chamber of Commerce, "The Xenia flood of May 1886, which killed 28 people, had a small tornado associated with it, but the waters were the big story."

Northeastern Tornadoes: May 31, 1985

In just three hours, rapidly-developing severe storms produced the most tornadoes Ohio had ever experienced in a single day (up to that time). A massive F5 twister tore a 47-mile path of destruction through Portage and Trumbull counties, killing 11 people, before moving into Pennsylvania. Other tornadoes were reported in Licking, Coshocton, Columbiana, Madison, Stark, and Adams counties.

June

The Cardington Tornado: June 13, 1981

At 2:23 p.m., an F3 tornado shredded the village's nine-block downtown killing four people and injuring at least 56.

Shadyside Flood: June 14, 1990

After weeks of soaking rains, Belmont County was hit with a deluge that dropped three to four inches of rain in a single hour. A total of 5.5 inches of rain fell in the valleys of the Wegee and Pipe Creeks. It was more than the hillsides could support. A wall of water and mud six feet high carried away trees, cars and entire buildings. As the debris slammed into bridges, it got stuck and created temporary dams. When those broke, even larger walls of water, mud and debris slammed into the valleys downstream. Eighty homes were destroyed and more than 250 damaged. At least 26 bodies were recovered in the Ohio River.

Lorain Tornado: June 28, 1924

The deadliest tornado in Ohio history claimed at least 85 lives in Lorain and Sandusky. It destroyed more than nine city blocks along Sandusky's downtown waterfront. The funnel traveled onto Lake Erie (technically, becoming a waterspout) for nearly 30 minutes before coming ashore again at Lorain where it smashed its way down a three-mile path. Nearly every downtown business was damaged or destroyed. Fifteen people were killed in the State Theatre, the largest single-building tornado death toll in Ohio's history. According to Schmidlin's research, there was evidence of a car smashing into the fourth floor of a brick building before crashing to the ground.

July

Intense Heat: July 8-15, 1936

This was one of the warmest weeks ever documented in Ohio. Temperatures reached triple-digits across the entire state. At Paulding, the thermometers read 111°F. Observers in Bowling Green and Van Wert reported highs of 110°F. Columbus tied its all-time record of 106°F and Toledo hit 105°F.

Most Tornadoes in One Day: July 12, 1992

Twenty-eight tornadoes in a single day. It was a devastating afternoon and evening across northern Ohio from Toledo to Cleveland, twisters dropped out of the sky destroying homes, businesses, trees, and cemeteries. Amazingly, no one was killed and only 36 injuries were reported. July 1992 became the month with most tornadoes (44) and 1992 the busiest tornado year (61).

Hottest Temperature and Summer: July 21, 1934

Hundreds died across the midwest as record-setting heat and drought invaded the region. The all-time state record of 113°F was set at Gallipolis. Columbus set its current all-time record high of 106°F (which was tied again in July 1936). Circleville, Marysville, Coshocton also set records. The heat wave pushed the month's average temperature high enough to make it the hottest month ever recorded in Ohio.

September

Remnants of Hurricane Ike: Sept. 14, 2008

After pounding the Gulf Coast as a Category 2 hurricane, the remnants of Ike arrived in Central Ohio on a bright, sunny, warm, late-summer afternoon. It came and went in a matter of hours. With gusts of 75 mph, it uprooted trees, tore down power lines, and ripped away roofs. Power was out in some areas for more than two weeks. Damage estimates nationwide hit $30 billion.

The Xenia Tornadoes - Part 4: Sept. 20, 2000

Another F4 tornado touched down in Xenia following a path similar to the 1974 twister. One man was killed at the Greene County Fairgrounds when a tree fell on his car and more than 100 others were injured. An estimated 300 homes and businesses were damaged and at least three churches were destroyed.

October

Circleville Tornado: Oct. 13, 1999

An F3 tornado ravaged parts of Circleville, damaging at least a dozen homes and business. Winds were reported up to 206 mph. Only four injuries were reported. Warnings were issued and tornado sirens were activated 15 minutes before the storm arrived, giving residents time to take safety precautions.

November

Great Lakes Hurricane: Nov. 9-12 1913

With winds of nearly 80 mph and 18-25 inches of snow, this was a full-on blizzard of epic proportions. Across the Great Lakes, 12 ships sank killing at least 235 sailors. Freezing and rain and wet snow brought down trees as well as electric, telegraph, and telephone lines. Roofs collapsed under the weight of the heavy, wet snow. Food shortages developed because trains and trucks were stranded in the deep snow.

Central Ohio Tornadoes: Nov. 10, 2002

Nineteen tornadoes ravaged parts of Central and Northwestern Ohio as unseasonably-warm air helped fuel strong storms. In Union County, an EF3 tornado destroyed the stables used by a therapy-horse service. Another EF3 touched down for nearly 10 miles in Logan County. And an EF4 twister infamously tossed cars into the front row of a movie theatre just moments after patrons escaped. In all, five people were killed.

Thanksgiving Blizzard: Nov. 23-27, 1950

Some portions of Ohio were buried under 20-30 inches of snow and drifts that reached second-story windows. Winds of up to 60 mph brought down trees and power lines and buildings collapsed under the weight of the snow. The Ohio National Guard was called out to deliver food and get victims to hospitals. In the midst of the storm, Michigan beat Ohio State in a low-scoring football game that became known as the "Blizzard Bowl."

December

Christmas Snow & Ice Storm: Dec. 23, 2004

Two days before Christmas, a massive winter storm dumped 10-20 inches of snow across the state along with a layer of ice. Southern and southeastern Ohio were coated with enough to bring down power lines, knocking out power to tens of thousands of homes. At least four deaths were blamed on the storm. Damage estimates surpassed $85 million.

WEATHER FOLKLORE

*"Look at that moon, will you! Tsk-tsk-tsk.
Potato weather, for sure."*

— Mrs. Gibbs, *Our Town* by Thornton Wilder

Humans are observant. For millennia, people have looked to the skies and watched the clouds, the sun and the stars. And they've noticed patterns. Some patterns are easier to identify than others; some happen over and over in a single year and others only reveal themselves a few times in a generation. Once those curious observers deciphered the patterns, the heavens began to tell stories and predict the future.

The early observers passed along their discoveries orally. They created clever phrases and poems to make them easier to remember. Those stories have become our folklore.

Many folkloric stories stand up to scientific fact and reasoning. They're based on real-world, anecdotal evidence. The early observers may not have understood thermodynamics, but they knew a mackerel sky pretty consistently appeared shortly before rainfall. Their knowledge of atmospheric light refraction was rudimentary at best, but they knew a red sky early in the day meant trouble was on the way. In many instances, the folklore actually can be used for basic, short-term forecasting. Some concepts, though, are just plain hokum.

Among the many:

- Thunder in February, freeze in May.

- Blackbirds sitting together in rows on the telephone wires, means rain is coming.

- A ring around the sun or moon, means rain or snow coming soon.

- When grass is dry at morning light, look for rain before the night.

- The sudden storm lasts not three hours ; the sharper the blast, the sooner 'tis past.

- Cold is the night when the stars shine bright.

- No weather's ill if the wind be still.

- Waning Moon. Plant biennials, perennials, bulb and root crops.

- Waxing Moon. Plant annuals that produce their yield above ground.

- When your joints all start to ache, rainy weather is at stake.

Red in the Morning...

Red sky at night, sailor's delight.
Red sky in morning, sailor take warning.

This is probably one of the most recognized and oft-quoted pieces of weather folklore. You've heard it a million times. And it comes in several iterations:

A rainbow in the morning, is the shepherd's warning.

A rainbow at night is the shepherd's delight.

Evening red and morning gray will set the traveler on his way,

But evening gray and morning red will bring down rain upon his head.

They are all based on a fairly straightforward weather concept: a stormy sky to the west often means rain is coming your way; and a stormy sky to the east often means the rain has just passed. This is all assuming, of course, that you are in the northern hemisphere where our weather patterns tend to move from west to east.

The stunning colors we see at sunrise and sunset are created as sunlight passes through the gasses and particles in the atmosphere; they scatter the blue end of the spectrum, leaving the vibrant reds, oranges, and yellows to bounce off the clouds. When the sky is clear, the sunsets aren't quite as spectacular because only the sun's orb itself shines in brilliant, fiery colors.

The perfect sunrise or sunset needs just enough clouds to fill the sky with color, but not enough to obscure the horizon.

If the sky is red at sunset (Sailor's Delight), it means the western sky is clear and allowing the scattered sunlight to pass by and bounce off the clouds in the east. That's an indication that the rain is moving out of the region.

When the sky is red at sunrise (Sailor's Warning), the scattered sunlight is passing through the clear sky to the east and bouncing off the clouds in the western sky, indicating rain may be moving into the area.

Rain before seven...

Rain before seven, fine by eleven.

Rain is often caused by either frontal passage or convection, sometimes both. As a cold front rolls through the region, it often creates a distinct line of showers and thunderstorms. Many times, it only takes a few hours for the front to pass. Once the front has gone by, it often takes the precipitation with it. Convective showers and storms are often short-lived because they are dependent on the day's surface (diurnal) heating.

In both cases, the rain comes and goes within a matter of hours. So, on occasion, this piece of folklore holds true. Late-day and overnight convective storms will usually fall apart by morning. And a front that is passing in the morning will usually be east of the area by afternoon. However, frontal passage can happen at any time of the day or night so, if it is raining at seven, keep your umbrella handy at lunchtime, just in case.

Trees turning their leaves...

**When leaves show their undersides,
be very sure that rain betides.**

Leaves turning silver a change will deliver.

In many cases, rain moves into the area as a cold front or low-pressure center gets closer or passes through. Those weather systems also cause stronger winds and, often, a shift in wind direction.

Trees tend to grow where they get enough sunlight to sustain themselves. Their leaves turn up to face the sun. The sunny side has lots of chlorophyll and that makes the leaves a beautiful green. When the wind picks up, or changes direction, the leaves are blown a different way and we see their underside.

So, seeing the backs of the leaves is not so much an indicator portending of rain, as much as a change in the winds. They do, however, often go together.

Onion skins and winter...

**Onion skins very thin, mild winter coming in;
Onion skins thick and tough, coming winter cold and rough.**

This one has been attributed to selective memory; people only remember when it was right and tend to forget when it missed the mark.

Put simply, plants can't forecast. They have no sense of foreboding, no extra-sensory perception, no innate long-term signal reading. They can't prepare for anything. They are, however, very good indicators of the past. Tree rings are an excellent record of rainfall, extreme heat, and severe cold. But an onion can't lay on an extra layer because it feels an El Nino winter coming on. It can adapt for next year but not give us a heads-up for this year.

Sorry, this one is bunk.

Mares Tales & Mackerel Skies

Mares' tails and mackerel scales
Make tall ships take down their sails.

A mackerel sky means rain within 24 hours.

"Mares' tails" and "mackerel scales" are common names for specific types of clouds. Mares' tails are wispy, cirrus clouds made of ice crystals very high in the sky. They're usually formed by updrafts in the atmosphere that carry moisture high enough to condense, then turn to ice. A mackerel sky is made of slightly-lower-altitude clouds called cirrocumulus; they're still very high but not quite as high as mares' tails and they're water vapor instead of ice. They're similar to the puffy cumulus clouds we see during wet weather, but they're much, much higher.

As high pressure moves away from the region, we'll often see cirrus clouds. And as a cold front or low-pressure center moves closer, we'll see other clouds, like cirrocumulus, begin to form. The progression of clouds gets lower and lower as the front approaches.

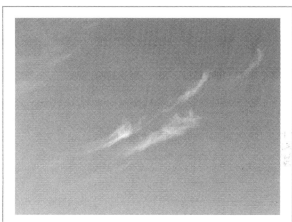

Cirrus clouds and wispy "mare's tales" high in the sky on a bright afternoon.

So, seeing mares' tails (high pressure leaving) followed by mackerel scales (lower pressure approaching), you might be good to guess that some unsettled weather is on the way.

Fog Foretells of Snows

This one was new. Hadn't heard it before Margo's message arrived via Facebook in October 2014:

> Can u tell me where i can find out how many fogs we had in august in lancaster?
> Suppose to tell u how many snows we will have. Please help. :-}-;

So, the number of foggy mornings in August portends of the number of coming snows during this winter? By that logic, our winter can never have more than 31 snows. Love the sound of that!

Just for fun, 'cause that's what we think is fun, we did some research. Here's how it stacks up for the past several years:

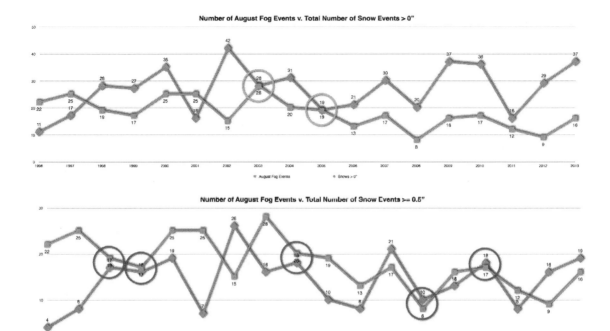

Between 1996 and 2013, for snow events of a trace or more, the fog events matched twice: 2003 and 2005. The numbers for all the other years were back and forth across the chart. For snow events of 1/2" or greater, the fog numbers came within two events on five occasions, but never actually matched. I think we'd have to call this one, "mildly unreliable at best."

Cicadas Predict the First Frost

**When the cicadas begin to sing,
it's 90 days 'til the first frost.**

Cicadas are the creepy-looking bugs, about the size of your thumb, that sit in the trees and make a deafeningly-loud buzzing noise on summer afternoons and evenings. Some broods, the periodical cicadas, only emerge every few years (some broods take 17 years!). Others, the annual or "dog-day" cicadas, come out every year. The annual guys are said to predict when we'll get our first frost of the season.

Usually in late July or early August, the males will start their mating routine. They use membranes in their abdomens to create a loud noise meant to attract females. Turns out, the ladies like a guy with rhythm and a loud hummer.

There's no scientific indication that the insects have any kind of long-range weather-predicting abilities or atmospheric sensibilities. But their timing is often relatively good; their mating rituals just happen to keep pace with our average frost patterns.

On average, in Columbus, the season's first frost is around Oct. 10, about 90 days after the cicadas often start making noise. How convenient.

When the annual cicadas begin to sing, many believe that it's a indication that the first frost is only 90 days away. Photo of *Tibicen linnei* by Bruce Marlin, 2003.

Woolly Bears: Can a Caterpillar Really Predict the Weather?

Some people will say the answer is a resounding, "Yes!" Others will tell you the Woolly Bear (aka Woolybear, Woolly Worm) is just about as accurate as the Groundhog.

"Woolly Bear" is the common name for the Isabella Tiger Moth (*Pyrrharctia isabella*) while it's in its larval stage. They're fuzzy with black bands on the ends and an orange band in the middle (although sometimes they can be all black, too). There are also some variations that have up to 13 alternating bands of black and orange.

The folklore says if the middle, orange band is wide, we'll have a mild winter. If the black bands are bigger, it's going to be a severe winter.

Joan from Columbus writes:

The stripes on a woolly bear caterpillar allegedly can predict the severity of the upcoming winter. Meh.
Photo emailed by "Saint Croix."

> "We were at Old Man's Cave today and saw only one wooly worm. It was totally black. What does that mean regarding the weather this winter???"

And Laura from Cambridge says:

> "The weather was talking about woolly worms. What does it mean when they are white? What kind of weather does that mean?"

The different colorations can come from a lot of things. Not every caterpillar conforms to the norm. They're all different, just like people. Some may have more orange or more black or more than three stripes or no stripes at all. It's also possible you've found a wholly different, fuzzy, caterpillar species (there are a bunch of them).

In the late 1940s, Dr. C. H. Curran from New York's American Museum of Natural History began collecting caterpillars and studying their colors. He found a slight correlation between the orange segments and mild winters. But even he acknowledged that the sample size was too small and wasn't proof of anything. He, his wife, and their friends started the Original Society of the Friends of the Woolly Bear and used "the experiment" as a tongue-in-cheek excuse for getting out of the city each autumn.

There is some scientific evidence to suggest that the amount of brown or orange on the caterpillar may actually indicate winter severity. The catch is, it tells us about *last year's* winter, not the coming winter. It is reactive rather than predictive.

It's still very fun folklore. Every autumn for more than 40 years, the folks in Vermillion, Ohio, have held a Woollybear Festival to celebrate! (And legendary, now-retired, Cleveland meteorologist Dick Goddard from FOX8 has been the host for most of them!)

Groundhog Day

The theory goes, if the groundhog pops up on Feb.2, and sees his shadow, he'll run back into his burrow and we'll have six more weeks of winter. If there's no shadow, he's a happy camper, he'll stay above ground and we'll have an early spring.

In truth, the big rodent has a 50-50 chance of getting it right. Punxsutawney Phil (in Pennsylvania) and Buckeye Chuck (in Marion, Ohio) often have different forecasts. They win some and they lose some. But their forecast record isn't much better than just flipping a coin.

As it turns out, there's no statistical correlation between clouds at the beginning of February and warmer temperatures in the next six weeks. Likewise, there's no link between sunshine on 2/2 and extra-wintry conditions for a couple of months.

WMRN's Charlie Evers introduced "Buckeye Chuck" to Central Ohio and he was declared the "Official State Groundhog" by the Ohio General Assembly in 1979. Chuck claims a record of nearly 80% accuracy compared to his Pennsylvania counterpart's less-than 30%.

Besides, spring begins around March 20 anyway, which is conveniently about six weeks after Groundhog Day.

Three Snows After the Forsythia Blooms

A lot of Central Ohioans absolutely swear by this one. And, some years, it's spot on. Look for the bright, yellow blooms of the forsythia bushes to burst forth in the late winter. Once they appear, we only have three snows left for the season.

Given the timing of the Heating Degree Days needed for the bushes to produce flowers (see our earlier discussion on that), they often blossom in late March or early April, sometimes even earlier. When we're in a warm enough cycle to generate the HDDs for forsythia growth, we're on a path toward warmer weather and fewer snows. So, having only three remaining snows is plausible.

The big question, though, is how to count the snows. How widespread does it have to be? How deep? Does a dusting count? It's folklore. It's up to your imagination; there are no set rules.

But is that actually Forsythia?

The bright, yellow blooms of Witch Hazel and Forsythia look very similar. You have to get up close to tell the difference. The witch hazel flowers have stringy, spindly petals attached to a reddish base. The forsythia blossoms have four to six petals attached to a green base and tend to have a "fuller," less wiry appearance. Witch hazel tends to burst forth much earlier in the season, often mid-winter. Witch hazel has even been called "The Queen of Winter." Forsythia usually blooms in late-winter or early-spring.

Witch Hazel   Forsythia

Left: Arnold's Promise Witch Hazel (*Hamamelis x intermedia*) at Schiller Park in German Village with mid-winter blooms; Right: Forsythia (*Forsythia ovata*) in Victorian Village with late-winter blooms.

Funny Fruit Formulates Frosty Forecasts

It's a funny-looking little fruit that looks like an apple, a tomato, and a pumpkin somehow combined their DNA.

The American Persimmon (*Diospyros virginiana*) grows on 30-foot trees that thrive from warm, sun-soaked Florida to the chilly, southern half of Ohio. The fruit is smaller than your fist, starts out green, and turns a bright orange when it's sweet and ripe. The tree's dark wood is solid and strong and was a prized material for making golf clubs. And folklore tells us that persimmons are pragmatic prognosticators. Or at least the seeds are.

Persimmons grow in parts of Ohio and folklore says the seedlings buried deep in the fruit's seeds can predict the forthcoming winter weather..

Before turning your persimmon into pie, sauce, or candy, pull out the seeds and slice them open. You'll find a bright, white shape buried in the gooey, meaty interior. Oddly, those shapes tend to have three, recognizable, culinary variations: knife, fork, and spoon.

Spoon shapes suggest a winter with heavy snow. Fork shapes hint at a mild winter. And knife shapes suggest a very cold winter.

Each persimmon has multiple seeds. Count the number of each shape and create your winter forecast! Slice your persimmons safely and happy forecasting!

ASTRONOMY

Humans have watched the night sky for millions of years. The stars and the heavens have guided generations of storytellers, navigators, and farmers. The Ohio mound builders created enormous earthen monuments to honor the heavens and it's movements. The tiny twinkling lights, high above our heads, have always been an inspiration to us.

Learning about the moon and the stars requires a little more than walking outside on a clear night and looking skyward. It's awe inspiring. The more we learn about our place in the universe, the more fascinating and humbling it becomes.

Staring up at a beautiful, clear sky filled with innumerable stars, it's hard not to feel very, very small. Every one of those twinkling dots in the sky is a star, many of them like our very own sun. Are there other solar systems like ours? Are there other planets like ours? Is it possible that we are alone? All we can do is keep asking questions and keep searching for answers.

Constellations and Stars

In many ways, our universe is regular and predictable. Our current understanding of science and the laws of physics are helping us understand our relationship to the cosmos. We still have a lot to learn but we have come a long way from when our Neanderthal ancestors were first mesmerized by the twinkling lights dancing across the night sky.

Thousands of years ago, our ancestors began noticing patterns in the stars' annual dance. They noticed that some stars only appeared around the time of the harvest. Some constellations hid themselves from view during the cold, dark winter. Certain specks danced independently from sunset until dawn. And the sun and the moon moved in regular intervals east to west and north to south.

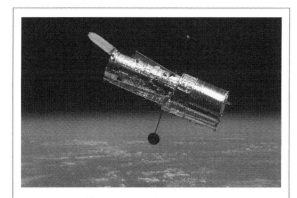

The Hubble Space Telescope looks deep into space and provides glimpses of the workings of our universe. Photo courtesy NASA/ESA.

The timing of their patterns and the relationship between the stars' locations inspired countless stories about the origins of man and the universe. Many of the gods and their stories could be seen right there in the heavens. Orion. Leo. Capricorn. Ares. Hercules. The Pleiades. Every human culture has looked at the stars and wondered about the origins of the universe.

We still do. Incredible tools like the Hubble Space Telescope allow scientists to look back in time as light arrives from the oldest known places in the cosmos. They've been able to catch a fleeting glimpse of the very beginning of the universe. And every answer brings up countless, fascinating, new questions.

Identifying some of the constellations is a good way to start exploring the night sky. Here in the mid-latitudes of the northern hemisphere, it's easy to begin with the "Big Dipper" or "Plough," part of Ursa Major. (Our counterparts in the southern hemisphere might start with the Southern Cross.) On a clear night, look for four bright stars that form a box and three more nearby stars that connect to form a "handle." You've just found your first constellation!

While you're at it, imagine drawing a line up from the far edge of the Big Dipper's bowl, farther into the night sky. The brightest star along that line will be Polaris, the North Star (which also happens to be at the far-end of the Little Dipper's handle).

The only way to explore the constellations is to spend time staring up at the night sky. Take a star chart, an astronomy book, or your favorite astronomy app, get away from the city lights, and find the stars yourself. Let your inner geek shine through. The first time you see the Milky Way or the International Space Station, you'll be amazed at what a thrill it really is!

The Moon

Most of the planets in our solar system have moons. Some have more than others. Our Earth has only one. It doesn't get a fancy name that elicits stories of the ancient gods or conjures up memories of a famous scientist. It's called simply... the moon.

The moon and Venus appear over Broadcast Lake outside the WSYX-WTTE studios, October 4, 2016.

Our moon circles the earth in an orbit roughly 250,000 miles away. In astronomical terms, it's practically on top of us, just a hop, skip, and a jump away. It circles the planet in about 29 days, going in and out of the Earth's shadow and occasionally lining up between us and the sun (see syzygy).

There are a few important things to know about the Earth's moon:

- it is *not* made of green cheese,
- it reflects the sun's light; it doesn't give off its own,
- the "Man in the Moon" is a pattern of shadows created by a series of craters, not an alien drawing,
- despite the wailing of conspiracy theorists, Americans *have* actually visited the moon and they've brought back rocks and surface samples.

Phases of the moon

The moon's cycle or "lunation" takes about 29.5 days[14]. That timing keeps it just slightly out of sync with our Gregorian calendars and allows us to occasionally have two full moons in a single calendar month.

The moon goes through eight distinct phases during each cycle:

On its way from new to full, the moon is "waxing" with the lit portion on the right. As it lunates from full to new, the moon is "waning" with the lit portion to the left.

New Moon	Waxing Crescent	First Quarter	Waxing Gibbous
Full Moon	Waning Gibbous	Last Quarter	Waning Crescent

---

[14] More precisely, lunation takes an average of 29 days, 12 hours, 44 minutes, and 3 seconds.

Moon Names

Both ancient and modern cultures have been so fascinated by the moon that they've given it names for each of its full appearances. Many of the names are related to what's going on at that time of the year or the animals that are active at the time.

January	Wolf Moon	Old Moon	Moon After Yule	Wolf Moon
February	Snow Moon	Snow Moon	Hunger Moon	
March	Worm Moon	Crow Moon	Worm Moon	Sap Moon
April	Pink Moon	Egg Moon	Grass Moon	Fish Moon
May	Flower Moon	Planting Moon	Milk Moon	Flower Moon
June	Strawberry Moon	Strawberry Moon	Rose Moon	Hot Moon
July	Thunder Moon	Hay Moon	Full Buck Moon	
August	Grain Moon	Green Corn Moon	Full Sturgeon	
September	Corn Moon	Harvest Moon	Fruit Moon	Barley Moon
October	Hunter's Moon	Harvest Moon	Travel Moon	
November	Frost Moon	Beaver Moon		
December	Moon Before Yule	Long Night Moon	Cold Moon	

According to *The Old Farmer's Almanac*, "the Harvest Moon is the full Moon that occurs closest to the autumnal equinox." Depending on the timing of the moon's phase, it could happen in September or October.

Blue Moon

When people say, "It only happens once in a blue moon," they mean it's a rare occurrence or that it only happens once in a great while. That's because a Blue Moon only happens once in a great while.

The term "Blue Moon" has nothing to do with shadows or colors of the lunar surface. It's actually about the number of times we see a full moon during a specific period of time. And it has two definitions. There is great debate about which one is acceptable.

The most popular definition is "the second full moon in a calendar month." Since the moon's cycle is

The full moon rises over the Franklin Park Conservatory in Columbus.

roughly 29.5 days, now and then you'll have two full moons in a single month. The timing has to be just right.

The second, much more complex definition involves the number of moons per season. There are roughly three months between an equinox (beginning of spring/fall) and a solstice (beginning of summer/winter). When there are four full moons between a solstice and an equinox (i.e. in a season), the third one is a Blue Moon. You'll note it's not based on the beginning and end of the calendar months, but the dates of the astronomical events. By this definition, a Blue Moon happens only seven times every 19 years.

Incidentally, the way the timing works out, also once every 19 years, there is no full moon in February.

Oh, and a Black Moon, according to Wiccan culture, is the second *new* moon in a calendar month. AstronomyCafe.net says it can also be called a Spinner Moon, Finder's Moon, or Secret Moon.

The Super Moon

From Facebook:

> Angela posted to Marshall McPeek:
>
> Marshall Why are people so excited about a super Moon tonight? what is a super Moon ?

A "supermoon" is a full or new moon that makes a closer-than-average pass by the earth. The moon's orbit is not perfectly round; it's elliptical and slightly off center. So, its distance from the earth changes depending on where it is along its orbital path.

To actually understand the term "supermoon," first we need to suss out a few other words.

> **apogee**: the time, about every 29.5 days, when the moon is at its farthest point to the earth.
>
> **perigee**: the time, about every 29.5 days, when the moon is at its closest point to the earth.
>
> **proxigee**: the closest perigee of the year.
>
> **syzygy**: the straight-line alignment of three or more celestial bodies.

The only real effect of the perigee and apogee is in coastal areas. The moon's gravitational pull on the earth is what causes ocean tides. During perigee, the moon's pull is slightly greater and the tides are a little higher (usually only a few inches).

Astrologer Richard Nolle created the term "supermoon" in 1979 in an article for *Horoscope* magazine and defined it as:

> "...a perigee-syzygy, a new or full moon (syzygy) which occurs when the Moon is at 90% or greater of its mean closest approach to Earth (perigee)."

Given the breadth of that definition, it means many years have four or even six supermoons.

North Pole Sunset with the Moon

When you see the image to the right circulating on the internet, before you send it to your entire address book with a message explaining how, "we'll never see anything like it again in our lifetimes," take a deep breath and, just for a moment, ponder the (astro)physics depicted in the image.

For the moon to look that large in the sky, it would have to be tens of thousands of miles closer to Earth. It also would have to be orbiting much, much faster than it is now; otherwise, the added gravitational pull would bring it crashing into the planet.

This is digital artwork. It's beautiful. But it's fantasy.

It's actually entitled "Hideaway" and was created by German artist Inga Nielsen. She says she created it using a free software download

Image circulating on the internet, usually via email, that comes with a caption saying, "This is the sunset at the North Pole with the moon at its closest point last week. A scene you will probably never get to see in person, so take a moment and enjoy God at work at the North Pole." The original image of a fictional alien landscape was imaginatively created by German artist Inga Nielsen.

called TerraGen by Matt Fairclough. It is prominent on her website, Gate to Nowhere, and was turned into a 2009 calendar cover. Much to Nielsen's surprise, the image has been making the rounds on the internet since at least 2006 and has even been featured by NASA as an Astronomy Photo of the Day[15] (with an explanation of why it's *not* real).

Yes, it's pretty. No, it is not a photo from the north pole. Well, not Earth's north pole anyway.

---

[15] "Hideaway" was the Astronomy Photo of the Day on June 20, 2006.

The Planets

"Mary's violet eyes make John stay up nights (permanently)."

Many of us learned to name the planets, in order, by using a simple phrase, a mnemonic device. Let's be honest, for most of us, "Mercury, Venus, Earth, Mars, Jupiter, Saturn, Uranus, Neptune" doesn't roll off the tongue like poetry. But we can easily remember that John thinks Mary's eyes are as lovely as the heavens themselves.

- Mary's - Mercury
- Violet - Venus
- Eyes - Earth
- Make - Mars
- John - Jupiter
- Stay - Saturn
- Up - Uranus
- Nights - Netpune
- Permanently - Pluto (when Pluto was still considered a planet)

You can make up your own or try these:

- My very early morning jam sandwich usually nauseates people.
- Mother very easily made Jane stop using nail polish.
- Make very easy mash, just squash up new potatoes.
- My very easy method just speeds up naming planets.
- My very energetic mate just swam under North Pier.
- My very energetic mother jumps skateboards under Nan's patio.

In 2006, after Pluto was demoted to "minor planet" by the International Astronomical Union, new phrases popped up to drop the last p-word (including some with more than a hint of sarcasm).

- Many very educated men just screwed up nature.
- Many very elderly men just snooze under newspapers.
- My very educated mother just served us nachos.

Once you can name them, try finding them in the sky. For a few of them, you won't even have to wait until the sun goes down.

Mercury

This one is really difficult to see in Ohio. It tends to sit so close to the horizon that the trees and buildings get in the way. If you can get a good view across Lake Erie or maybe over a wide-open field that's large enough, you might see just enough of the horizon to pick out the little, reddish speck near the time of sunrise or sunset.

Venus

Venus flies high in the sky during most of the year. It shines very brightly; you definitely won't need a telescope to see it. Sometimes it camps out near the moon. Other times you'll see it glistening near the horizon. Keep and eye on the rise-and-set times to get your best view of the second rock from the sun.

Interestingly, Venus orbits the sun in the same direction as the rest of the planets in our solar system, but it rotates backward (from above the north pole, it rotates clockwise, the other planets turn counterclockwise). If you lived there, you'd see the sun rise in the west and set in the east.

Earth

You see this one all the time.

It's big. Really big.

This image of Mercury was created by NASA engineers who stitched together several mosaics that were taken January 14, 2008, by the space agency's Messenger probe.

The Jet Propulsion Laboratory assembled this image of Venus using data and images gathered by NASA's Magellan spacecraft, the Pioneer Venus Orbiter, and several Soviet spacecraft.

Mars

You can see our sister planet, Mars, without a telescope. Sometimes, the bright, little dot even takes on a distinct, reddish hue. Some years are better for seeing Mars than others, depending on its position around the sun, relative to Earth. 2014 provided some outstanding views of the Red Planet.

Scientists have discovered evidence that water once flowed on Mars and it may have been just enough for microbes to evolve on the Martian surface. In 2013, NASA's rover, Curiosity, found actual water in the soil (about 2 percent by weight).

The Mars Hoax

There are lots of false facts running around on the internet and in your email Inbox. A kind viewer sent us a copy of this one that turns up every August. You may have seen it, too.

NASA's Hubble Space Telescope took this picture of Mars on June 26, 2001, when Mars was approximately 43 million miles from Earth, the closest Mars has been to Earth since 1988.

> From: Skip
> Subject: Astronomy Question
> I received the following email last night and am curious as to its validity.
> IT'S AMAZING!
> *Two moons on 27 August*
> *27th Aug the Whole World is waiting for...*
> Planet Mars will be the brightest in the night sky starting in August. It will look as large as the full moon to the naked eye. This will culminate on Aug. 27th when Mars comes within 34.65M miles of earth. Be sure to watch the sky on Aug. 27th 12:30 am. It will look like the earth has 2 moons. The next time Mars may come this close is in 2287.
> Share this with your friends as NO ONE ALIVE TODAY will ever see it again.

This one is just plain false. Mars is still just a little red dot in the sky. It's true that the planets can be slightly closer to each other at certain times, but they can never look as big as the moon. It's a matter of distance. The planets are millions and millions of miles farther away than the moon (it's less than 250,000 miles from here). That's why the moon looks so much bigger. It's that much closer.

A false image of Mars appearing to be as large as the moon makes the email rounds every August. This is hokum. Delete immediately. Do not forward.

Snopes.com helps debunk lots of email myths and reports that this email message started in 2003 when Mars made a close pass by the earth, within a mere 35,000,000 miles. With a telescope, it did, indeed, appear much larger than usual. *With a telescope.*

Bottom line: Mars will never look as big as the moon in our sky. It's not possible. Physics, geometry and optics prevent it. Just delete that email. Don't forward it or post it on Facebook. Please.

Happy stargazing!

Jupiter's Great Red Spot is prominent in this four-image composite from NASA's Cassini spacecraft. The small, dark spot is a shadow from one of Jupiter's moons, Europa.

Jupiter

The largest planet in our solar system also is visible with the naked eye, but still looks only like a bright speck in the night sky. Like the sun, it rises in the east and sets in the west. You'll need a telescope if you want to see it up close and personal; check out the Great Red Spot when you have the planet captured in your viewfinder.

If you're lucky, you may even catch sight of a few of its more than four dozen moons. Io, Europa, Ganymede, and Callisto are the largest. All four were discovered by Galileo in 1610.

NASA JPL launched the Juno space probe on August 5, 2011, to study Jupiter.

Saturn

Like Venus, you'll need nothing more than your eyes to find Saturn dancing across the sky. It shines brilliantly in the morning and evening sky. If you do have a telescope, it's worth pointing it at the sixth planet so you can check out its magnificent rings.

Two images from the Cassini spacecraft were combined to create this phenomenal image of Saturn and its seemingly-delicate rings, May 7, 2004. Image courtesy: NASA/JPL.

As of 2014, Saturn claims at least 62 moons or satellites, excluding its rings. Titan, Enceladus, Mimas (which has a crater that makes it look like the Death Star from "Star Wars"), Rhea and Tethys are some of the largest.

The Cassini spacecraft, after circling and studying Saturn for years, ended its mission by intentionally crashing into the planet in September 2017.

Uranus

For this one, you're going to need a telescope. The gas giant Uranus isn't visible to the un-aided eye. When you see it, you'll notice its distinctive blue-green color. It's an "ice giant" buried under an atmosphere of hydrogen, helium, methane, ammonia, and some water.

It rotates in the same direction as the rest of the planets but it has a peculiar tilt, like it's been knocked over (82°, compared to Earth's 23.5°). At times, its poles are pointed almost directly at the sun, giving it super-extreme seasons. Summer lasts about 21 Earth years!

Neptune

Beautiful, bright blue Neptune is only visible with a telescope. It was first discovered mathematically because of a wobble in Uranus' orbit but wasn't confirmed visually as a planet until 1846. It's an enormous, gas giant with winds estimated to be nearly 1,500 mph. And it has its own Great Dark Spot and a Small Dark Spot storming across its surface.

Covered in clouds, Uranus looked like a smooth, bluish sphere when NASA's Voyager 2 spacecraft snapped this photo in December 1986.

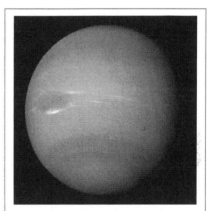

NASA's Voyager 2 captured this image of Neptune in August 1989 showing the Great Dark Spot and the Small Dark Spot along with some wispy, white clouds of methane ice.

Pluto

Poor Pluto. It used to be a planet. It was the smallest, farthest planet in our solar system. But in 2006, after a long, contentious debate, the International Astronomical Union (IAU) changed its definition of "planet." Now our beloved little Pluto is considered a lowly "dwarf planet" meaning, even though it is round and has a moon named Charon, it "has not cleared the neighborhood around its orbit, and is not a satellite."

You'll need a powerful telescope, a descent star chart, and some good tracking skills to find it in the night sky.

"Planet Nine"

In January 2016, scientists at the California Institute of Technology announced they believe they have mathematically discovered another planet in our solar system. While dong some research around the Kuiper Belt, they found an unusual gravitational signature that was affecting other icy objects and cosmic debris. They think the unnamed body "has a mass about 10 times that of earth and orbits 20 times farther from the sun" than Neptune, they said in a news release. They've nicknamed it, "Planet Nine."

Now, they're hoping other scientists can use the calculations and find physical evidence of a giant planet in the super-distant reaches of our solar system.

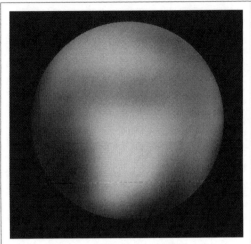

Before 2015, we didn't have any close-up pictures of Pluto. NASA, the European Space Agency, and Marc W. Buie of the Southwest Research Institute used images from the Hubble Telescope to create "best-fit color image/maps" like the one above.

Now, thanks to NASA's New Horizons spacecraft, we have incredible, high-resolution images like this showing Pluto's surface features and its enormous "heart".

The planets appear in the night and twilight sky throughout the year. And sometimes they may seem to flicker, pulse, or even change color. It's not a UFO (this time). It's just our celestial neighbors.

Mike sent a question by email:

> Hi Marshall
> I have noticed the most twinkling star (?) in the south-eastern sky every morning at 6 a.m. at about 20 degrees. It seems to change color from blue to red to white. Could it be a pulsar or what is this heavenly body? Someone told me it was Venus but I don't think the south-east location is correct for it to be Venus. Thank you!
> Mike

Around the time he sent his message, both Jupiter and Venus had been in the eastern, early-morning sky, as they often are.

The color changes he saw were caused much closer to home, not by the planets themselves. The light reflected from the planets arrives here very steadily, but the Earth's atmosphere can play tricks with it. Ripples in the atmosphere can refract and distort the light which is why stars (and planets) sometimes seem to "twinkle" or even change color.

If you see the same light from outside our protective atmosphere, it will appear almost exactly the same the way it left the stars and planets.

Meteor Showers

It's amazing how much stuff is flying around in space. And little pieces of rock and ice get pulled in by Earth's gravity all the time. Almost all of it burns up as it careens through the atmosphere, creating a ball of fire with a trail of ash, steam, and dust.

Those fireballs are meteors. If the pieces actually make it to the ground, they're called meteorites.

Thousands of meteors flash through the sky every month. The daytime sky is (usually) too bright for us to see them. But they make quite a show in the inky nighttime sky. They look almost like stars falling from the heavens; that's how they picked up the nickname "shooting stars" or "falling stars."

There are dozens of meteor showers every year. Some are more spectacular than others with more frequent flashes and streaks. They happen when the earth passes through a particularly dusty part of the solar system. And each shower appears to come from a

A meteor streaks through the night sky near San Jose, California, during the 2009 Leonid Meteor Shower. (Photo by Navicore, via Wikipedia.)

particular point in the night sky. Most are named for the constellation from which they emanate.

The best displays are usually after midnight local time. If you're lucky, your favorite shower will coincide with a new moon when there's less light to ruin the show.

There's a lull between the Quarantids in January and the Lyrids in April.

To know where to look, find the constellation for which the shower is named (Orionids = Orion, Leonids = Leo) and watch that area of the dark, night sky.

Camelopardalids

The Camelopardalids first appeared in May 2014. Well, they were supposed to anyway. Astronomers predicted they could produce a spectacular show as the earth passed through the dust trail of a comet that was first discovered in 2004 and labeled "209P/Linear." The debris was left behind sometime during a pass in the 1800s. This was a shower that had the potential to rival the spectacular Perseids that streak across the sky every August.

The meteors were expected to radiate out from a constellation called "the giraffe," or Camelopardalis, near Polaris, the North Star.

Umm, yeah. If you stayed up all night on May 24, you got nothing more than a stiff neck. Bupkis. The Camelopardalids turned out to be a complete dud. Meh. It happens.

Meteor Shower Calendar	
Date Range	Meteor Shower
Jan 1 to 10	Quarantids
Apr 16 to 25	Lyrids
Apr 19 to 26	Eta Aquariids
Jul 11 to Aug 10	Alpha Capricornids
Jul 13 to Aug 26	Perseids
Jul 21 to Aug 23	Delta Aquariids
Sep 7 to Nov 19	Southern Taurids
Oct 4 to Nov 14	Orionids
Oct 7 to 8	Draconids
Oct 19 to Dec 10	Northern Taurids
Nov 5 to 30	Leonids
Dec 4 to 16	Geminids
Dec 17 to 23	Ursids

Perseids

The Perseids are often one of the best meteor showers of the year.

Find a dark place, away from the city lights, a few hours before dawn. Take a lawn chair or a blanket so you can be comfortable staring at the sky for extended periods of time. Then just lie back and watch the show. When the shower peaks, usually close to Aug. 12 or 13, you should see 60 to 80 meteors every hour. Yes, one or two a minute. It's very cool!

The Perseids are pieces of dust burning up in Earth's atmosphere as we pass through the debris stream of the Swift-Tuttle Comet. We hit it every August. The comet itself is long gone, but it left a trail millions of miles long.

As the dust particles hit the earth's atmosphere, they burn up. Vaporize. We see them as streaks in the night sky.

The best concentration of "shooting stars" will be near the constellation "Perseus," (that's how they get the name "Perseids"). The easiest thing to do is just keep watching the Northeast sky between 2:00 a.m. and dawn (about 6:30 a.m.). Try not to focus too much. Using your peripheral vision is best. You won't miss them!

Leonids

In mid-November, the Leonids light up the night sky as we pass through the debris left behind by the Tempel-Tuttle comet. At their peak, in a very dark sky, away from the city lights, you can sometimes see up to 100 meteors per hour streaking across the sky. They will appear to emanate from the constellation Leo.

The Leonids tend to be brighter than some of the other showers and many of the debris particles are large enough to create long, lingering trails. Viewing is best when the shower coincides with a new moon but some of the meteors are vivid enough to be seen even in bright moonlight.

Geminids

Pull on a heavy coat and head out into the cold if you want to catch the Geminids as the streak across the dark, night sky. They usually peak in mid-December but they're active for the first-half of the month.

Look for the constellation Gemini and follow it across the sky from late-evening until dawn. The meteors will seem to radiate out from the celestial twins.

They're brilliant and should be easy to see, even if the moon is bright. And, if you're lucky, you might notice they fall toward the earth in spectacular colors.

International Space Station

Seeing the International Space Station is a "geek moment," to be sure. Once you've done it, you'll feel compelled to do it over and over again.

The ISS soars about 250 miles above the earth at more than 17,000 miles per hour. With the combination of its forward momentum and the pull of Earth's gravity, the ISS is, literally, falling around the planet. The station is well within the planet's gravity field but because it is in constant free fall, it creates weightlessness.

Astronauts from around the globe spend months in the station's microgravity environment performing experiments that help ground-based scientists test theories, invent new products, and create new scientific techniques.

You can see the ISS each time its orbit brings it over Ohio. No telescope needed. Sometimes, when the orbit is just right, you can see it several times in a single night. It only takes about 92 minutes for it to fly all the way around the planet.

NASA's website has a calculator that will help you determine when the ISS is going to pass overhead and from what direction. At the designated time, look for a large, bright "star" that moves quickly, in a straight line, across the sky. If you're watching at the right time, you won't miss it. And you'll never forget it.

Other Satellites

Other satellites fly over Ohio all the time, too. They're usually much fainter but you can still see them with the naked eye.

Find a dark place, away from the bright lights of the city, and stare up at the sky for a little while. Be patient. Sometimes it takes quite a while before you spot one. It will look like any other star, just a speck in the night sky. Except it'll move.

This image of the ISS was taken as the Space Shuttle Atlantis was moving away from the station after undocking in May 2010. Image courtesy: NASA/STS-132

Some track slowly. Some move more quickly. It depends on their orbit.

Throw down a blanket, lie down and get comfortable, then let your eyes wander the sky. Be aware of your peripheral vision. Like meteors, satellites like to lurk there.

Some satellites you won't be able to see so easily because they don't appear to move. They are in a geosynchronous orbit (they stay in the same place over the earth) at 22,300 miles above the planet. Like the ISS, they're falling around the planet but they're also going fast enough to keep up with the earth's rotation -- that's really, really fast.

CENTRAL OHIO CLIMATOLOGY

"Climate is what we expect, weather is what we get."

- [questionably attributed to] Mark Twain

Climate v. Weather

With the political debate about climate change and the warming of the atmosphere, it is important to understand the difference between climate and weather.

In general, weather refers to the day-to-day conditions that are covered by your local forecast. Climate is the long-term average conditions covering decades, centuries, and millennia. A recent analogy held that climate is like your personality while weather is akin to your daily mood.

When scientists discuss climate change, they are talking about the long-term averages. Despite the passionate discussions, a single, super-hot summer or one brutally-cold winter is not direct evidence of climate change.

Climatologists and meteorologists ask different kinds of questions. Like these:

Climatologists ask: How much have sea surface temperatures risen or fallen in the past 10 to 50 years? Are average polar temperatures warmer or colder now compared to 100 or 1,000 years ago? What compositional changes have happened in our atmosphere in the past 200 years?

Meteorologists ask: How warm are sea surface temperatures this season and how will that affect this season's hurricanes? How cold is the polar air mass that is moving into our forecast region this week? Will an Ozone Action Day be necessary today given the particle pollution in the air?

Record highs and record lows are fascinating statistics. Meteorologists love to keep track of them. But record highs and lows are daily anomalies and are not useful in a climatological discussion. One cold winter doth not an ice age make; a sizzling summer maketh not a global catastrophe. However, raise or lower the global average temperatures by two or three degrees on a consistent, long-term basis and you've got real trouble on your hands.

Holiday & Event Climatology

Long-range forecasting is very, very difficult.

We can't tell you what the exact temperature will be or whether it will be raining during your graduation/wedding/picnic six months from now. But we can use some climatological data to get a feel for the general characteristics of that time of year.

For some cases, the best forecast is actually persistence. In other words, what has happened before is likely to continue; today's weather is likely to be similar to yesterday's weather. It's not a fantastic way to create a forecast but it still has a chance of being right.

A better way to forecast long range is with averages. If you can discern what is typical for a given day, there's a good chance that's what will happen again. The averages exist because those conditions tend to happen more frequently than the extremes. By knowing the climatology of a particular day or week, we can make a decent guess as to what the weather *might* be like during that same sample period in the future.

While it can't replace the accuracy of a meteorological forecast within 24 hours of the event, a climatological prediction stands a pretty good chance of being close.

In the following pages, we'll look at the climatological data for specific events and holidays. We'll see some records and some averages. And we'll get a feel for the general weather patterns during those times of the year.

Columbus Area Climatology at a Glance (1871-2017)

Average Annual Temperatures

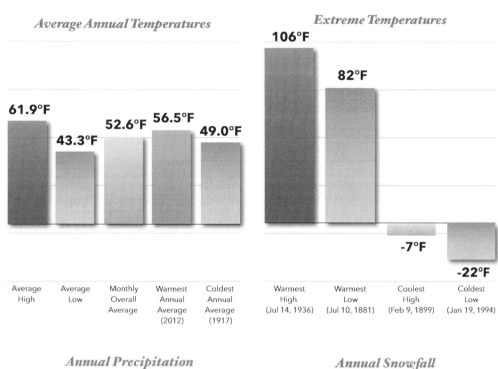

Average High	Average Low	Monthly Overall Average	Warmest Annual Average (2012)	Coldest Annual Average (1917)
61.9°F	43.3°F	52.6°F	56.5°F	49.0°F

Extreme Temperatures

Warmest High (Jul 14, 1936)	Warmest Low (Jul 10, 1881)	Coolest High (Feb 9, 1899)	Coldest Low (Jan 19, 1994)
106°F	82°F	-7°F	-22°F

Annual Precipitation

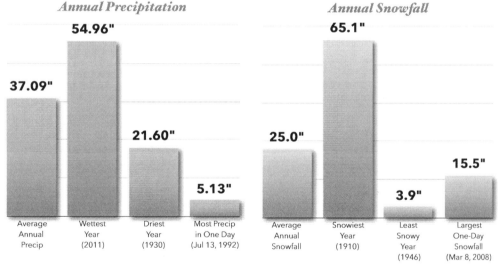

Average Annual Precip	Wettest Year (2011)	Driest Year (1930)	Most Precip in One Day (Jul 13, 1992)
37.09"	54.96"	21.60"	5.13"

Annual Snowfall

Average Annual Snowfall	Snowiest Year (1910)	Least Snowy Year (1946)	Largest One-Day Snowfall (Mar 8, 2008)
25.0"	65.1"	3.9"	15.5"

January at a Glance

Average Temperatures

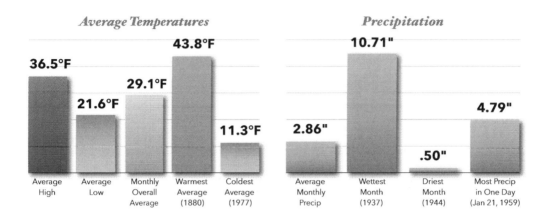

36.5°F — Average High
21.6°F — Average Low
29.1°F — Monthly Overall Average
43.8°F — Warmest Average (1880)
11.3°F — Coldest Average (1977)

Precipitation

2.86" — Average Monthly Precip
10.71" — Wettest Month (1937)
.50" — Driest Month (1944)
4.79" — Most Precip in One Day (Jan 21, 1959)

Extreme Temperatures

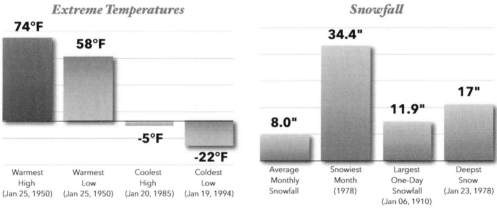

74°F — Warmest High (Jan 25, 1950)
58°F — Warmest Low (Jan 25, 1950)
-5°F — Coolest High (Jan 20, 1985)
-22°F — Coldest Low (Jan 19, 1994)

Snowfall

8.0" — Average Monthly Snowfall
34.4" — Snowiest Month (1978)
11.9" — Largest One-Day Snowfall (Jan 06, 1910)
17" — Deepst Snow (Jan 23, 1978)

Avg. Frequency of Precip

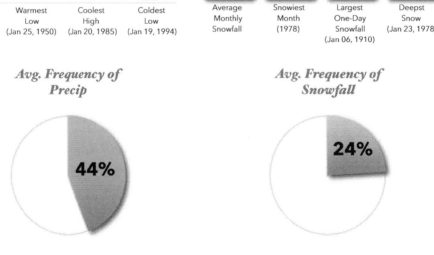

44%

Avg. Frequency of Snowfall

24%

New Year's Day Climatology

The average New Year's Day in the Columbus area is mostly cloudy with a high temperature around 39°F and a roughly 70% chance of rain or snow. Where there is snow on the ground, it averages about 1" deep.

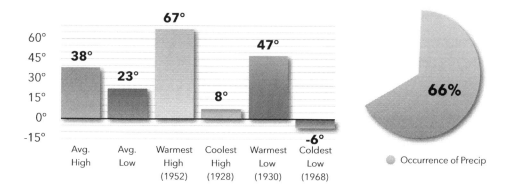

○ Occurrence of Precip

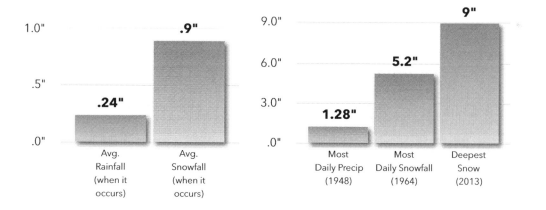

Based on data for the Columbus area, January 1, 1879-2018.

Rev. Dr. Martin Luther King, Jr., Day Climatology

The average Rev. Dr. Martin Luther King, Jr., Day in the Columbus area is mostly cloudy with a high temperature around 35°F and a roughly 70% chance of rain or snow.

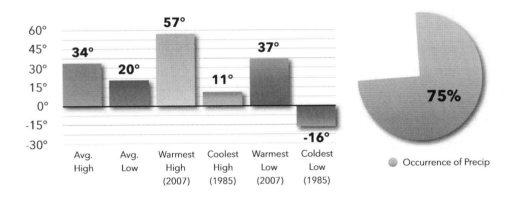

Occurrence of Precip

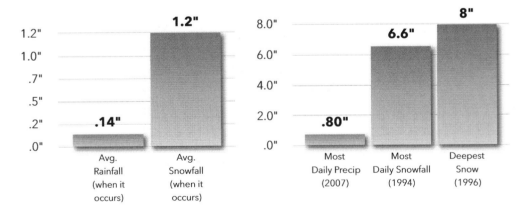

Based on data for the Columbus area, the third Monday of January, 1983-2018.

February at a Glance

Average Temperatures

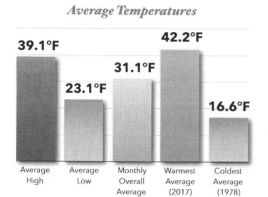

39.1°F — Average High
23.1°F — Average Low
31.1°F — Monthly Overall Average
42.2°F — Warmest Average (2017)
16.6°F — Coldest Average (1978)

Precipitation

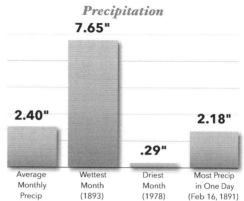

2.40" — Average Monthly Precip
7.65" — Wettest Month (1893)
.29" — Driest Month (1978)
2.18" — Most Precip in One Day (Feb 16, 1891)

Extreme Temperatures

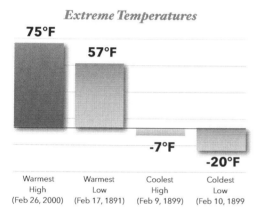

75°F — Warmest High (Feb 26, 2000)
57°F — Warmest Low (Feb 17, 1891)
-7°F — Coolest High (Feb 9, 1899)
-20°F — Coldest Low (Feb 10, 1899)

Snowfall

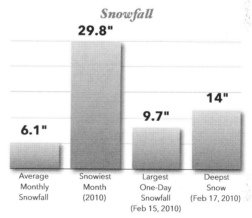

6.1" — Average Monthly Snowfall
29.8" — Snowiest Month (2010)
9.7" — Largest One-Day Snowfall (Feb 15, 2010)
14" — Deepst Snow (Feb 17, 2010)

Avg. Frequency of Precip

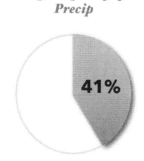

41%

Avg. Frequency of Snowfall

21%

Valentine's Day Climatology

The average Valentine's Day in the Columbus area is mostly cloudy with a high temperature around 40°F and a nearly 70% chance of rain or snow.

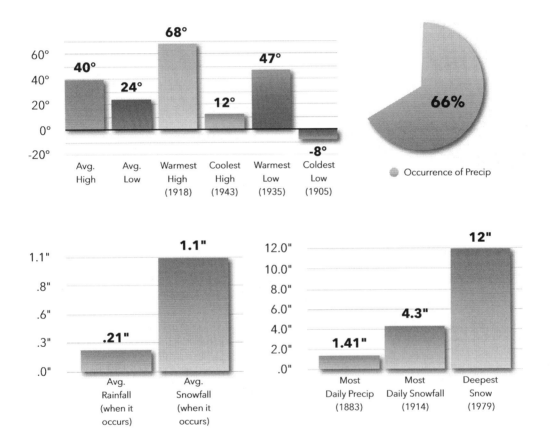

Based on data for the Columbus area, February 14, 1879-2018.

Presidents' Day Climatology

The average Presidents' Day in the Columbus area is mostly cloudy with a high temperature around 43°F and a roughly 60% chance of rain or snow.

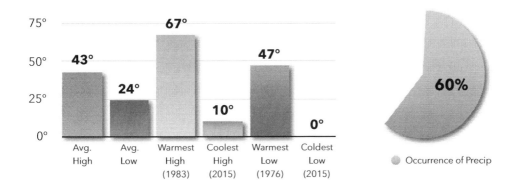

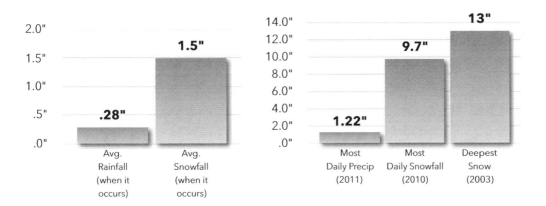

Based on data for the Columbus area, the third Monday of February, 1971-2018.

March at a Glance

Average Temperatures

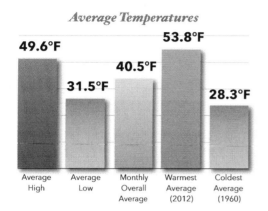

- 49.6°F — Average High
- 31.5°F — Average Low
- 40.5°F — Monthly Overall Average
- 53.8°F — Warmest Average (2012)
- 28.3°F — Coldest Average (1960)

Precipitation

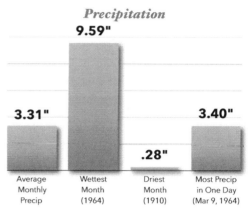

- 3.31" — Average Monthly Precip
- 9.59" — Wettest Month (1964)
- .28" — Driest Month (1910)
- 3.40" — Most Precip in One Day (Mar 9, 1964)

Extreme Temperatures

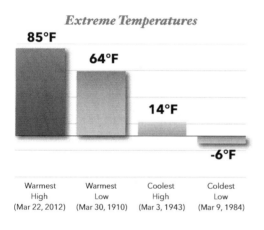

- 85°F — Warmest High (Mar 22, 2012)
- 64°F — Warmest Low (Mar 30, 1910)
- 14°F — Coolest High (Mar 3, 1943)
- -6°F — Coldest Low (Mar 9, 1984)

Snowfall

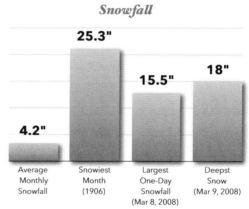

- 4.2" — Average Monthly Snowfall
- 25.3" — Snowiest Month (1906)
- 15.5" — Largest One-Day Snowfall (Mar 8, 2008)
- 18" — Deepst Snow (Mar 9, 2008)

Avg. Frequency of Precip

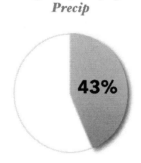

43%

Avg. Frequency of Snowfall

14%

St. Patrick's Day Climatology

The average St. Patrick's Day in the Columbus area is mostly cloudy with a high temperature around 49°F and a roughly 60% chance of rain or snow.

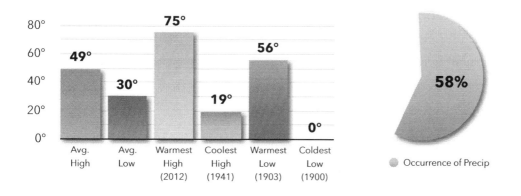

58%

○ Occurrence of Precip

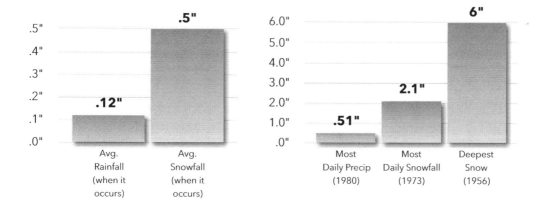

Based on data for the Columbus area, March 17, 1879-2018.

Easter Sunday Climatology

The average Easter Sunday in the Columbus area is mostly cloudy with a high temperature around 60°F and a roughly 60% chance of rain.

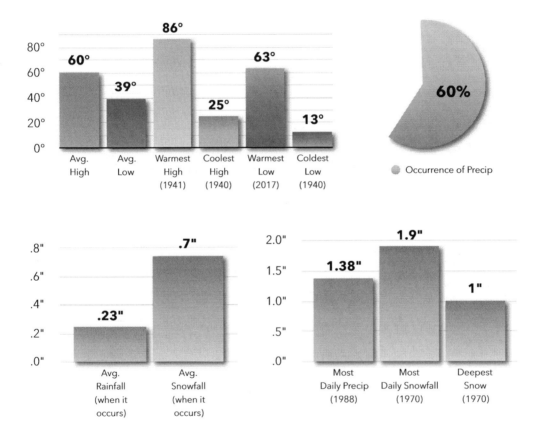

Based on data for the Columbus area, Easter Sunday, 1879-2018.

April at a Glance

Average Temperatures

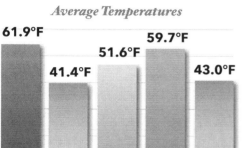

61.9°F	41.4°F	51.6°F	59.7°F	43.0°F
Average High	Average Low	Monthly Overall Average	Warmest Average (2017)	Coldest Average (1907)

Precipitation

3.26"	7.14"	.67"	2.30"
Average Monthly Precip	Wettest Month (2011)	Driest Month (1971)	Most Precip in One Day (Apr 19, 1940)

Extreme Temperatures

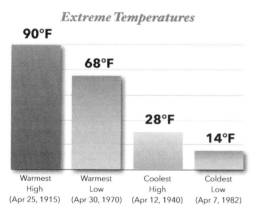

90°F	68°F	28°F	14°F
Warmest High (Apr 25, 1915)	Warmest Low (Apr 30, 1970)	Coolest High (Apr 12, 1940)	Coldest Low (Apr 7, 1982)

Snowfall

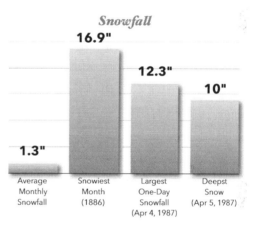

1.3"	16.9"	12.3"	10"
Average Monthly Snowfall	Snowiest Month (1886)	Largest One-Day Snowfall (Apr 4, 1987)	Deepst Snow (Apr 5, 1987)

Avg. Frequency of Precip

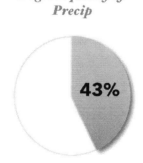

43%

Avg. Frequency of Snowfall

3%

Columbus Crew SC Home Opener Climatology

The average Columbus Crew SC Opening Day in the Columbus area is mostly cloudy with a high temperature around 59°F and a roughly 60% chance of rain.

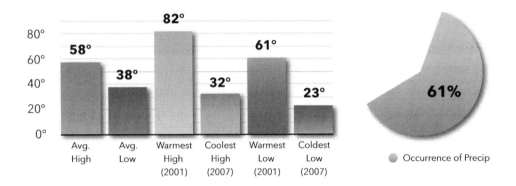

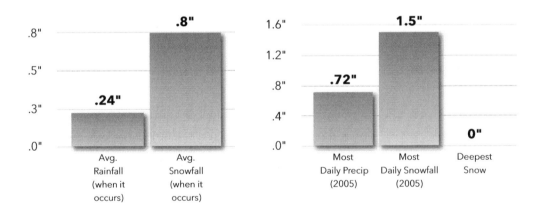

Based on data for the Columbus area, home opening days, 1996-2018.

Earth Day Climatology

The average Earth Day in the Columbus area is mostly cloudy with a high temperature around 64°F and a roughly 60% chance of rain. Since 1970, only one Earth Day has included snowfall in Columbus; a trace in 1986.

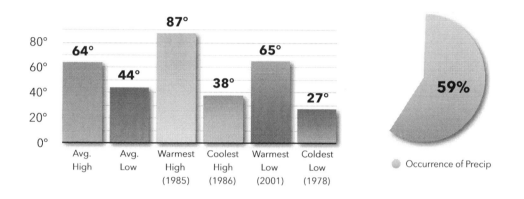

Occurrence of Precip

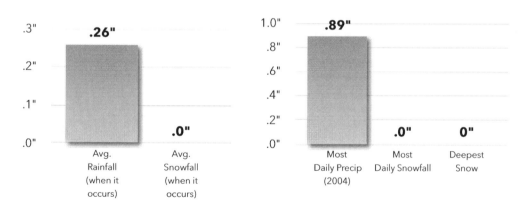

Based on data for the Columbus area, April 22, 1970-2018.

May at a Glance

Average Temperatures

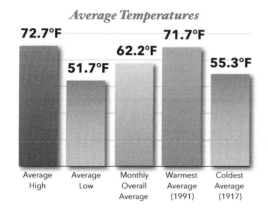

72.7°F — Average High
51.7°F — Average Low
62.2°F — Monthly Overall Average
71.7°F — Warmest Average (1991)
55.3°F — Coldest Average (1917)

Precipitation

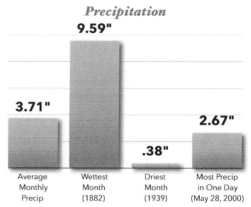

9.59" — 3.71" — .38" — 2.67"

Average Monthly Precip
Wettest Month (1882)
Driest Month (1939)
Most Precip in One Day (May 28, 2000)

Extreme Temperatures

96°F — Warmest High (May 31, 1895)
75°F — Warmest Low (May 26, 1880)
37°F — Coolest High (May 9, 1923)
25°F — Coldest Low (May 10, 1966)

Snowfall

.8" — .8"
.0" — 0"

Average Monthly Snowfall
Snowiest Month (1989)
Largest One-Day Snowfall (May 7, 1989)
Deepst Snow

Avg. Frequency of Precip

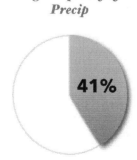

41%

Avg. Frequency of Snowfall

Memorial Day Climatology

The average Memorial Day in the Columbus area is partly cloudy with a high temperature around 77°F and a roughly 50% chance of rain.

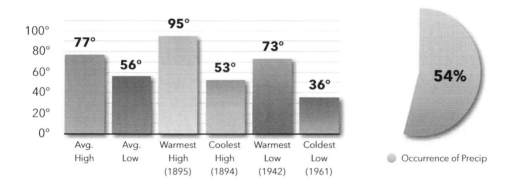

Occurrence of Precip

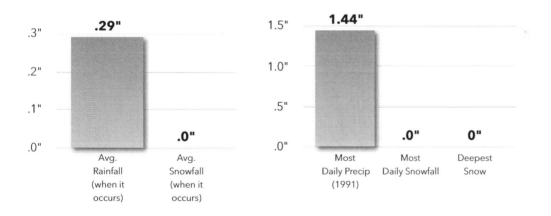

Based on data for the Columbus area, Memorial Day, 1879-2018.

Memorial Tournament Climatology

The average Memorial Tournament Days in the Columbus area are partly cloudy with a high temperature around 77°F and a roughly 50% chance of rain.

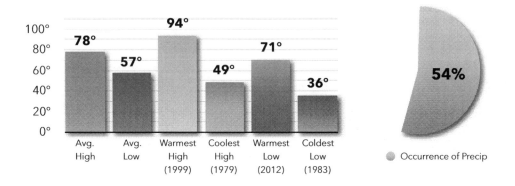

78°	57°	94°	49°	71°	36°
Avg. High	Avg. Low	Warmest High (1999)	Coolest High (1979)	Warmest Low (2012)	Coldest Low (1983)

54%

● Occurrence of Precip

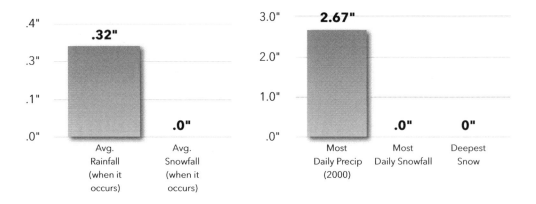

.32"	.0"
Avg. Rainfall (when it occurs)	Avg. Snowfall (when it occurs)

2.67"	.0"	0"
Most Daily Precip (2000)	Most Daily Snowfall	Deepest Snow

Based on data for the Columbus area, tournament days (Thursday through Sunday), 1976-2018.

The monument to Chief Leatherlips overlooks the Scioto River in a park near Dublin.

Wyandot Chief Leatherlips (Shateyoranyah) was executed by his own tribe in 1810 for being loyal to the local white settlers. Many people think he still haunts the Dublin area, specifically, the Muirfield Village Golf Club. His burial site is said to be in the trees just beyond the practice fairway. He is said to have cursed the area because of the crowds, traffic and disruption caused by the annual Memorial Tournament. That, they say, is why it rains on the tournament almost every year: the Curse of Chief Leatherlips.

In a June 1, 1977, article, the Associated Press reported that Barbara Nicklaus, the wife of course designer and tournament founder Jack Nicklaus, once tried to placate Leatherlips, hoping that he would lift the curse. She reportedly left a glass of gin at the Leatherlips Monument and at his burial site. It kept raining.

June at a Glance

Average Temperatures

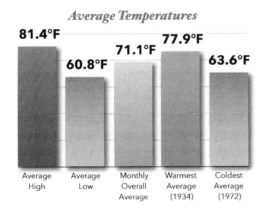

81.4°F — Average High
60.8°F — Average Low
71.1°F — Monthly Overall Average
77.9°F — Warmest Average (1934)
63.6°F — Coldest Average (1972)

Precipitation

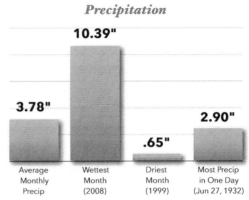

3.78" — Average Monthly Precip
10.39" — Wettest Month (2008)
.65" — Driest Month (1999)
2.90" — Most Precip in One Day (Jun 27, 1932)

Extreme Temperatures

102°F — Warmest High (Jun 28, 1944)
77°F — Warmest Low (Jun 29, 1934)
51°F — Coolest High (Jun 23, 1972)
35°F — Coldest Low (Jun 11, 1972)

Avg. Frequency of Precip

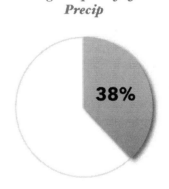

38%

Columbus Arts Festival Climatology

The average Columbus Arts Festival day in the Columbus area is partly cloudy with a high temperature around 79°F and a less than 50% chance of rain.

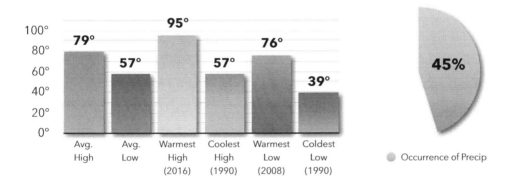

Occurrence of Precip

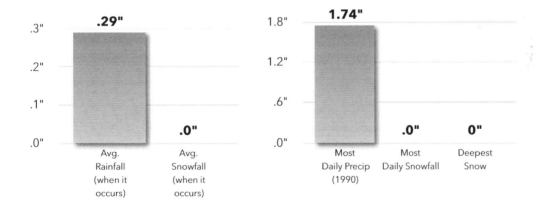

Based on data for the Columbus area, Arts Festival days, 1974-2018.
(Festival data is missing for 1962-1973, 1975, and 1982-1984.)

227

The Arts Festival has racked up 14 daily-record low temperatures, the coldest of which was 39°F on Tuesday, June 5, 1990.

The 2008 festival endured two daily-record high temperatures, both of 92°F, on Friday, June 6, and Sunday, June 8. But the hottest festival day was June 11, 2016, when the thermometer read 95°F.

Five daily-record high temperatures have been recorded on festival days, two of which happened during the 2008 festival, one each in 1989, 2015, and 2016.

A total of 18.46" of rain have fallen on festival days. The heaviest was a deluge of 1.74" on June 8, 1990. Hail was also reported that day. The next wettest day was Thursday, June 1, 2006, with 1.16" rainfall.

1990 Columbus Arts Festival
May 30 - June 9
High Temperatures

The 1990 Arts Festival had wild temperature swings. One day set a record-low of 39°F. Other days during the same festival had high temperatures in the 50s, 60s, 70s, and 80s.

Only three festival days have had more than an inch of rainfall. They happened during celebrations in 1990, 1995, and 2006.

Eighty-five percent of festival days have enjoyed high temperatures of 70°F or warmer. Only seven-percent have been in the 90s.

Tour de Grandview Climatology

The average Tour de Grandview race day in the Columbus area is partly cloudy with a high temperature around 84°F and a roughly 50-50 chance of rain.

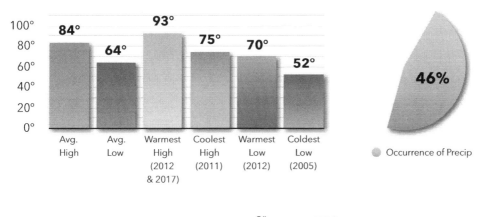

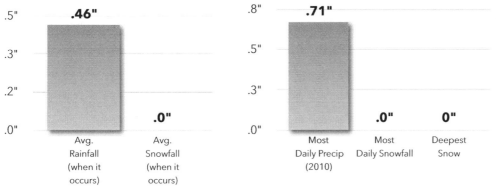

Based on data for the Columbus area, Tour de Grandview race days, 2005-2018.

July at a Glance

Average Temperatures

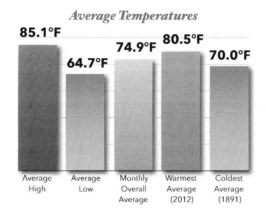

85.1°F — Average High
64.7°F — Average Low
74.9°F — Monthly Overall Average
80.5°F — Warmest Average (2012)
70.0°F — Coldest Average (1891)

Precipitation

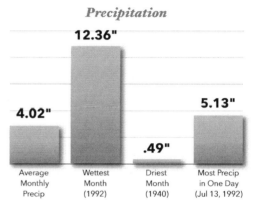

4.02" — Average Monthly Precip
12.36" — Wettest Month (1992)
.49" — Driest Month (1940)
5.13" — Most Precip in One Day (Jul 13, 1992)

Extreme Temperatures

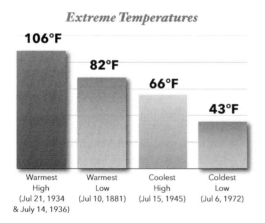

106°F — Warmest High (Jul 21, 1934 & July 14, 1936)
82°F — Warmest Low (Jul 10, 1881)
66°F — Coolest High (Jul 15, 1945)
43°F — Coldest Low (Jul 6, 1972)

Avg. Frequency of Precip

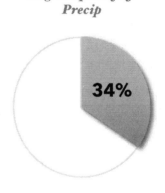

34%

Independence Day Climatology

The average Independence Day in the Columbus area is partly cloudy with a high temperature around 84°F and a roughly 50-50 chance of rain.

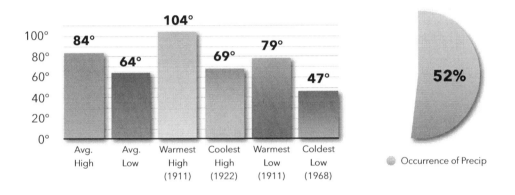

Occurrence of Precip

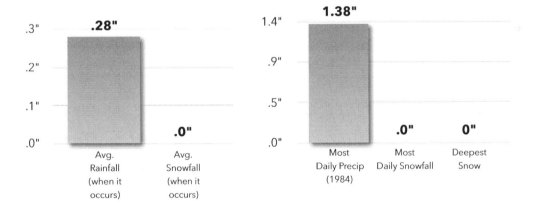

Based on data for the Columbus area, July 4, 1878-2018.

Columbus Jazz & Rib Fest Climatology

The average Columbus Jazz & Rib Fest day in the Columbus area is partly cloudy with a high temperature around 86°F and a roughly 40-50% chance of rain.

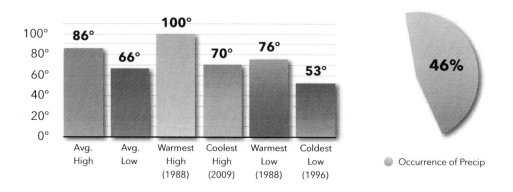

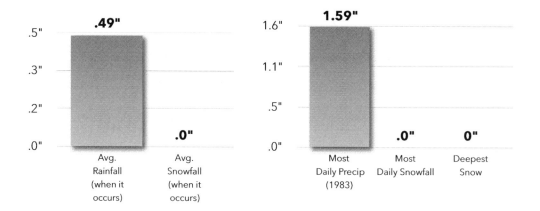

Based on data for the Columbus area, third Friday, Saturday, and Sunday of July 1980-2018.

August at a Glance

Average Temperatures

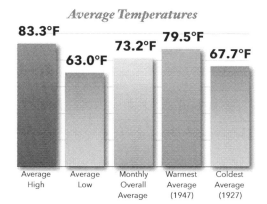

- 83.3°F — Average High
- 63.0°F — Average Low
- 73.2°F — Monthly Overall Average
- 79.5°F — Warmest Average (1947)
- 67.7°F — Coldest Average (1927)

Precipitation

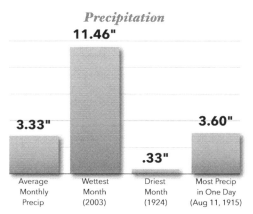

- 3.33" — Average Monthly Precip
- 11.46" — Wettest Month (2003)
- .33" — Driest Month (1924)
- 3.60" — Most Precip in One Day (Aug 11, 1915)

Extreme Temperatures

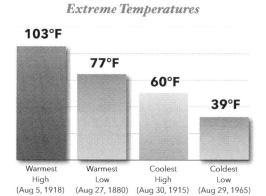

- 103°F — Warmest High (Aug 5, 1918)
- 77°F — Warmest Low (Aug 27, 1880)
- 60°F — Coolest High (Aug 30, 1915)
- 39°F — Coldest Low (Aug 29, 1965)

Avg. Frequency of Precip

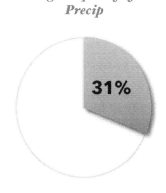

31%

Ohio State Fair Climatology

The average Ohio State Fair day in the Columbus area is partly cloudy with a high temperature around 83°F and a roughly 40% chance of rain.

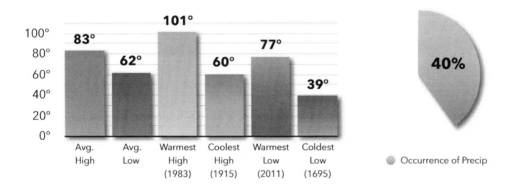

Occurrence of Precip

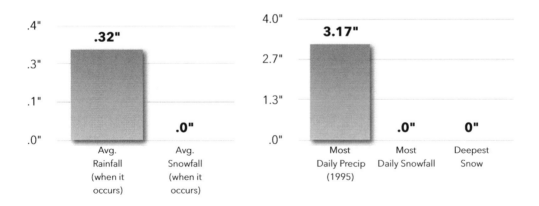

Based on data for the Columbus area, Ohio State Fair days (except 1888 and 1942-1945), 1886-2018.
A total of 1,235 days.

Pelotonia Climatology

The average Pelotonia riding day in the Columbus area is mostly cloudy with a high temperature around 83°F and a nearly 60% chance of rain.

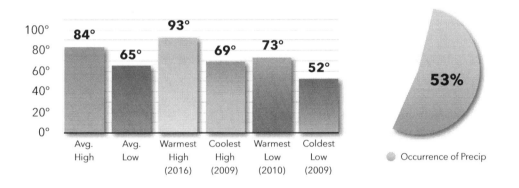

Occurrence of Precip

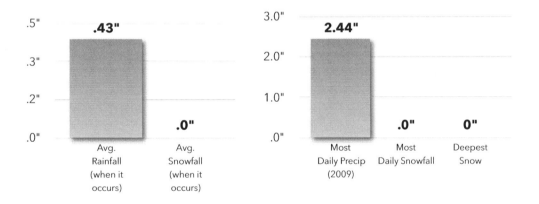

Based on data for the Columbus area, Pelotonia riding days, 2009-2018.

All-Ohio Balloon Festival Climatology

The average All-Ohio Balloon Festival day in the Marysville area is mostly sunny with a high temperature around 83°F and a roughly 40% chance of rain.

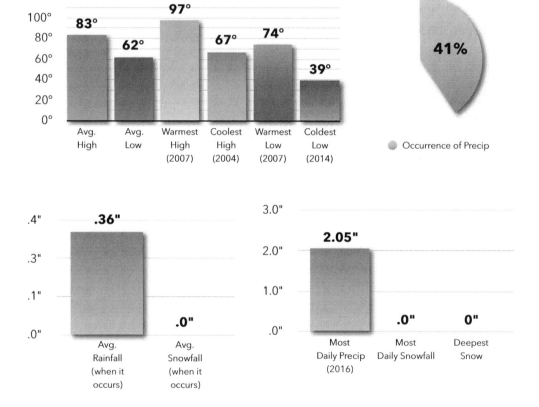

Based on data for the Marysville area, second Thursday, Friday, and Saturday of August, 1975-2018.

Ohio Cup Vintage Base Ball Festival Climatology

The average Ohio Cup Vintage Base Ball Festival day in the Columbus area is mostly sunny with a high temperature around 84°F and a roughly 40% chance of rain.

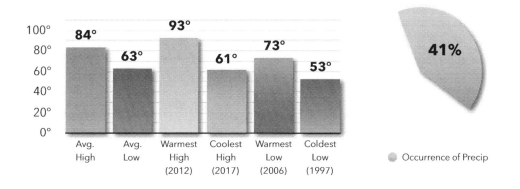

- **84°** Avg. High
- **63°** Avg. Low
- **93°** Warmest High (2012)
- **61°** Coolest High (2017)
- **73°** Warmest Low (2006)
- **53°** Coldest Low (1997)

41% ● Occurrence of Precip

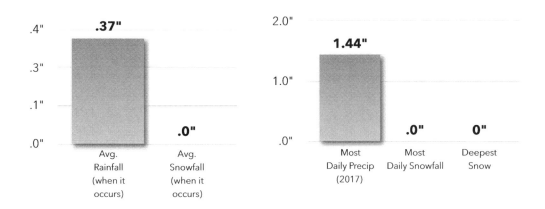

- **.37"** Avg. Rainfall (when it occurs)
- **.0"** Avg. Snowfall (when it occurs)
- **1.44"** Most Daily Precip (2017)
- **.0"** Most Daily Snowfall
- **0"** Deepest Snow

Based on data for the Columbus area, Ohio Cup days, fourth Saturday and Sunday of August, 1996-2018.

September at a Glance

Average Temperatures

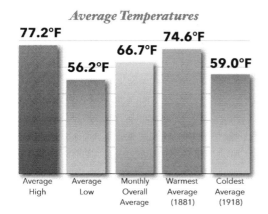

77.2°F — Average High
56.2°F — Average Low
66.7°F — Monthly Overall Average
74.6°F — Warmest Average (1881)
59.0°F — Coldest Average (1918)

Precipitation

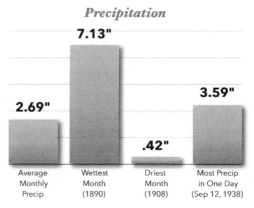

2.69" — Average Monthly Precip
7.13" — Wettest Month (1890)
.42" — Driest Month (1908)
3.59" — Most Precip in One Day (Sep 12, 1938)

Extreme Temperatures

100°F — Warmest (Sep 2, 1953)
75°F — Warmest Low (Sep 10, 2013)
48°F — Coolest High (Sep 29, 1967)
31°F — Coldest Low (Sep 30, 1963)

Avg. Frequency of Precip

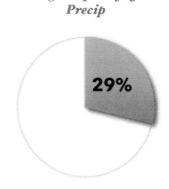

29%

Labor Day Climatology

The average Labor Day in the Columbus area is partly cloudy with a high temperature around 82°F and a roughly 40% chance of rain.

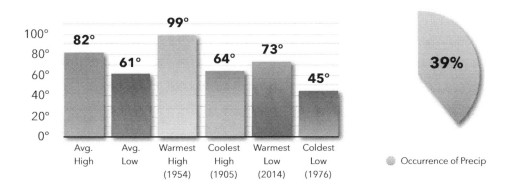

Occurrence of Precip

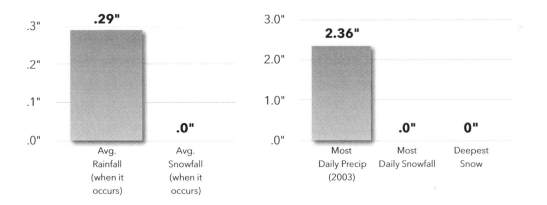

Based on data for the Columbus area, first Monday of September, 1894-2018.

Marion Popcorn Festival Climatology

The average Popcorn Festival day in the Marion area is mostly sunny with a high temperature around 78°F and a roughly 30% chance of rain.

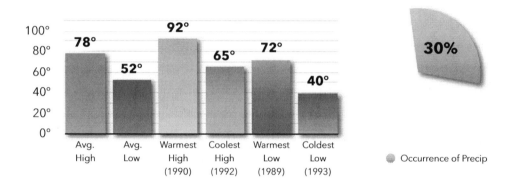

			Warmest High (1990)	Coolest High (1992)	Warmest Low (1989)	Coldest Low (1993)
	Avg. High 78°	Avg. Low 52°	92°	65°	72°	40°

30%

● Occurrence of Precip

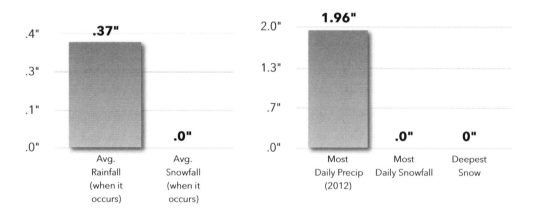

Avg. Rainfall (when it occurs)	Avg. Snowfall (when it occurs)	Most Daily Precip (2012)	Most Daily Snowfall	Deepest Snow
.37"	.0"	1.96"	.0"	0"

Based on data for the Marion area, festival days, first Friday, Saturday and Sunday after Labor Day, 1980-2017.

Little Brown Jug Climatology

The average Little Brown Jug race day in the Delaware area is partly cloudy with a high temperature around 76°F and a roughly 40% chance of rain.

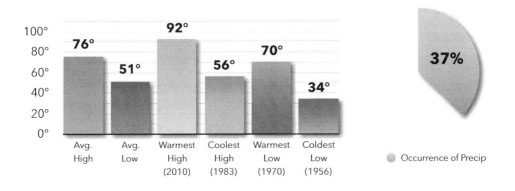

- Occurrence of Precip

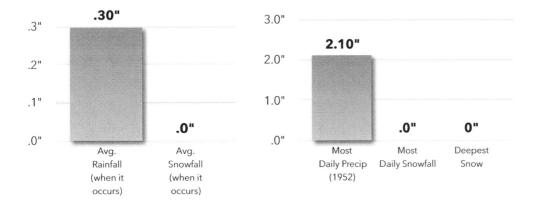

Based on data for the Delaware area (using NOWData from Marysville, the closest reliable reporting station), Little Brown Jug race days, 1946-2018.

October at a Glance

Average Temperatures

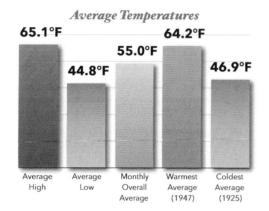

65.1°F — Average High
44.8°F — Average Low
55.0°F — Monthly Overall Average
64.2°F — Warmest Average (1947)
46.9°F — Coldest Average (1925)

Precipitation

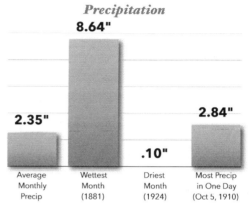

2.35" — Average Monthly Precip
8.64" — Wettest Month (1881)
.10" — Driest Month (1924)
2.84" — Most Precip in One Day (Oct 5, 1910)

Extreme Temperatures

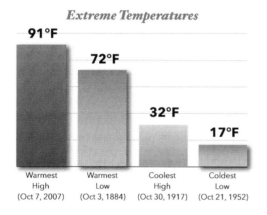

91°F — Warmest High (Oct 7, 2007)
72°F — Warmest Low (Oct 3, 1884)
32°F — Coolest High (Oct 30, 1917)
17°F — Coldest Low (Oct 21, 1952)

Snowfall

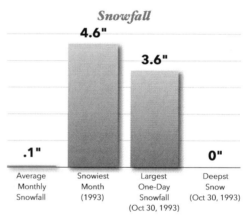

4.6" — Snowiest Month (1993)
.1" — Average Monthly Snowfall
3.6" — Largest One-Day Snowfall (Oct 30, 1993)
0" — Deepst Snow (Oct 30, 1993)

Avg. Frequency of Precip

29%

Avg. Frequency of Snowfall

Columbus Italian Festival Climatology

The average Italian Festival day in the Columbus area is partly cloudy with a high temperature around 70°F and a 30-40% chance of rain.

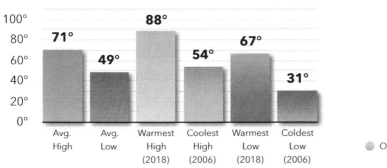

35%

Occurrence of Precip

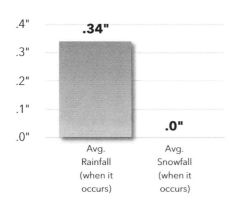

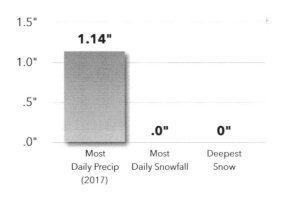

Based on data for the Columbus area, Italian Festival days, 2001-2018.

Columbus Marathon Climatology

The average Columbus Marathon race day in the Columbus area is mostly sunny with a crisp morning, an afternoon high temperature around 64°F, and a roughly 10-20% chance of rain or snow.

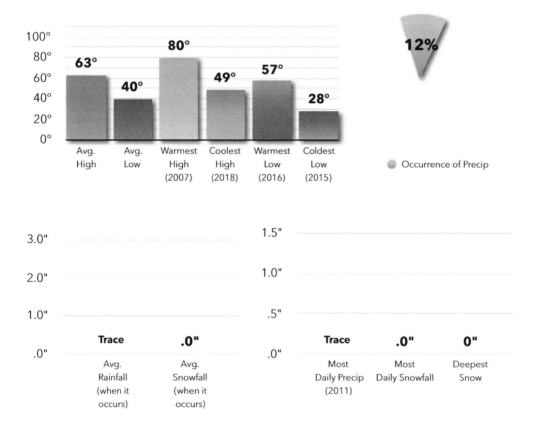

Based on data for the Columbus area, marathon race days, 2002-2018.

Circleville Pumpkin Show Climatology

The average Pumpkin Show day in the Circleville area is partly cloudy with a high temperature around 66°F and a roughly 40% chance of rain or snow.

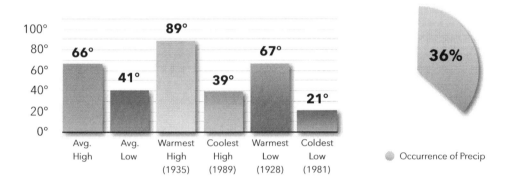

Occurrence of Precip

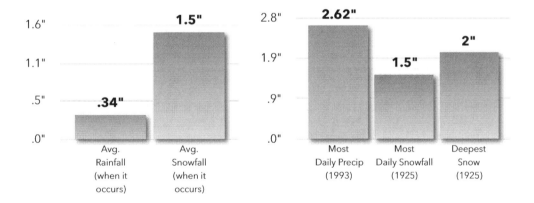

Based on data for the Circleville area, Pumpkin Show Days, third Wednesday through Saturday of October, 1903-2018.

Halloween Climatology

The average Halloween in the Columbus area is mostly cloudy with a high temperature around 60°F and a roughly 50% chance of rain or snow.

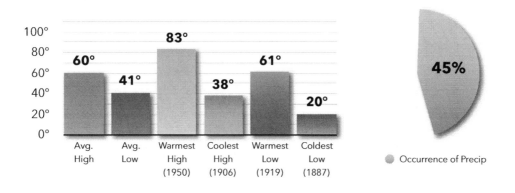

Occurrence of Precip

45%

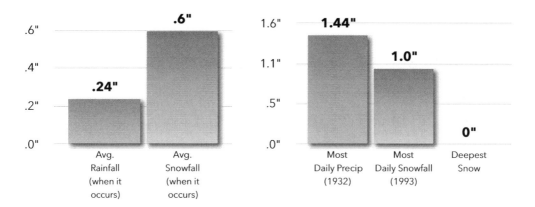

Based on data for the Columbus area, October 31, 1878-2018.

November at a Glance

Average Temperatures

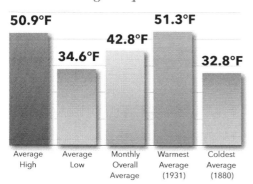

50.9°F	34.6°F	42.8°F	51.3°F	32.8°F
Average High	Average Low	Monthly Overall Average	Warmest Average (1931)	Coldest Average (1880)

Precipitation

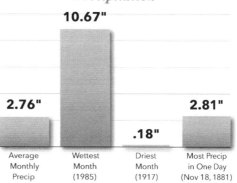

2.76"	10.67"	.18"	2.81"
Average Monthly Precip	Wettest Month (1985)	Driest Month (1917)	Most Precip in One Day (Nov 18, 1881)

Extreme Temperatures

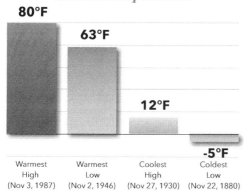

80°F	63°F	12°F	-5°F
Warmest High (Nov 3, 1987)	Warmest Low (Nov 2, 1946)	Coolest High (Nov 27, 1930)	Coldest Low (Nov 22, 1880)

Snowfall

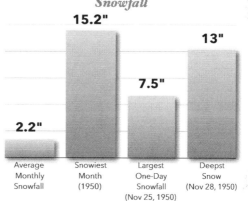

2.2"	15.2"	7.5"	13"
Average Monthly Snowfall	Snowiest Month (1950)	Largest One-Day Snowfall (Nov 25, 1950)	Deepst Snow (Nov 28, 1950)

Avg. Frequency of Precip

37%

Avg. Frequency of Snowfall

7%

Veterans Day Climatology

The average Veterans Day in the Columbus area is mostly cloudy with a high temperature around 53°F and a roughly 50% chance of rain or snow.

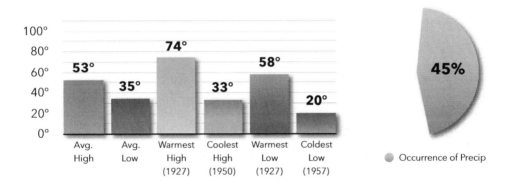

Occurrence of Precip

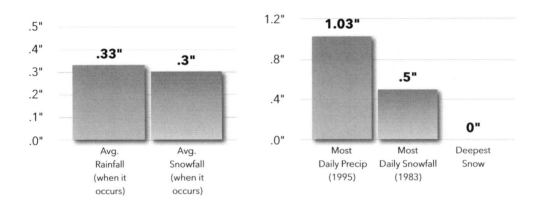

Based on data for the Columbus area, November 11, 1919-2018.

Thanksgiving Climatology

The average Thanksgiving Day in the Columbus area is mostly cloudy with a high temperature around 46°F and a roughly 60% chance of rain or snow.

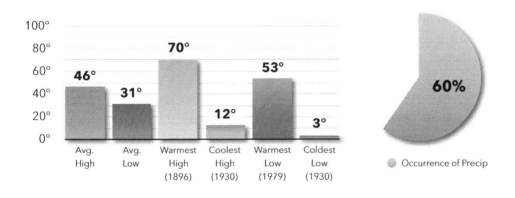

● Occurrence of Precip

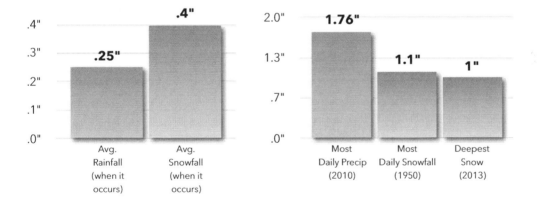

Based on data for the Columbus area, Thanksgiving Day, 1878-2018.

OSU v. Michigan Game Day Climatology

The average OSU v. Michigan game day in the Columbus or Ann Arbor areas is partly cloudy with a high temperature around 48°F and a roughly 40% chance of rain or snow.

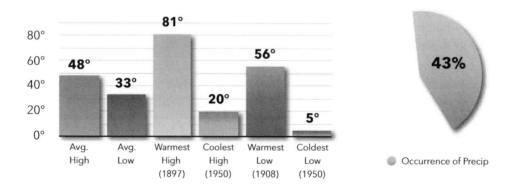

Occurrence of Precip

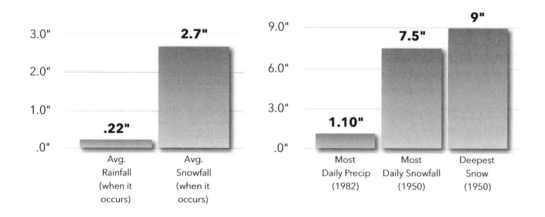

Based on data for the Columbus and Ann Arbor areas, game days, 1897-2018.

December at a Glance

Average Temperatures

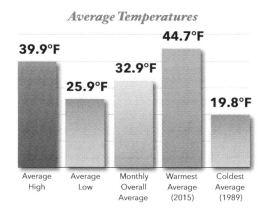

- **39.9°F** — Average High
- **25.9°F** — Average Low
- **32.9°F** — Monthly Overall Average
- **44.7°F** — Warmest Average (2015)
- **19.8°F** — Coldest Average (1989)

Precipitation

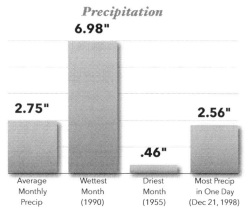

- **2.75"** — Average Monthly Precip
- **6.98"** — Wettest Month (1990)
- **.46"** — Driest Month (1955)
- **2.56"** — Most Precip in One Day (Dec 21, 1998)

Extreme Temperatures

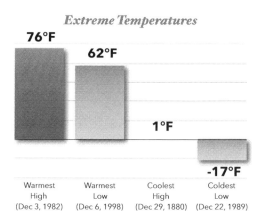

- **76°F** — Warmest High (Dec 3, 1982)
- **62°F** — Warmest Low (Dec 6, 1998)
- **1°F** — Coolest High (Dec 29, 1880)
- **-17°F** — Coldest Low (Dec 22, 1989)

Snowfall

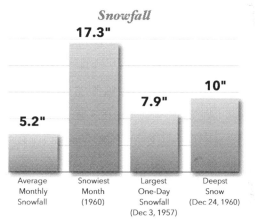

- **5.2"** — Average Monthly Snowfall
- **17.3"** — Snowiest Month (1960)
- **7.9"** — Largest One-Day Snowfall (Dec 3, 1957)
- **10"** — Deepst Snow (Dec 24, 1960)

Avg. Frequency of Precip

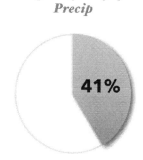

41%

Avg. Frequency of Snowfall

17%

Charity Newsies Collection Day Climatology

The average Charity Newsies Collection Day in the Columbus area is mostly cloudy with a high temperature around 40°F and a roughly 60-70% chance of rain or snow.

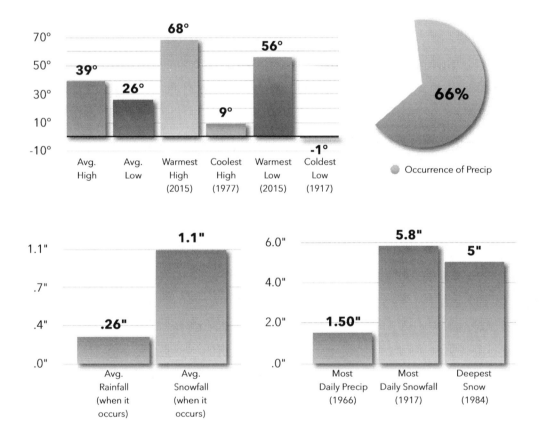

Based on data for the Columbus area, second Saturday of December, 1907-2018.

Christmas Day Climatology

The average Christmas Day in the Columbus area is mostly cloudy with a high temperature around 36°F and a roughly 70% chance of rain or snow.

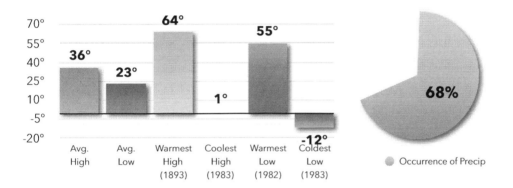

● Occurrence of Precip

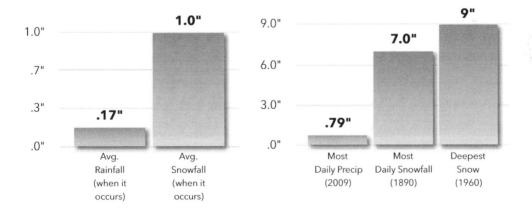

Based on data for the Columbus area, December 25, 1878-2018.

What is a White Christmas?

Let's be honest, a White Christmas is a state of mind. But there are also meteorological definitions for it, too. According to the US National Climatic Data Center, a White Christmas is "a snow depth of at least 1 inch on Christmas morning." Important to note that it's a snow depth, not necessarily new snow. That means whatever is already on the ground counts!

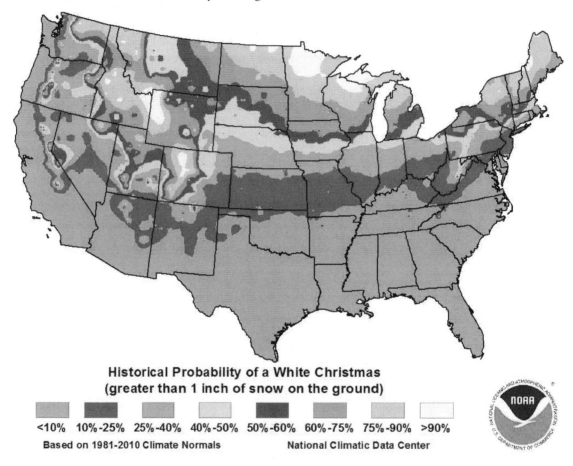

Historical Probability of a White Christmas
(greater than 1 inch of snow on the ground)

<10%   10%-25%   25%-40%   40%-50%   50%-60%   60%-75%   75%-90%   >90%

Based on 1981-2010 Climate Normals   **National Climatic Data Center**

In Ohio, our best chance for a White Christmas is in the far-northeastern corner where they get a lot of lake-effect snow. Cleveland's chances are about 50-50 and Columbus lies on a statistical line that gives us anywhere from a 10% to a 40% chance.

Not everyplace uses the same definition of White Christmas. In the United Kingdom, the Met Office defines a White Christmas as "a single snow flake (perhaps amongst a shower of rain and snow mixed) to be observed falling in the 24 hours of 25 December." Remember that Britain's climate is very different from ours!

New Year's Eve Climatology

The average New Year's Eve in the Columbus area is mostly cloudy with a high temperature around 39°F and a roughly 70% chance of rain or snow.

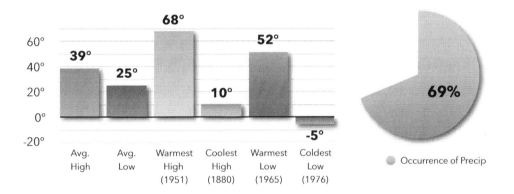

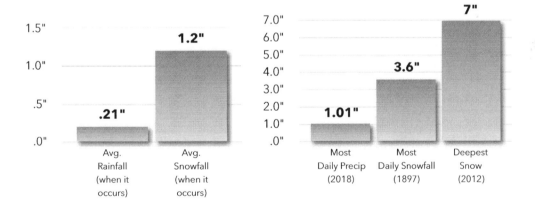

Based on data for the Columbus area, December 31, 1878-2018.

Columbus Daily Record High Temps (Jan - Jun), 1879-2017

	Jan		Feb		Mar		Apr		May		Jun	
1	67	1952	66	1989	65	1997	81	2010	88	1942	96	1934
2	64	2000	64	1903	73	1992	84	2010	88	1959	96	1895
3	64	1950	63	1890	75	1974	80	2010	89	1959	99	1895
4	67	1997	66	1890	78	1976	82	1986	89	1955	97	1895
5	65	1998	64	1986	78	1983	82	1988	92	1952	95	1925
6	68	1946	62	2008	76	1973	84	2010	91	1959	95	1925
7	68	2008	61	1925	77	2009	85	1893	88	2015	95	1933
8	68	2008	72	1937	80	1974	83	2001	89	1936	98	1933
9	62	1949	66	2001	77	1974	83	2013	93	1896	95	1999
10	59	1975	69	1932	79	2009	84	2011	94	1936	98	1911
11	66	1890	74	1999	76	1990	88	1930	92	1896	95	2016
12	67	2017	69	1984	75	1990	86	1930	90	1881	94	1954
13	69	2005	68	1938	78	1990	86	1941	88	2014	95	1956
14	70	1932	68	1918	78	2012	86	1883	91	1991	94	1994
15	64	1932	70	1954	79	1990	84	2010	92	1991	96	1897
16	60	1949	72	1883	79	1945	86	1896	91	1900	96	1957
17	64	2017	67	1911	75	2012	88	1896	92	1900	97	1994
18	68	1996	66	2017	77	1903	89	1896	93	1962	99	1944
19	67	1907	70	1939	78	2012	85	2002	92	1964	98	1994
20	68	1906	77	2018	84	2012	85	1896	91	1962	97	1994
21	72	1906	71	1997	85	2012	86	1987	92	1941	98	1988
22	71	1906	70	1930	85	2012	87	1985	93	1941	97	1988
23	68	1967	72	2017	81	1907	88	1960	90	1939	96	1948
24	66	1950	78	2017	84	1910	88	1960	90	1975	97	1914
25	74	1950	74	2000	84	1929	90	1915	93	1975	101	1988
26	70	1950	75	2000	80	1907	89	1948	94	1911	100	1952
27	68	1916	71	1996	81	2007	88	1990	94	1911	101	1944
28	66	1914	65	2016	83	1910	85	1914	94	1911	102	1944
29	67	2013	70	2012	83	1910	86	1899	94	1914	100	1934
30	65	2013	-	-	82	1998	89	1942	95	1895	99	1901
31	66	2002	-	-	83	1998	-	-	96	1895	-	-

Columbus Daily Record High Temps (Jul - Dec), 1878-2017

	Jul		Aug		Sep		Oct		Nov		Dec	
1	98	1953	97	1955	99	1953	89	1952	80	2016	67	1970
2	98	1911	99	1991	100	1953	88	1919	79	2016	72	1982
3	101	1911	100	1955	99	1953	89	1953	80	1987	76	1982
4	104	1911	99	1955	96	1953	89	1959	78	1987	68	1982
5	98	2012	103	1918	99	1954	90	1951	76	1977	70	2001
6	101	2012	102	1918	99	1954	89	2007	77	1975	73	1998
7	101	2012	98	1918	98	1939	91	2007	78	1938	69	1998
8	102	1936	96	2012	98	1939	90	2007	74	1945	69	1966
9	105	1936	98	1930	95	1939	88	1939	76	1975	66	1952
10	103	1881	98	1944	96	1983	87	2010	72	1949	72	1971
11	104	1936	96	1944	96	1895	86	1928	74	1927	66	2007
12	103	1936	97	1881	96	1897	84	1938	75	1949	68	2015
13	101	1936	98	1936	95	1939	85	1969	74	1955	65	1901
14	106	1936	96	1959	98	1939	86	1897	74	1909	65	2015
15	100	1988	95	1944	97	1939	90	1897	71	1971	64	1971
16	100	1988	96	1913	96	1939	88	1897	72	1953	64	1984
17	100	1887	97	1988	94	1955	83	1968	76	1958	67	1984
18	99	1887	94	1940	95	1955	83	2016	75	2016	63	1967
19	98	1930	101	1936	97	1895	85	1953	73	1985	61	1895
20	101	1934	101	1983	97	1895	84	1953	74	1942	62	1895
21	106	1934	99	1936	96	1895	83	1953	73	1934	69	2013
22	104	1901	98	1936	95	1895	83	1947	74	1931	68	2013
23	99	1933	95	2007	93	2010	83	1947	72	1931	65	2015
24	102	1934	96	2007	92	2010	82	1963	68	1931	66	1889
25	104	1934	99	1959	93	1900	81	1963	68	1908	64	1893
26	102	1934	98	1948	92	2017	83	1963	70	1896	69	2016
27	102	1936	100	1948	92	2017	81	1963	75	1990	68	2008
28	100	1952	97	1948	92	1959	81	1927	71	2005	68	1984
29	98	1940	98	1953	96	1953	80	1922	70	1927	67	1889
30	99	1940	100	1953	92	1953	80	1927	71	1934	63	1964
31	100	1999	98	1953	-	-	83	1950	-	-	68	1951

Columbus Daily Record Low Temps (Jan - Jun), 1879-2017

	Jan		Feb		Mar		Apr		May		Jun	
1	-6	1968	-3	1978	-2	1967	15	1923	30	1978	41	1910
2	-13	1879	-13	1951	0	1980	20	1907	30	1994	39	1966
3	-20	1879	-10	1985	1	1980	18	1879	30	1978	41	1929
4	-10	1879	-9	1985	1	1943	24	1995	31	2005	41	1988
5	-16	1884	-10	1918	1	1978	15	1881	32	1979	39	1990
6	-20	1884	-11	1977	2	1901	19	1881	29	1968	43	1993
7	-7	2014	-2	1977	4	1960	14	1982	31	1974	39	1977
8	-9	1968	-13	1977	-2	1960	19	1972	31	1954	40	1977
9	-5	1979	-17	1899	-6	1984	18	1972	30	1983	39	1913
10	-11	1982	-20	1899	2	1984	20	1997	25	1966	41	1988
11	-11	1886	-11	1885	8	1948	23	1882	33	1997	35	1972
12	-13	1918	-8	1917	1	1948	21	1976	35	1976	43	1980
13	-14	1977	-13	1899	5	1960	21	1920	34	1996	46	1903
14	-14	1964	-8	1905	8	1993	20	1950	34	1996	44	1959
15	-12	1893	-4	1978	4	1993	22	1935	36	1984	47	1959
16	-13	1977	-5	1904	4	1900	22	1962	32	2016	43	1969
17	-19	1977	-7	1979	0	1900	25	1962	34	1891	44	1980
18	-17	1994	-7	1936	9	1941	22	1953	34	1973	47	1986
19	-22	1994	-6	1936	8	1885	21	1953	34	2002	47	1959
20	-19	1985	-9	1885	1	1885	22	1904	36	1929	45	1914
21	-16	1985	-8	1885	8	1885	22	1953	34	1883	46	1992
22	-16	1936	-8	1963	6	1888	27	1978	33	2002	41	1992
23	-15	1936	-4	1885	9	1885	23	1986	34	1963	44	1918
24	-15	1963	-11	2015	11	1974	28	2015	36	1956	46	1982
25	-15	1884	-7	1900	5	1974	25	1919	33	1925	43	1979
26	-9	1948	-10	1963	13	2001	26	1972	37	1969	48	1961
27	-8	1936	-11	1963	15	1955	28	1971	34	1961	45	1981
28	-15	1963	0	2015	15	1955	28	1967	36	1971	48	1950
29	-13	1963	0	1884	14	1887	28	1977	38	1949	48	1923
30	-5	1966	-	-	16	1915	30	1971	36	1984	47	1988
31	-6	2004	-	-	9	1923	-	-	38	1984	-	-

Columbus Daily Record Low Temps (Jul - Dec), 1878-2017

	Jul		Aug		Sep		Oct		Nov		Dec	
1	44	1988	48	1952	42	1967	30	1899	24	1949	7	1964
2	48	1988	50	1976	43	1967	32	1974	25	1954	1	1886
3	50	1924	45	1965	46	1967	31	1888	20	1991	0	1966
4	47	1968	49	1950	44	1997	29	1987	18	1991	3	1966
5	49	1972	46	1951	45	1950	31	1968	14	1991	8	1976
6	43	1972	48	1948	40	1984	30	1980	20	1953	3	1977
7	48	1983	51	1994	40	1988	29	1952	20	1971	-1	1882
8	49	1984	46	1989	39	1951	29	1889	13	1971	-4	1882
9	49	1963	51	1989	39	1883	29	1989	17	1995	-8	1917
10	45	1963	45	1972	41	1924	29	1925	19	1957	-8	1958
11	50	1963	48	1967	39	1917	24	1964	20	1957	-9	1917
12	51	1973	45	1967	44	1985	27	1964	16	1911	-2	1962
13	50	1940	48	1967	38	1964	28	1988	14	1911	-7	1960
14	47	1950	45	1964	38	1975	28	1988	12	1986	-1	1898
15	49	1930	43	1964	40	1923	30	1894	15	1916	-4	1958
16	52	1967	46	1979	40	1916	31	1970	12	1883	-14	1951
17	52	1896	48	1981	37	1959	26	1977	13	1959	-12	1989
18	53	1976	48	1962	34	1959	25	1976	10	1880	-7	1989
19	50	1979	49	1977	40	1929	25	1896	-3	1880	-8	1884
20	50	1929	50	1977	37	1956	24	1972	11	1914	-10	1963
21	48	1970	44	1950	31	1962	17	1952	5	1880	-10	1989
22	50	1966	46	1982	37	1995	24	1952	-5	1880	-17	1989
23	51	1981	46	1952	33	1995	23	1969	-1	1880	-14	1989
24	53	1985	47	1971	35	1983	21	1981	8	1950	-12	1983
25	52	1911	46	1887	33	1967	23	1960	5	1950	-12	1983
26	52	1911	48	1958	35	1950	23	1962	7	1950	-5	1983
27	45	1962	46	1968	36	1991	20	1962	3	1930	-14	1950
28	50	1962	44	1887	36	1942	21	1976	7	1930	-10	1950
29	51	1968	39	1965	32	1961	21	1925	3	1887	-10	1880
30	49	1981	45	1976	31	1963	20	1895	-4	1958	-12	1880
31	52	1895	43	1915	-	-	20	1887	-	-	-5	1976

Columbus Daily Warmest Low Temps (Jan - Jun), 1879-2017

	Jan		Feb		Mar		Apr		May		Jun	
1	47	1930	51	1988	50	1972	59	2007	68	1942	73	1895
2	49	2005	42	1983	57	1976	58	1946	64	1899	73	1943
3	55	1997	44	1890	58	1976	58	1963	69	2018	72	1943
4	57	1997	55	1890	61	1974	59	1928	65	1902	73	1943
5	52	2007	54	2008	60	1961	63	1929	66	1895	75	1925
6	55	1998	42	1991	55	1983	65	1929	67	1941	73	1899
7	57	2008	50	1887	56	1974	66	2010	67	1930	76	2008
8	55	2008	48	1925	56	1921	67	2001	67	1880	75	1933
9	50	1935	47	1938	54	1879	63	1922	68	2000	77	1914
10	43	1960	53	1932	53	1879	61	2013	67	1979	75	1914
11	55	1890	52	1932	60	1973	63	1981	68	1936	74	1880
12	57	1890	49	1882	56	1990	63	2018	68	2011	76	1880
13	51	1995	50	1938	55	1990	63	2018	70	1881	74	2017
14	54	1995	47	1935	58	2007	61	1941	67	2004	73	1994
15	45	1953	55	2018	58	1990	62	1941	65	2018	73	1981
16	44	1990	51	1883	59	1945	64	1896	66	2015	74	1891
17	50	1913	57	1891	56	1903	63	2002	68	1899	75	1939
18	48	1996	52	1961	58	2012	63	1941	71	1889	75	1944
19	50	1951	49	1981	59	1903	67	1896	70	1911	74	2018
20	49	2006	60	2018	63	1921	62	1917	70	1996	73	1931
21	56	1906	56	1997	62	2012	64	1977	71	2013	73	1933
22	50	1933	54	2017	61	1907	65	2001	69	1941	73	1996
23	57	1967	52	2017	60	1907	62	1925	71	1925	73	1884
24	56	1967	59	2017	58	2007	66	1925	71	1991	74	1930
25	58	1950	55	1930	58	2017	63	1881	71	1991	76	1879
26	48	1954	54	2000	57	1916	63	1915	75	1880	73	1998
27	53	1916	48	1996	61	1998	66	1915	73	2014	75	1969
28	45	1914	55	1880	61	1998	65	1914	71	2012	77	1944
29	52	2002	43	1976	60	1946	64	1991	71	2012	77	1934
30	51	1916	-	-	64	1910	68	1970	73	1991	76	1927
31	49	2016	-	-	61	1998	-	-	71	2018	-	-

Columbus Daily Warmest Low Temps (Jul - Dec), 1978-2017

	Jul		Aug		Sep		Oct		Nov		Dec	
1	77	1931	75	2006	75	1880	68	1881	60	1974	53	1914
2	75	1879	75	2006	75	1880	69	2018	63	1946	53	1982
3	77	1879	75	2006	74	1937	72	1884	58	1977	61	1982
4	79	1911	74	1890	74	1943	70	1926	61	1977	59	1982
5	77	1999	76	1918	73	2014	71	1884	61	1977	54	2001
6	77	1921	77	1918	75	1899	69	1941	61	1977	62	1998
7	77	1881	77	1918	73	1945	68	1879	60	1977	54	1966
8	76	1921	76	2007	73	1945	68	2018	58	1977	59	1966
9	80	1881	76	2007	74	1881	69	2018	61	1888	51	1952
10	82	1881	75	2016	75	2013	68	2018	56	2002	51	1897
11	78	1881	76	2016	74	2013	67	1879	58	1927	50	1899
12	78	1881	77	2016	72	1936	68	1879	60	1879	56	2015
13	77	1936	75	2016	74	1936	65	1879	59	1985	56	1929
14	76	1936	75	1918	74	1927	62	1879	59	1993	50	1906
15	77	1880	74	1938	74	1998	62	1897	57	1927	53	1891
16	78	1887	75	1995	72	1931	65	1928	57	1928	50	2012
17	77	1887	73	2017	70	2016	68	1879	61	1958	51	2006
18	78	1942	72	2009	72	1942	69	2016	57	2015	46	1889
19	75	2013	76	1947	74	1895	63	1985	61	1985	51	1957
20	78	1930	74	1947	71	1978	60	1979	60	1942	52	1895
21	80	1934	75	1936	74	1895	64	1979	58	1931	57	2013
22	79	1934	76	1936	74	1931	61	1979	60	1931	47	2017
23	76	2012	74	1898	70	1970	61	2001	56	1931	51	2015
24	78	2010	74	1947	71	1970	59	2012	55	2001	57	1964
25	78	1934	74	1975	71	1881	61	2010	52	1987	55	1982
26	77	1940	72	2018	69	1958	62	1984	54	1887	52	1940
27	76	1941	77	1880	68	1929	61	1918	60	1990	52	1940
28	77	2011	76	1880	69	1973	61	1984	56	1960	53	1984
29	75	1940	74	1960	67	1986	59	2004	54	2006	50	1984
30	79	1999	75	1881	71	1986	60	1974	54	2014	55	1936
31	78	1999	74	1932	-	-	61	1919	-	-	52	1965

Columbus Daily Coolest High Temps (Jan - Jun), 1879-2017

	Jan		Feb		Mar		Apr		May		Jun	
1	8	1928	10	1971	15	1980	33	1919	44	1909	52	1889
2	10	2018	4	1951	17	1925	33	1886	42	1940	54	1907
3	-4	1879	6	1996	14	1943	33	1936	41	1940	57	1956
4	4	1879	4	1912	20	2002	32	1903	45	1917	55	1945
5	0	1884	7	1917	20	1890	33	1898	43	1917	60	1998
6	-1	1884	5	1895	18	1920	34	1920	43	1917	60	1894
7	6	1912	3	1895	17	1920	32	2007	47	1917	61	1907
8	-1	1970	-2	1895	17	1996	30	1972	45	1947	62	1913
9	6	1970	-7	1899	18	1932	34	1892	37	1923	61	1910
10	-4	1982	-1	1899	23	1933	36	1918	43	1960	59	1972
11	4	1886	2	1899	24	1998	33	1882	46	1966	60	1910
12	0	1895	4	1899	22	1896	28	1940	48	1960	55	1985
13	10	1893	7	1899	23	1888	30	1950	48	1914	61	1978
14	12	1917	12	1943	21	1895	32	1950	42	1895	63	1933
15	-3	1893	8	2015	21	1916	37	1943	47	1927	52	1917
16	4	2009	10	2015	24	1900	36	1935	49	2011	64	1917
17	-2	1977	9	1903	19	1941	37	2018	51	2011	68	2003
18	0	1994	9	1993	25	1967	36	1953	52	2002	61	1950
19	-1	1994	8	2015	21	1885	39	1901	44	1894	69	1958
20	-5	1985	7	1885	17	1885	38	1901	48	1894	61	1992
21	0	1984	12	1963	21	1885	38	1901	49	1894	61	1992
22	11	1885	10	1963	22	1885	38	1986	42	1883	54	1972
23	4	1936	12	1889	25	1940	41	1927	55	1931	51	1972
24	3	1963	15	1967	25	1940	40	1883	55	1940	58	1972
25	3	1897	14	1900	29	1940	42	1919	47	1925	65	1889
26	9	1897	14	1963	22	1894	43	1976	54	1901	66	1928
27	9	1936	18	2015	28	1904	40	1931	54	1902	67	1886
28	6	2014	25	2015	29	1923	46	1913	56	1891	63	1923
29	6	1977	14	1884	25	1887	45	1908	52	1984	62	1914
30	5	1966	-	-	30	1881	41	1908	53	1894	66	1943
31	8	1899	-	-	24	1923	-	-	47	1910	-	-

Columbus Daily Coolest High Temps (Jul - Dec), 1878-2017

	Jul		Aug		Sep		Oct		Nov		Dec	
1	67	1914	70	1920	62	2017	50	1920	38	1917	25	1964
2	70	1929	70	1927	61	2017	48	1888	34	1954	13	1886
3	68	1915	67	1880	60	1974	51	1888	28	1951	17	1929
4	69	1922	68	1971	63	1891	47	1980	27	1991	23	1886
5	68	1972	70	1884	62	1885	48	1935	33	1951	25	1899
6	70	1983	67	1951	64	1924	44	1952	31	1967	22	1958
7	68	1918	64	1976	64	1888	44	1889	31	1971	11	1977
8	67	1899	71	1922	61	1914	48	1921	32	1976	14	1882
9	68	1947	66	1972	62	1943	47	1915	34	1913	4	1917
10	69	1917	67	1882	57	1924	41	1906	27	1913	4	1917
11	71	1917	70	1924	61	1968	42	1906	33	1950	10	1917
12	67	1940	68	1964	63	1940	44	1909	30	1920	10	1962
13	69	1990	66	1931	58	1902	47	1907	25	1911	13	1962
14	71	1960	70	2013	54	1953	46	1937	33	2018	16	1917
15	66	1945	66	1979	58	1949	46	2009	24	1933	10	1914
16	70	1892	66	1879	59	1959	47	2009	26	1933	7	1951
17	73	1925	66	1943	54	1981	45	1943	29	1891	9	1989
18	67	1939	68	1941	54	1981	38	1972	19	2014	11	1901
19	68	2000	65	1927	51	1918	37	1880	22	1880	9	1963
20	68	1958	68	1956	56	1918	39	1989	22	1937	12	1901
21	68	1958	66	1930	51	1918	39	1913	19	1880	11	1989
22	70	2009	65	1923	52	1913	42	1925	15	1880	4	1989
23	68	1909	67	1891	57	1887	41	1937	24	1880	11	1960
24	74	1911	67	1942	51	1950	40	1929	20	1950	4	1983
25	71	1920	66	1987	51	2001	35	1962	20	1950	1	1983
26	71	1962	66	1968	53	1899	38	1962	25	1977	13	1925
27	69	2004	64	1885	53	1984	37	1957	12	1930	7	1925
28	70	1925	65	1986	50	1967	40	1967	21	1930	8	1880
29	71	1981	68	1946	48	1967	35	1925	18	1929	1	1880
30	70	1971	60	1915	49	1924	32	1917	16	1929	2	1880
31	69	1925	67	1967	-	-	38	1906	-	-	10	1880

Columbus Daily Record Precipitation (Jan - Jun), 1879-2017

	Jan		Feb		Mar		Apr		May		Jun	
1	1.28	1948	1.42	1988	1.10	2007	1.23	1970	2.07	1893	1.16	2006
2	0.95	1947	0.90	1970	1.08	1940	1.51	1977	1.92	1935	2.09	1980
3	2.41	2000	0.69	1903	0.74	1951	1.95	2018	1.16	2011	2.66	1941
4	2.09	2004	0.90	1997	3.25	1964	1.64	2011	1.44	1990	1.61	2008
5	2.21	2005	1.21	1908	2.87	1897	1.06	1917	1.97	1882	1.38	2002
6	1.43	1950	1.41	1893	2.55	1945	1.10	1938	1.42	1916	1.22	1923
7	1.15	1913	0.79	1999	1.48	1903	2.26	1895	1.25	2012	1.21	1940
8	1.44	1920	0.84	1881	0.99	1961	1.07	1895	2.06	1972	2.13	1924
9	0.86	1898	1.62	1893	3.40	1964	1.52	1897	1.12	1909	1.98	1972
10	1.79	1924	1.33	1959	1.70	1952	1.59	1990	1.03	2014	2.50	1986
11	2.10	2005	0.82	2009	1.08	1890	1.33	1948	1.74	1933	2.89	2004
12	1.13	1916	0.77	1930	1.38	1977	0.66	1948	1.92	1918	1.84	1973
13	1.10	2007	1.36	1948	2.33	1907	1.12	1991	1.93	1886	2.71	2003
14	2.10	1937	1.41	1883	1.37	1922	1.45	1922	1.14	1938	2.49	1964
15	1.59	1890	1.72	1990	1.69	1919	2.06	2018	1.07	1985	1.13	1943
16	1.29	1885	2.18	1891	1.12	1963	2.23	1998	1.11	1960	1.73	1997
17	1.30	1953	0.74	1910	0.51	1980	0.94	1924	1.64	1945	1.48	1973
18	0.79	1927	0.83	1914	2.04	2012	1.61	1885	1.47	1927	1.55	1939
19	0.91	1986	1.58	1981	2.32	1943	2.30	1940	1.49	2017	1.94	1973
20	1.74	1900	1.94	1882	1.60	1984	1.51	1964	1.44	1984	2.00	2015
21	4.79	1959	1.22	2011	1.03	1955	1.15	1928	1.83	1901	2.49	1885
22	1.33	1937	0.96	1971	1.75	1879	1.44	1887	1.48	1960	1.55	1942
23	1.00	1996	2.15	1975	1.95	2007	1.64	1882	1.92	1968	2.75	2016
24	1.65	1937	2.16	1890	2.14	1913	1.72	1970	1.82	1885	1.83	1969
25	0.68	1952	1.44	1929	2.89	1913	1.74	1950	1.72	1944	2.26	1882
26	2.88	1952	1.55	1887	1.55	1949	1.24	2012	1.82	1968	2.31	2008
27	1.06	1949	1.47	1910	1.58	1916	1.36	1966	1.44	1991	2.90	1932
28	0.80	2009	0.56	1954	1.45	2005	0.81	2013	2.67	2000	2.50	1902
29	1.16	1969	0.64	2012	2.18	1974	1.82	1996	2.12	1982	1.50	1902
30	1.37	1947	-	-	1.47	1987	2.03	1983	1.29	1972	1.41	2005
31	1.18	1982	-	-	0.78	2017	-	-	2.07	1997	-	-

Columbus Daily Record Precipitation (Jul - Dec), 1878-2017

	Jul		Aug		Sep		Oct		Nov		Dec	
1	2.89	1993	1.83	1938	2.36	2003	2.23	1881	1.80	2018	0.91	1878
2	1.95	1994	2.18	1964	2.04	1982	1.67	1881	1.46	1970	1.37	1991
3	1.54	1892	1.93	1898	1.80	1988	1.69	1986	0.91	1985	1.41	1978
4	1.38	1984	1.65	1919	1.10	2011	1.57	2006	1.86	1936	1.26	1916
5	1.48	1949	3.17	1995	1.67	1915	2.84	1910	1.72	2017	1.95	2011
6	2.67	1955	2.00	1976	1.95	1890	2.23	2013	1.91	1880	1.10	1971
7	2.40	1943	2.35	1935	1.05	1934	1.61	1998	1.16	1972	1.15	1950
8	1.93	1952	1.39	1996	1.72	1885	1.14	2017	1.08	1897	1.74	1978
9	2.03	1965	1.87	1969	1.59	1991	1.21	1990	1.91	1895	1.42	1901
10	2.61	1979	1.49	1966	1.82	1894	0.72	1991	2.38	1985	1.22	1966
11	3.76	1897	3.60	1915	2.17	2011	0.71	2006	1.03	1995	1.26	1964
12	2.31	1990	1.59	1949	3.59	1938	0.71	2001	0.92	1925	1.21	1911
13	5.13	1992	1.03	1896	2.20	1979	0.90	1893	1.33	1993	1.26	1927
14	2.38	1985	1.44	1886	2.66	1979	0.89	1954	1.26	1897	1.50	1901
15	3.39	1947	2.44	2003	1.79	1911	1.18	1914	1.32	1989	1.27	1982
16	2.01	1995	1.26	1934	1.46	1996	0.98	1993	1.82	1955	2.26	2000
17	2.39	1931	2.06	1972	1.46	1913	1.54	2006	1.61	1993	1.71	2001
18	2.26	1953	1.81	1941	1.20	1975	1.92	2004	2.81	1881	1.57	1990
19	2.25	1969	1.83	1880	1.22	1902	1.83	2011	0.94	1950	1.74	2008
20	2.85	1988	2.37	2007	0.92	2000	0.77	1983	1.48	1906	1.02	1903
21	2.04	1928	1.40	1913	1.52	2013	1.54	1929	1.18	1883	2.56	1998
22	2.31	2013	1.47	1917	1.74	2003	1.39	1983	1.51	1920	0.98	1879
23	3.06	2002	1.86	1979	1.93	2000	2.31	2007	1.79	1891	1.88	1921
24	3.01	1896	1.65	1999	1.32	2018	1.39	1926	0.95	1900	1.63	2008
25	1.61	1945	1.52	1879	0.91	1994	1.66	1939	1.76	2010	0.79	2009
26	2.31	1995	0.80	1882	1.47	1890	1.03	1997	1.44	1897	1.37	1895
27	2.49	1926	1.89	1992	1.29	1886	1.21	2006	1.58	2001	1.19	2015
28	1.72	1896	2.44	2009	2.07	1996	1.25	2015	1.22	1968	0.91	1988
29	2.20	1878	2.51	2008	2.38	1896	2.17	1883	0.69	1919	1.13	1915
30	2.84	1886	2.64	2003	1.39	2016	0.78	1878	1.37	2010	1.59	1990
31	2.36	2004	2.35	2001	-	-	1.44	1932	-	-	0.89	1887

Columbus Daily Record Snowfall (Jan - Jun), 1884-2017

	Jan		Feb		Mar		Apr		May		Jun	
1	5.2	1964	5	1965	3.6	2015	1.5	1961	T	1909	0	2017
2	6.4	1999	2.4	1985	5	1891	2.6	1886	T	1940	0	2017
3	5	1911	4.4	1961	3.6	1960	2	1911	T	1930	T	1995
4	5.2	1994	7.1	2014	2.3	1922	12.3	1987	T	1957	0	2017
5	2.5	2003	9	2010	8.6	1962	2.9	1886	0	2017	0	2017
6	11.9	1910	4.7	1972	4.5	1967	6.1	1886	0	2017	0	2017
7	8.8	1996	4.4	2018	5	2008	1.2	1886	0.8	1989	0	2017
8	5.6	1999	8.9	1971	15.5	2008	2	1916	T	1947	T	1990
9	3.1	1996	4.4	2010	7.2	1999	3.9	1982	0.3	1923	0	2017
10	4.9	1985	4.2	1923	2.5	1971	2	1890	0	2017	0	2017
11	6.3	1893	4.5	1910	6.6	1906	0.2	1990	T	1966	0	2017
12	4.4	1895	6.6	1979	4.5	1970	6.3	1973	0	2017	0	2017
13	6	1917	5.9	2007	5.2	1958	1	1920	0	2017	0	2017
14	5.6	2009	4.3	1914	2.5	1940	1	1907	T	1895	0	2017
15	6.7	1965	9.7	2010	4.5	1916	0.9	2014	T	1904	0	2017
16	4.8	1936	8.9	2003	6.7	1956	0.4	1935	0	2017	0	2017
17	6.6	1994	6.8	1910	2.1	1973	1	1961	0	2017	0	2017
18	3.1	1985	3.4	1979	1.9	1934	4.1	1953	0	2017	0	2017
19	5	1956	4.4	1929	9.6	1906	0.5	1969	0	2017	0	2017
20	6.8	1978	5.8	1911	3.9	1996	2.4	1910	0	2017	0	2017
21	4.5	1926	6.8	2015	0.9	2018	2	1901	0	2017	T	1955
22	5.9	1966	2	1900	4	1968	0.8	1893	0	2017	0	2017
23	3.2	1963	5.2	1914	3.8	1974	0.2	2005	0	2017	0	2017
24	5.7	1948	3.8	1990	3	1912	3	2005	0	2017	0	2017
25	4.7	1988	4.2	1934	2	1899	T	1977	T	1950	0	2017
26	4.4	1978	5.2	1894	2.3	1930	T	1933	0	2017	T	1998
27	4	1888	6.4	1967	1.3	1926	T	1932	T	2001	0	2017
28	4.7	2009	7.2	1984	0.8	1887	T	1961	0	2017	0	2017
29	3.6	1925	1.4	1952	1.9	1970	T	2014	0	2017	T	1994
30	3.5	1909	-	-	1.7	1987	2.4	1908	0	2017	0	2017
31	3.5	1949	-	-	4	1987	-	-	0	2017	-	-

Columbus Daily Record Snowfall (Jul - Dec), 1884-2017

	Jul		Aug		Sep		Oct		Nov		Dec	
1	T	1953	T	1953	0	2017	0	2016	0.2	1954	6	1952
2	T	1994	0	2017	0	2017	0	2016	4.7	1966	3	1936
3	0	2017	0	2017	0	2017	0	2016	1	1966	7.9	1957
4	T	1995	0	2017	0	2017	T	2014	3.5	1936	2.9	1921
5	T	2012	0	2017	0	2017	0	2016	1.2	1992	5.7	1984
6	T	1955	0	2017	0	2017	0	2016	1.8	1971	5.1	2013
7	0	2017	0	2017	0	2017	0	2016	3	1894	1.7	2007
8	0	2017	0	2017	0	2017	0	2016	0.5	1900	5.8	1917
9	0	2017	0	2017	0	2017	T	1979	5	1913	1.6	1956
10	0	2017	0	2017	0	2017	0.1	1906	2.5	1913	3.6	1932
11	0	2017	0	2017	T	2011	T	1906	0.5	1983	4.6	1960
12	0	2017	0	2017	0	2017	T	2006	2.2	1886	2.9	2010
13	0	2017	0	2017	0	2017	T	2006	2	1886	3.6	1945
14	T	2000	0	2017	0	2017	T	1937	1.2	1911	5.8	1951
15	0	2017	0	2017	0	2017	0	2016	1.3	2018	4.2	1989
16	0	2017	0	2017	0	2017	T	2004	3.5	1920	1.8	1953
17	0	2017	0	2017	0	2017	0	2016	6	1980	4.1	1981
18	0	2017	0	2017	0	2017	T	1992	0.9	1984	5.5	1951
19	0	2017	0	2017	0	2017	0.4	1989	4.1	1955	4.3	1995
20	0	2017	0	2017	0	2017	T	1992	0.9	1887	6.5	1960
21	0	2017	0	2017	0	2017	T	1989	1.9	1995	4.3	1981
22	0	2017	T	2007	0	2017	1	1925	0.3	2002	6	1916
23	0	2017	0	2017	0	2017	0.6	1917	1.4	2005	5.4	1947
24	0	2017	0	2017	0	2017	T	2013	1.4	1971	2.7	1980
25	T	1994	0	2017	T	1994	1.3	1962	7.5	1950	7	1890
26	0	2017	0	2017	0	2017	T	2001	5.2	1900	5	1933
27	0	2017	0	2017	0	2016	T	2008	3.1	1931	3	2009
28	T	2000	0	2017	0	2016	0.5	1925	6.2	1958	3.6	1999
29	0	2017	0	2017	T	1967	T	2012	4	1966	5.9	2012
30	0	2017	0	2017	0	2016	3.6	1993	4	1972	2.2	1976
31	0	2017	T	1949	-	-	1	1993	-	-	3.6	1897

267

What We Do on TV

"Tonight's forecast: dark. Continued dark overnight, turning to partly light in the morning."

- Comedian George Carlin as Al Sleet, The Hippy-Dippy Weatherman

When you want to know how to dress for the day ahead, whether to push back your tee time or when it'll be good to mow the lawn, you'll probably look for a weather forecast. It's available online and on your smartphone, but most people still get it from the radio or the TV while they're rushing through the morning routine. Hot, cold, wet, or dry; it's good to be prepared.

Broadcast meteorologists are constantly monitoring the conditions and updating the forecasts. Today's forecasters have lots of training and most of us have at least a few years of living in Central Ohio.

Lots of Education

Years ago, the weatherperson you saw on TV had very little (if any) meteorological training. They collected the Weather Bureau's forecast from the UPI wire service, used a grease pencil to scribble some temperatures on an erasable map, added some magnetic weather symbols, and recited the pre-prepared forecast. For some stations, the only requirements for the job were overtly cosmetic. But the days of "The Weather Bunny" are long gone.

The overwhelming majority of women and men presenting the forecast on television today are trained specialists with extensive education and years of experience. They are meteorologists, not just "presenters." It's important for them to understand the constantly-changing dynamics of the atmosphere. When severe weather strikes the area, lives can be at stake.

The National Weather Association and the American Meteorological Society provide Seals of Approval for broadcast meteorologists who meet specific educational and experiential criteria and pass the organizations' written and on-camera tests.

To earn the American Meteorological Society's Seal of Approval or the golden seal as a Certified Broadcast Meteorologist, the AMS requires seal holders to have education in some pretty specific disciplines including:

- ✦ atmospheric thermodynamics,

- ✦ dynamic, synoptic, and mesoscale meteorology,

- ✦ atmospheric physics, with emphasis on cloud/precipitation physics and solar and terrestrial radiation,

- ✦ atmospheric measurements, instrumentation, or remote sensing,

◆ and advanced dynamics, agricultural meteorology, air pollution meteorology, applied climatology, aviation meteorology, broadcast meteorology, hydrology or hydrometeorology, physical oceanography, tropical meteorology, and weather forecasting.

There are some grueling classes with some daunting math and science but most of us weather nerds find it absolutely fascinating.

Create the Graphics, text, social media

Creating a forecast is only the first step. For it to be useful, people have to be able to see it, read it and hear it. We create lots of different versions of the forecast and make them available on lots of platforms. So, whether you look for the forecast on TV, listen for it on the radio or look it up on your smartphone, it's there when you want it.

All of the graphics you see on television, online and posted in social media are created and updated every day. Some of them are updated every few minutes. Some of them are even live. It takes a lot of time plus a slew of computers and specialized software.

The First Warning Weather Center, like most broadcast meteorology departments, is lined with computers, each of which is assigned very specific tasks. One computer monitors watches and warnings 24 hours a day. Another is dedicated to radar. Several are tasked with collecting enormous amounts of data. And another's sole purpose is to create the animated maps and graphics you see on TV. They all communicate with each other and share data. It's an IT nightmare.

Part of the First Warning Weather Center at WSYX-ABC6 and WTTE-FOX28.

The on-air graphics computer has specialized software that automatically taps into the available weather data. That way, we can show you the most up-to-date temperatures, satellite and radar data and model information. Plus, we can create our own graphics to help tell the day's weather story (like when you send us pictures of weather events in your backyard).

Once the visuals are ready, we use them on all of the available platforms. Some graphics are sent to the website automatically every few minutes, we post a few manually and others end up in your Facebook or Twitter feeds.

Present it on TV & Radio

We post the forecast on line several times a day. We also give the forecast to our radio partners. (Sometimes we are live on the radio; sometimes it's recorded.) But television is still where the majority of people get their weather updates. During the morning news casts, you'll see a weather report every few minutes. You'll see it several times during the noon newscast, Then again at 5 p.m., 6 p.m., 10 p.m., and 11 p.m. Seven days a week.

It takes a lot of practice to interact with maps and graphics superimposed on the Big Green Wall! Photo by Adam Aaro.

Besides the computers, our biggest tool for TV is the Big Green Wall. The Wall is where we present the forecast. It is truly part of the "magic of TV." In the studio, it looks as if we are waving our arms randomly in front of a giant, blank, florescent-green wall. In the control room, though, they replace the green with video. That's why it looks like we are actually standing in front of a series of maps. We use monitors to see what we are pointing at. It takes a lot of practice and some serious getting used to.

On television, our goal is to make the weather forecast useful. That also means making it understandable. Rarely will we talk about things like mesoscale convective complexes or hard-core thermodynamics. We can when it's necessary, but usually that would just be confusing. It's more important to help people plan their day.

How It Works: Central Ohio DMA

Television is a business. It's a very expensive business. It costs a lot of money to obtain a broadcast license, put up a transmitter, build studios and pay the enormous electric bill. Buying programming, gathering content and producing newscasts costs even more. You get it free because the stations sell advertising to pay those bills.

The ad rates are determined by ratings. The Nielsen Company is the largest provider of television surveys and ratings. To keep track of it all, they sub-divide the entire country into 210 television "markets" based on population. The Designated Market Areas (DMAs) range from the New York City metro area (6.539% of the US population) to Glendive, California (0.004%).

The counties highlighted on the map make up the Columbus Designated Market Area (DMA). The extra-highlighted counties are considered to be the "core metro" area.

1. New York
2. Los Angeles
3. Chicago
4. Philadelphia
5. Dallas
6. San Francisco
7. Boston
8. Washington, DC
9. Atlanta
10. Houston

19. Cleveland (including Akron and Canton)
32. Columbus
36. Cincinnati
64. Dayton
76. Toledo
113. Youngstown
157. Steubenville & Wheeling
188. Lima
204. Zanesville

The Columbus DMA includes an enormous area covering 23 counties[16] and nearly 2.5 million people:

The Federal Communications Commission uses the same DMAs when assigning "areas of responsibility." In order to maintain their broadcast licenses, the stations in each market are required to keep the public informed of certain emergencies and safety messages, for example, weather warnings. When the National Weather Service issues watches and warnings, broadcast stations are required to pass them along to all the counties affected in their DMAs. That's why you'll see the Columbus stations talking about warnings from Bucyrus to Piketon and London to Cambridge. They're responsible for more than just Franklin County.

---

[16] Zanesville is a very interesting, one-county market, surrounded by the Columbus DMA. The only TV station in Muskingum County is WHIZ, the local NBC affiliate. So, the county is excluded from ratings surveys for Columbus' NBC station but included for the ABC, CBS, CW, and FOX stations.

Other Jobs in Meteorology

Only a tiny fraction of meteorologists work in the media. There are thousands of "mets" in dozens of other industries including:

- ✦ insurance companies
- ✦ airlines
- ✦ electric, gas and petroleum companies
- ✦ National Weather Service
- ✦ PGA
- ✦ education and research
- ✦ NASA
- ✦ commodities trading
- ✦ computer programming and development

And they're good gigs. After assessing work environment, the stress of the job, the hiring outlook, and income, CareerCast.com listed "meteorologist" as #21 of the 200 best jobs of 2014 in its annual Jobs Rated report (down from #6 in 2011). The American Meteorological Society estimates more than 30,000 Americans currently have jobs involving the atmospheric sciences.

Have a question?

Do you have a weather-related question? Send us a message! Your question might appear in the McWeather or Wait Ten Minutes blogs or maybe in a future edition of this book!

email: questions@WaitTenMinutes.com

Plus, you'll find updates and interactive features at WaitTenMinutes.com!

Have an awesome weather photo?

We're always thrilled to see new photos of Central Ohio weather events! If you have a cool picture you want to share (and maybe see in a future edition), send it our way!

email: photos@WaitTenMinutes.com

ABOUT THE AUTHOR

Marshall McPeek

Marshall McPeek is a longtime Columbus meteorologist and journalist. He joined the WSYX-ABC6 and WTTE-FOX28 First Warning Weather team in September 2013 and was named Chief Meteorologist in 2018.

Marshall grew up in Central Ohio (in Bucyrus, the Bratwurst Capital of the World) and graduated Summa Cum Laude from Ohio University's Honors College with a degree in journalism. He received his meteorology training from Mississippi State University and has earned the American Meteorological Society's prestigious designation as a Certified Broadcast Meteorologist (CBM #501).

Marshall started his broadcast career in Bucyrus at WBCO-AM/WQEL-FM when he was just 14 years old. Since then, the dinosaurs have disappeared, man has discovered fire and Marshall has worked for stations in Toronto, Cleveland (x2), Southern Illinois, Toledo, and Columbus. Central Ohio viewers may remember his 11-year stint co-hosting the weekend-morning broadcasts on WCMH-NBC4. He came to ABC6/FOX28 after running off to Key West, Florida, where he founded a successful marketing business, MRM Media & Marketing, LLC, and produced The Keys Home Show.

When he's not staring at the radar or being mesmerized by passing clouds, Marshall enjoys exploring the back roads of Central Ohio and meeting the interesting people who make this one of the most fascinating places in the country. He loves to travel and looks forward to meeting you on his excursions!

Marshall has earned the American Meteorological Society's Seal of Approval (Seal #1416) and is an AMS Certified Broadcast Meteorologist (CBM #501).

Made in the USA
Lexington, KY
13 February 2019